2/6/57

To raise temp in constant temp. bath, raise needle from Hg. When Hg comes up with needed temp make contact and temp will remain constant.

To move needle down, turn clockwise.

To lower temp, turn on faucet (cold H_2O goes into cooling coils) and turn needle into Hg.

Experiments in Physical Chemistry

by ***Otto F. Steinbach***

ASSISTANT PROFESSOR OF CHEMISTRY
QUEENS COLLEGE
FLUSHING, N. Y.

and ***Cecil V. King***

PROFESSOR OF CHEMISTRY
NEW YORK UNIVERSITY
NEW YORK, N. Y.

American Book Company NEW YORK CINCINNATI CHICAGO
BOSTON ATLANTA DALLAS SAN FRANCISCO

Steinbach and King: *Experiments in Physical Chemistry*

MADE IN U.S.A. E. P. 3

Photograph on cover courtesy Standard Oil Co. (N. J.)

Preface

In presenting this book to the teachers and students of physical chemistry, the authors have kept in mind the practical requirements of the laboratory as well as the diversified needs of students who are preparing for various careers.

In many of the experiments the apparatus described has been kept as simple as possible both to keep costs low and to make it easy to obtain and assemble; yet it is designed to give results of a degree of precision and accuracy which is in accordance with the requirements of the experiment and in keeping with the traditions of physical chemistry. The instructor should find it easy to make modifications or substitutions according to the supplies he has at hand, or the needs of his own course.

Experimental procedures have been described in some detail in order to expedite the laboratory work for the student and, as much as possible, to release the instructor's time for more important things. Similarly, the methods of calculating results have been given explicitly in the belief that the average student needs detailed assistance in solving such problems if he is not to waste a great deal of time. The treatment of errors has been introduced into many of the experiments so that the student may learn how to evaluate each technique in its proper setting. The authors believe this to be of invaluable assistance in learning to plan an investigation, design methods, and understand results correctly.

A wide variety of experiments is presented so that the instructor may choose in accordance with the apparatus he has available and the needs of his students, or may vary the experiments from year to year. The experiments are all of standard types, since the authors believe that a description of the use of radioactive materials, for example, would be out of place in a book of this type. The same, in general, may be said of the study of electronic circuits or the polarograph and of the measurement of dielectric constants or of infrared or ultraviolet absorption.

Each experiment is preceded by a brief theoretical introduction so that the student may have the fundamental principles clearly in mind as he begins work in the laboratory. The later experiments are in general more difficult and comprehensive than those in the earlier sections. The instructor may think some of these suitable for study without doing the experimental work, or suitable only for students of exceptional ability or those who have extra time available.

References have been selected with two views in mind. Those indicated by footnotes are specific ones dealing directly with the experiment; the others are more general in nature and show applications of the principles involved or give different experimental approaches to the same problem.

Most of the symbols employed correspond to those used in the textbook *Physical Chemistry* by Gucker and Meldrum. Such variations as occur have been introduced to increase the clarity of designation.

The authors wish to acknowledge the direct and indirect assistance of various colleagues, and of former students who were "guinea pigs" in the earlier stages of development of this book. They also wish to express their appreciation to the reviewer of the manuscript for his excellent advice and criticism.

Contents

Introduction

Mathematical Procedures

Certain definite procedures have been accepted by scientific workers for use in the recording of observational data, the calculations of experimental results, and the estimation of errors in the results. These procedures are not based upon empirical rules; they have a sound theoretical basis. The serious student of science must learn the necessary mathematical techniques. The methods most useful in the physical chemistry laboratory are outlined below and additional information may be obtained from special treatises on the theory of measurements and errors.[1]

Errors Scientists recognize that the true or absolute values of many experimental quantities can never be known exactly because of unavoidable errors in the measurements. From a suitable set of measurements a "most probable value" may be calculated. If Q is the most probable value of a certain quantity, the true value Q_t may lie within the range $Q \pm R$, where R represents the range of uncertainty of the most probable value.

The term *precision* is used to indicate the concordance within a set of measurements from which the "most probable value" is to be chosen. The term *accuracy* indicates the agreement of a measurement with the correct value Q_t. It is easy to see that a series of measurements may be highly precise in that they agree well among themselves, yet all of them and the chosen "most probable value" may be highly inaccurate.

Errors may be broadly divided into two classes, namely, *accidental* (indeterminate) and *constant* (determinate) errors. For example, a set of weights may be calibrated to evaluate, so far as possible, the constant errors otherwise involved in its use. On the other hand, it may be found that the rest point of an analytical balance seems to vary a few tenths of a division in repeated observations, or different observers find a slightly different rest point. The accidental or indeterminate error involved may vary in magnitude and sign even though equally reliable observations are made. It is obvious that in evaluating constant or

[1] See Brownlee, *Industrial Experimentation;* Crumpler and Yoe, *Chemical Computations and Errors;* Margenau and Murphy, *Mathematics of Physics and Chemistry;* Mellor, *Higher Mathematics*, Chap. 9; Sherwood and Reed, *Applied Mathematics in Chemical Engineering;* "Symposium on Statistical Methods," *Anal. Chem.*, **19,** 943 (1947), **20,** 1241 (1948).

determinate errors, as in calibrating weights, accidental or indeterminate errors will also be present.

Unknown constant errors can in general only be detected by employing different procedures, methods, instruments, or observers. For example, if a known weight is placed on one balance pan and an unknown weight on the other, a constant difference may be observed. However, this difference may be fictitious if the arm ratio of the balance is not unity and another unknown constant error may thus be present. If the arm ratio were known exactly, or the weights were interchanged and new readings taken, this constant error would become determinate.

Accidental errors Variable errors that result from unknown causes are classified as accidental errors. In the example previously cited, the fact that a different observer or even the same one finds a different rest point in repeating a weighing suggests that the laws of chance may be involved, since each reading has an equal probability of being correct. In fact, if a large number of readings are made, for example, a thousand or more, a curve similar to Fig. 1 will be obtained on plotting the value of a given reading as abscissa against the number or frequency of times the reading occurs as ordinate.

Certain information concerning the occurrence of accidental errors is obvious from this diagram: (1) Since the curve is symmetrical, positive

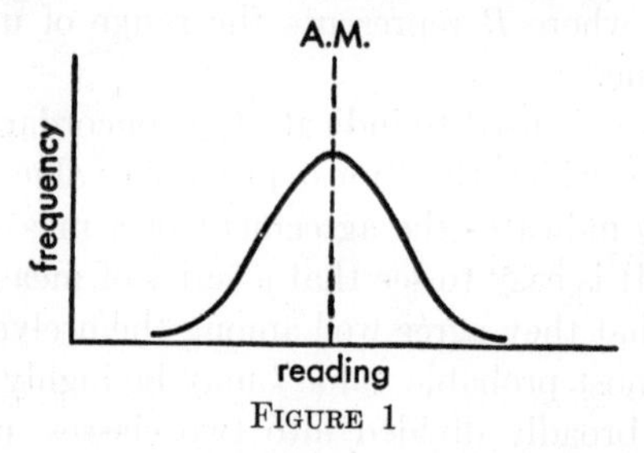

FIGURE 1

and negative errors of similar magnitude occur with equal frequency. (2) Small errors occur much more frequently than large ones; the curve approaches the horizontal axis for large errors of either sign.

When such a series of measurements has been obtained, involving only random accidental errors, the question arises: What is the most probable value of the quantity measured? The answer is the *arithmetical mean*, which may be defined as the sum of all the observed values divided by n, the number of observations. Thus if $Q_1, Q_2, Q_3, \cdots Q_n$ represent the observed values, the arithmetical mean ($A.M.$) is given by

$$A.M. = \frac{Q_1 + Q_2 + Q_3 + \cdots Q_n}{n} \quad (1)$$

The value of the $A.M.$ corresponds to the center of the curve in Fig. 1 and to the maximum frequency of the readings; the sum of the positive and negative deviations from the $A.M.$ equals zero:

$$(A.M. - Q_1) + (A.M. - Q_2) + (A.M. - Q_3) + \cdots (A.M. - Q_n) = 0$$

Further, the sum of the squares of the deviations (a positive quantity) is a minimum when the $A.M.$ is used rather than any other value.

If a second series of measurements of the same quantity is made with a different instrument, the arithmetical mean may agree closely while the reliability of the individual measurements may be obviously different. Accordingly, various methods have been devised to decide upon the reliability of the single observation and of the arithmetic mean.

The average error The average error, or average deviation (a) of the individual observation, is computed by adding all the deviations from the $A.M.$ ($d = A.M. - Q$) without regard to sign and dividing the sum by the number of observations:[1]

$$a = \pm \frac{\Sigma d}{n} \tag{2}$$

If one additional observation were made and its deviation from the $A.M.$ were no larger than the average, its numerical value would fall in the range of $A.M. \pm a$ units. According to probability theory, approximately 56 out of every 100 observations will fall in this range.

Since the number of observations in a series is ordinarily limited and the computed $A.M.$ will not be the same as the $A.M.$ of a very large number of values, one may well ask, "What is the error of the computed $A.M.$?" It has been found that the average error (A) of the $A.M.$ is inversely proportional to the $\sqrt{n}$. Thus

$$A = \pm \frac{a}{\sqrt{n}} \tag{3}$$

or

$$A = \pm \frac{\Sigma d}{n\sqrt{n}} \tag{4}$$

The result of a series of observations may be recorded as $A.M. \pm A$, the average error of the mean, $\pm A$, being used as a measure of the reliability of the result.

The root-mean-square error For some types of measurement the calculation of the root-mean-square error, or *standard deviation*, is preferred. The standard deviation (σ) of the individual observations by

[1] When the number of observations is small, the following equation may be applied:

$$a = \pm \frac{\Sigma d}{\sqrt{n(n-1)}}$$

this method is equal to the square root of the sum of the squares of the deviations from the *A.M.* divided by n:

$$\sigma = \pm \sqrt{\frac{\Sigma d^2}{n}} \tag{5}$$

Additional observations have the probability of 66 in 100 of falling within $\pm\sigma$ of the *A.M.*

For a small number of observations the "Student" deviation (s) is preferable:[1]

$$s = \pm \sqrt{\frac{\Sigma d^2}{n - 1}} \tag{6}$$

The standard deviation (σ_m) of the *A.M.* may be calculated by either of the equations

$$\sigma_m = \frac{\sigma}{\sqrt{n}} \tag{7}$$

or

$$\sigma_m = \frac{s}{\sqrt{n}} \tag{8}$$

the choice depending upon whether the standard deviation or the "Student" deviation has been used to determine the spread of the measures.

The probable error This term has a special definition: In a series of observations which fits the Gaussian curve (Fig. 1), it is a value such that half the deviations from the arithmetic mean are larger and half are smaller. Thus the error of a new observation has 50 chances out of 100 of being smaller than the probable error. The probable error of the individual observations in a series may be obtained by use of the equation

$$r = \pm 0.6745\,\text{[2]} \sqrt{\frac{\Sigma d^2}{n - 1}} \tag{9}$$

The probable error of the *A.M.* is related to r and d by

$$R = \pm \frac{r}{\sqrt{n}} \tag{10}$$

and

$$R = \pm\, 0.6745 \sqrt{\frac{\Sigma d^2}{n(n - 1)}} \tag{11}$$

[1] One of the advantages of employing the "Student" deviation as the error critique is that various tests are available for determining the significance or degree of confidence which may be placed in the results. This is especially necessary when the number of observations is limited. The importance of applying statistical methods for the analysis of data has become increasingly apparent. (See Brownlee and "Symposium on Statistical Methods.")

[2] When the number of observations is small (n = 2, 3, · · ·, 10) it has been suggested that the number 0.6745 be replaced by a more "realistic" constant. (Crumpler and Yoe, p. 195.)

Rejection of an observation Occasionally in a series of measurements, one or two values appear to be grossly in error, for instance, as if one weight were accidentally omitted in recording the total on a balance pan. A simplified procedure in this case is (*a*) to compute the *A.M.* and the average deviation (eq. 2), omitting the doubtful value, and (*b*) to obtain the deviation of the doubtful value from the *A.M.* If this deviation is equal to or greater than four times the average error found in (*a*), the observation may be rejected. A minimum of four observations must be obtained before this test can be applied. According to probability theory, 99.3 per cent of the observations in a given series have errors equal to or less than four times the average deviation.[1] Hence any observation which deviates more than this has only seven chances in one thousand of being a correct one.

Derived results In many experiments several quantities are measured to obtain the final result. For example, in determining the molecular weight of a gas which conforms to the ideal equation of state, the following equation is used:

$$M = \frac{gRT}{PV} \tag{12}$$

Upon substituting the measured quantities — mass g, temperature T, pressure P, and volume V — the calculated molecular weight M is obtained and is called a derived quantity or result. (The gas constant R may be treated as a mathematical constant not subject to error.) Each of the measured quantities is subject to constant and accidental errors, and the error of the derived result will depend upon the magnitude of these errors.

Two general methods are employed to calculate the error of such a derived result, the choice depending on the number and type of observations. If only one or two experiments are performed and the errors of the individual quantities are only estimated, the maximum error may be calculated. However if a series of carefully controlled experiments have been performed and the magnitude of the accidental errors of each measured quantity can be calculated by using equation 2, 5, or 9, then the various errors may be combined to give a more reliable estimate of the error of the derived result. We shall hereafter call this calculated error the "estimated error." Since positive and negative errors will occur simultaneously more often than all positive or all negative errors, the estimated error of a derived result will be smaller than the maximum error.

[1] It is more nearly correct to employ either four times the probable error or three times the standard deviation as the criterion for rejection.

The maximum error of a derived result In many cases the maximum error may be calculated very simply as follows: (*a*) The normal value of the function is calculated, using the observed or most probable values of the variables. (*b*) The maximum (or minimum) value is calculated, using some reasonable value for the error of each variable with the proper sign. The difference between (*b*) and (*a*) represents the maximum error. This method is satisfactory in principle, but since the result may be a small number obtained as the difference of two large numbers, the calculated error may not be very accurate.

A more generalized method is the following: If the derived result Q is some function f of the measured quantities $q_1, q_2, \cdots q_n$, then

$$Q = f(q_1, q_2, \cdots q_n) \tag{13}$$

The variation of Q with the quantities q is given by the total differential:

$$dQ = \frac{\partial f}{\partial q_1} dq_1 + \frac{\partial f}{\partial q_2} dq_2 + \cdots \frac{\partial f}{\partial q_n} dq_n \tag{14}$$

For small variations in q, the differential dq may be replaced by finite increments Δq:

$$\Delta Q = \frac{\partial f}{\partial q_1} \Delta q_1 + \frac{\partial f}{\partial q_2} \Delta q_2 + \cdots \frac{\partial f}{\partial q_n} \Delta q_n \tag{15}$$

As an illustration, equation 12 may be used; the partial differential coefficients are:

$$\frac{\partial M}{\partial T} = \frac{gR}{PV} \text{ or } \frac{M}{T} \qquad \frac{\partial M}{\partial g} = \frac{RT}{PV} \text{ or } \frac{M}{g}$$
$$\frac{\partial M}{\partial P} = -\frac{gRT}{P^2V} \text{ or } -\frac{M}{P} \qquad \frac{\partial M}{\partial V} = -\frac{gRT}{PV^2} \text{ or } -\frac{M}{V} \tag{16}$$

Each partial differential coefficient gives the rate of change of M with the variation of the corresponding variable, and when multiplied by the estimated error (Δq) of that variable, gives the corresponding error in M.

When the function Q involves powers of the variable other than plus or minus unity, a somewhat different method is preferable. Thus

$$Q = f(q_1^a, q_2^b, \cdots q_n^n) \tag{17}$$

On differentiating, dividing the result by equation 17, and substituting finite increments

$$\pm \frac{\Delta Q}{Q} = a\left(\frac{\Delta q_1}{q_1}\right) + b\left(\frac{\Delta q_2}{q_2}\right) + \cdots n\left(\frac{\Delta q_n}{q_n}\right) \tag{18}$$

That is, the fractional error in Q is equal to the sum of the partial fractional errors, each multiplied by the exponent of the quantity in the original function. The fractional errors multiplied by 100 give percentage errors. Obviously equation 18 can also be used when the exponents are plus or minus one.

The estimated error of a derived result If all errors in the measured quantities are of the accidental type which follow the normal distribution law, it can be shown that the following equations allow for partial cancellation of errors of opposite sign:

$$(\Delta Q)^2 = \left(\frac{\partial f}{\partial q_1}\right)^2 (\Delta q_1)^2 + \left(\frac{\partial f}{\partial q_2}\right)^2 (\Delta q_2)^2 + \cdots \left(\frac{\partial f}{\partial q_n}\right)^2 (\Delta q_n)^2 \qquad (19)$$

$$\left(\frac{\Delta Q}{Q}\right)^2 = a^2 \left(\frac{\Delta q_1}{q_1}\right)^2 + b^2 \left(\frac{\Delta q_2}{q_2}\right)^2 + \cdots n^2 \left(\frac{\Delta q_n}{q_n}\right)^2 \qquad (20)$$

In the above equations, the Δq's may be any one of the standard errors which are obtained from experimental results by employing equations 2, 5, or 9.

Application of the above equations to a numerical example will be shown below. It should be emphasized that none of the methods employed in the analysis of errors give any estimation of constant indeterminate errors arising from lack of instrument calibration, inadequate experimental method, approximate equations for calculations, etc.

Significant figures A significant figure in a numerical value is any digit, including zero when not used merely to locate the decimal point. The numbers 4356, 0.04356 and 435,600 each contain four significant figures; if the last number is written 4.35600×10^5, it contains six significant figures.

If the limit of error of a numerical value is known, it may be stated thus: 4356 ± 12. If the error is not stated, the last digit, other than zero, is assumed to be doubtful. Thus 4356 may represent a value between 4355.5 and 4356.5; 435,600 a value between 435,550 and 435,650.

In mathematical operations such as multiplication and division the number of significant figures in the final answer should not in general be greater than the least in any number used. For example the product of 404.25 by 23 is 9297.75, but the above rule requires rounding off to 9300. If the error in the number 23 is ± 0.5, the reason for rounding off is obvious.

In addition and subtraction, the number of significant figures retained in the answer should be not more than two uncertain figures. For example the sum of 4356 and 0.535 according to this rule is 4356.5.

Calculation of the maximum error and the estimated error of a derived result In many equations (such as eq. 12), the variables are composite quantities as they are obtained from two or more independent observations. For example, the mass may be the result of subtracting the weight m_1 of an empty weighing bottle from that of one containing sample m_2. While it is possible to substitute $m_2 - m_1$ for m and solve the resulting function by equations 13–20 as illustrated, it is not practical as the resulting equations may lead to cumbersome numerical computations. Accordingly the error of the composite quantity may be calculated from the known errors of the independent observations by means of the following equivalent equations, which are then employed as previously illustrated.

When the *maximum error* Δq_1 of the quantity q_1 is required from the combination of two independent observations whose values may be A and B, with possible errors of e_1 and e_2, by the process of addition, subtraction, etc., then:

$$q_1 \pm \Delta q_1 = (A \pm e_1) + (B \pm e_2) = A + B \pm (e_1 + e_2) \tag{21}$$

$$q_1 \pm \Delta q_1 = (A \pm e_1) - (B \pm e_2) = A - B \pm (e_1 + e_2) \tag{22}$$

$$q_1 \pm \Delta q_1 = (A \pm e_1) \times (B \pm e_2) = A \times B \pm (Ae_2 + Be_1) \tag{23}$$

$$q_1 \pm \Delta q_1 = \frac{A}{B + e_2} = \frac{A}{B} \pm \frac{Ae_2}{B^2} \tag{24}$$

$$q_1 \pm \Delta q_1 = \frac{A + e_1}{B} = \frac{A}{B} \pm \frac{e_1}{B} \tag{25}$$

When the *estimated error* Δq_1 of the final result q_1 is desired and this is obtained by the addition (or some other arithmetical manipulation) of the quantities affected with any one of the computed errors, the following formulas may be applied. (The computed error may be the average error, the root-mean-square error, or the probable error, eqs. 2–11.)

$$q_1 \pm \Delta q_1 = (A \pm e_1) + (B \pm e_2) = A + B \pm [e_1^2 + e_2^2]^{\frac{1}{2}} \tag{26}$$

$$q_1 \pm \Delta q_1 = (A \pm e_1) - (B \pm e_2) = A - B \pm [e_1^2 + e_2^2]^{\frac{1}{2}} \tag{27}$$

$$q_1 \pm \Delta q_1 = (A \pm e_1) \times (B \pm e_2) = A \times B \pm [(Ae_2)^2 + (Be_1)^2]^{\frac{1}{2}} \tag{28}$$ [1]

$$q_1 \pm \Delta q_1 = (A \pm e_1) \div (B \pm e_2) = \frac{A}{B} \pm \frac{\left[e_1^2 + \left(\frac{Ae_2}{B}\right)^2\right]^{\frac{1}{2}}}{B} \tag{29}$$ [2]

$$q_1 \pm \Delta q_1 = (A \pm e_1)^n = A^n \pm nA^{n-1} \times e_1 \tag{30}$$

$$q_1 \pm \Delta q_1 = 0.4343n \ln (A \pm e_1) = 0.4343n \ln A \pm \frac{0.4343ne_1}{A} \tag{31}$$

$$q_1 \pm \Delta q_1 = (A \pm e_1)^x = A^x \pm (A^x \cdot 2.303 \log A)(e_1) \tag{32}$$

A numerical example Assume that the following data have been obtained in an experiment on molecular weight and equation 12 is used to calculate the derived result M:

[1] This equation may be developed from $Q = f(A \times B)$ using equation 19.

[2] The function $Q = f(A/B)$ when developed by equation 19 gives this result; the remaining error functions can be developed in a similar manner.

q	$\pm\Delta q$
$g = 0.0828$ g.	± 0.0002
$T = 372.2°$ A	± 0.2
$P = 126$ mm.	± 2.0
$V = 100.75$ cc.	± 0.1
$R = 82.07$ cc. atm.	a constant

Substituting the values of q in equation 12

$$M = \frac{760 \times 82.07 \times 372.2 \times 0.0828}{126 \times 100.75} = 151.5$$

METHOD 1: Maximum error by maximum and normal values

Use $T = 372.4$, $g = 0.0830$, $P = 124$, and $V = 100.65$ to obtain $M_{\max}$.

$$M_{\max} = \frac{760 \times 82.07 \times 372.4 \times 0.0830}{124 \times 100.65} = 154.6$$

$$\pm\Delta M = M_{\max} - M = 154.6 - 151.5 = 3.1$$

The maximum error[1] is generally combined with the normal value which is now written as $M = 151.5 \pm 3.1$.

METHOD 2: Maximum error by equations 15 and 16

$$\frac{\partial M}{\partial T} = \frac{M}{T} = \frac{151.5}{372.2} = 0.407 \qquad \frac{\partial M}{\partial P} = -\frac{M}{P} = -\frac{151.5}{126} = -1.20$$

$$\frac{\partial M}{\partial g} = \frac{M}{g} = \frac{151.5}{0.0828} = 1830 \qquad \frac{\partial M}{\partial V} = -\frac{M}{V} = -\frac{151.5}{100.75} = -1.51$$

$$\begin{aligned} \pm\Delta M &= \left(\frac{M}{T}\right)\Delta T + \left(\frac{M}{g}\right)\Delta g - \left(-\frac{M}{p}\right)\Delta p - \left(-\frac{M}{V}\right)\Delta V \\ &= 0.407(0.2) + 1830(0.0002) + 1.20(2) + 1.51(0.1) \\ &= 0.0814 + 0.366 + 2.40 + 0.151 \\ &= 3.00 \\ \therefore M &= 151.5 \pm 3.0. \end{aligned}$$

Observe that in order to obtain the maximum error, the signs of the quantities Δp and ΔV are chosen to be negative so that all errors are added together in a positive sense.

One advantage of Method 2 is that the error contributed by the uncertainty in each measured quantity is clearly indicated. An improvement in procedure might be to measure the pressure more precisely, since its uncertainty contributes the major part of the calculated error.

METHOD 3: The estimated error (eq. 19)

Assuming that the values of Δq used in the previous illustration represent the probable errors[2] in a series of measurements of g, T, P, and V,

[1] The term "maximum error" as used here is not related to any of the errors in equations 2–11. It represents the largest error that could reasonably be expected.

[2] The resulting formulas are the same even though the average error or standard deviation is selected instead.

equation 19 or 20 may be used to compute the estimated error of M. The partial derivatives are the same as in Method 2 above, and

$$(\Delta M)^2 = \left(\frac{M}{T}\right)^2(\Delta T)^2 + \left(\frac{M}{g}\right)^2(\Delta g)^2 + \left(-\frac{M}{p}\right)^2(\Delta p)^2 + \left(-\frac{M}{V}\right)^2(\Delta V)^2$$
$$= (0.407)^2(0.2)^2 + (1830)^2(0.0002)^2 + (-1.20)^2(2)^2 + (-1.51)^2(0.1)^2$$
$$= 0.0066 + 0.134 + 5.76 + 0.023 = 5.92$$

Then $\pm\Delta M = 2.4$ and $M = 151.5 \pm 2.4$

The student is advised to carry out these calculations with equation 20, which of course gives the same final result.

The estimated error of the derived result is smaller than the maximum error as is to be expected. In the latter method, all errors are either positive or negative while in the former, partial cancellation of errors of opposite sign is possible.[1]

Graphical Procedures

The visual representation of experimental data takes the form of the graph. Each point representing the data should be made with a sharp pencil and surrounded by a small circle, the radius of which is sometimes used to represent the average error attached to the measurement. The scale should be chosen so that the general slope of the curve or line is about 45°. The graph does not necessarily include the origin, merely the limits of the data being sufficient unless an extrapolation is to be made. The best line representing the data need not pass through any of the points, but it should be drawn so that the number and distance of the points above and below the line are equal. A simple test is to obtain the average of the positive and negative deviations of each point from the curve in terms of x and y. If the curve is properly placed, then $\Sigma(+\Delta y) = \Sigma(-\Delta y)$ and $\Sigma(+\Delta x) = \Sigma(-\Delta x)$. The quantities $\Sigma|\Delta y/n|$ and $\Sigma|\Delta x/n|$ represent the average error of x and y. In some data the accuracy is greatest at the beginning of the measurements and least at the end (though it may also be just the opposite); more weight should be given to the points representing the accurate data.

The curve is best drawn by using a transparent straightedge, a French curve, a spline, or spring brass wire. There are various other methods for constructing curves, none of which are exact or above criticism. This is one of the reasons for choosing certain variables as ordinates and abscissas so that a straight line or a line of minimum curvature is obtained; furthermore extrapolations and interpolations can be made more satisfactorily with straight or slightly curved lines.

[1] Any one of the above values for the estimated error may be called a "precision measure" of the derived result.

The determination, from the graph, of the equation to represent the data After the graph has been constructed, it is often useful to have an empirical or interpolation equation to represent the data. If the points fall upon a straight line when y is plotted against x, the general equation

$$y = mx + b \tag{33}$$

can be employed. The two quantities obtained from the graph are the slope of the line m and the intercept b. The slope is most readily obtained by selecting two widely separated points on the line (x_1,y_1 and x_2,y_2), and employing the point slope equation, namely

$$m = \frac{y_2 - y_1}{x_2 - x_1} \tag{34}$$

NB.

The intercept b may often be obtained directly from the graph, for when $x = 0$ in equation 33 then $b = y$. However, the intercept is not always shown on the graph unless it happens to be within the range of the measurements. When this occurs, the following equation may be used to obtain the intercept b from two selected points:

$$y_2 = \left(\frac{y_2 - y_1}{x_2 - x_1}\right) x_2 + b \tag{35}$$

Many equations which are nonlinear with respect to the original variables become linear if suitable ones are chosen. For example, the integrated form of the Clausius-Clapeyron equation

$$\log P = \frac{-\Delta H}{2.303R} \cdot \frac{1}{T} + b \tag{36}$$

though not linear with respect to P and T becomes linear when $\log P$ and $1/T$ are used as the variables (y and x respectively).

The exponential equations

$$y = be^{mx} \tag{37}$$

and

$$y = bx^m \tag{38}$$

can be changed to linear ones by first taking logarithms:

$$\ln y = mx + \ln b \tag{39}$$

and

$$\ln y = m \ln x + \ln b \tag{40}$$

These equations are linear when $\ln y$ (or $\log y$) is plotted as ordinate versus x (eq. 39) or $\ln x$ ($\log x$) (eq. 40) as abscissa.

The determination of the equation from experimental data The construction and location of the curve on the graph depends upon the experience and particular choice of the experimenter. For example, if plots of the same data are prepared by several individuals, or even the same individual at different times, the slope of the curves may differ by as much as ±1 per cent. To overcome errors of plotting, the equation of the curve may be obtained directly from the experimental data. Several methods will be illustrated. However, the use of experimental data does not necessarily furnish a better interpolation equation than does the graphical solution, since all experimental values may not possess equal reliability.

1. *The method of selected points.* Select two points from the data, preferably widely separated, and substitute their values in the linear equation. Using the first and last data of Table 1, the following equations are obtained:

$$m \times 0.002679 + b = 2.88309$$
$$m \times 0.003092 + b = 1.96379$$

Solving the above simultaneous equations, one obtains $m = -2226$ and $b = 8.8465$. The final equation is then

$$y = -2226x + 8.8465 \qquad (41)$$

A test of the accuracy of equation 41 can be made by calculating y from the various experimental values of x, and subtracting these calculated values from the observed values of y. Each difference is known as a residual (R). This has been done and the residuals have been entered in the third column [$R(41)$] of Table 1. The method of selected points is not very reliable and is to be used only when a rapid and approximate solution is required.

TABLE 1

y	x	$R(41)$	$R(42)$	$R(43)$
2.88309	0.002679	0.0000	+0.0066	−0.0005
2.82866	.002705	+ .0035	+ .0100	− .0011
2.76567	.002732	− .0006	+ .0110	+ .0019
2.66229	.002778	+ .0032	+ .0094	+ .0053
2.51654	.002843	+ .0015	+ .0102	+ .0061
2.44560	.002875	+ .0011	+ .0011	+ .0020
2.26834	.002960	− .0118	− .0136	− .0037
2.19811	.002992	− .0118	− .0214	− .0055
2.08099	.003045	− .0127	− .0243	− .0034
1.96379	.003092	.0000	− .0221	+ .0048
		$\Sigma R = +$ .0093	$\Sigma R = +$ .0483	$\Sigma R = +$ .0201
		$\Sigma R = -$ .0371	$\Sigma R = -$ .0814	$\Sigma R = -$ .0142
		$\Sigma R = -$ .0278 Total	$\Sigma R = -$ .0331 Total	$\Sigma R = +$ .0059 Total

2. *The method of average points.* This method is quite similar to the previous one. The data are divided into two sets, and an average is found for each set. In this way, the two simultaneous equations can be formed and then solved.

Taking the average of the first, third, fifth, seventh, and ninth readings of x and y in Table 1, and the average of the second, fourth, sixth, eighth, and tenth readings, the two following simultaneous equations result:

$$0.002852m + b = 2.50293$$
$$0.002888m + b = 2.41969$$

The solution of these equations leads to

$$y = -2312x + 9.0967 \tag{42}$$

By grouping the observation equations together in different ways, each solution will give an empirical equation with different numerical coefficients. Thus, by grouping the first five observations and the last five,[1] and taking the average of the x's and y's, the two following simultaneous equations are obtained:

$$0.002747m + b = 2.73125$$
$$0.002991m + b = 2.19136$$

The solution of these leads to the following equation:

$$y = -2212x + 8.80761 \tag{43}$$

The residuals (R) obtained from equations 42 and 43 have been entered in columns four and five, respectively, of Table 1.

A comparison of the three equations shows that equation 43 is probably the best, as ΣR (sum of the residuals) is the least. This illustration shows that empirically derived equations may vary in both the slope and the intercept. As a comparison with the above equations, the values of x and y were plotted and the equation of the line was obtained by a graphical method, and it was found that $y = -2229x + 8.854$. The student may calculate and record the residuals (R) for this equation.

3. *Method of least squares.* The most reliable procedure, which, however, is the most laborious, is known as the method of least squares. In the previous methods, the coefficients m and b were supposed to be chosen so that the sum of the residuals is zero. The data in the residual columns show how closely this assumption is valid. In the method of least squares the coefficients m and b of the linear equation, are chosen so that the average of the sum of the squares of the residuals $\Sigma R^2/n$ is a

[1] This method of collecting the observation equations into equal successive groups is preferable to that previously illustrated.

minimum. This principle leads to equations 44 and 45; the theory may be obtained by the student from various texts.[1]

If the equation has the form $y = mx + b$

$$b = \frac{\Sigma x \cdot \Sigma(xy) - \Sigma(x^2) \cdot \Sigma(y)}{[\Sigma(x)]^2 - n\Sigma(x^2)} \tag{44}$$

$$m = \frac{\Sigma(x) \cdot \Sigma(y) - n\Sigma(xy)}{[\Sigma(x)]^2 - n\Sigma(x^2)} \tag{45}$$

The symbols have the same meaning as in the previous sections: Σ indicates sum and n is equal to the number of observations. In solving a problem it is best to tabulate the desired quantities as illustrated in Table 2. Upon substituting these data in equations 44 and 45, one obtains

$$y = 1.214x - 0.571 \tag{46}$$

The method of least squares occasionally fails to give an accurate solution when the numerical values of the numerator or the denominator or both are small numbers which are the difference of large numbers. It will be found that the coefficients become erratic when the differences approach the experimental error. However, a solution may be obtained by choosing a new axis and a new set of variables.[2]

In calculating the residuals of Table 2 and in applying the least squares equations 44 and 45, it is assumed that values of x are exact and all errors are in the measurement of y. If the opposite is true, residuals should be taken in the x direction, and in using the least squares method the coordinates should be reversed.

TABLE 2

y	x	x^2	xy	Residual in y from Eq. 16
6.0	5	25	30.0	−0.50
12.0	10	100	120.0	−0.43
17.0	15	225	255.0	+0.64
23.0	20	400	460.0	+0.71
30.0	25	625	750.0	−0.22
35.0	30	900	1050.0	+0.85
43.0	35	1225	1505.0	−1.08
$\Sigma y = 166$	$\Sigma x = 140$	$\Sigma x^2 = 3500$	$\Sigma xy = 4170$	$\Sigma R = -0.03$

After the best equation for a straight line has been decided upon, the error of the intercept b and the slope m may be estimated; for instance the "probable error" may be calculated from

[1] Mellor, *op. cit.*

[2] See Curtiss and Moulton, *Analytic Geometry.*

$$r_b = 0.6745 \left[\frac{\Sigma(d^2) \cdot \Sigma(x^2)}{(n-2)D}\right]^{\frac{1}{2}} \tag{47}$$

$$r_m = 0.6745 \left[\frac{\Sigma(d^2) \cdot n}{(n-2)D}\right]^{\frac{1}{2}} \tag{48}$$

where d is the deviation from the line in the y direction, n is the number of observations and D is the denominator in equations 44 and 45.

Occasionally the solution of a problem requires that the area under a curve be obtained. This may be measured with a mechanical integraph or by the method of counting squares. Another procedure is to obtain, first the weight of the graph paper and secondly the weight of the paper under the curve, the weighings being made upon an analytical balance. The ratio of the total area of the graph paper and the area under the curve is proportional to the ratio of the weights.

At times, the slope of a curve is determined by constructing a tangent at the point on the curve in question. The procedure of constructing the tangent with a straightedge is not very accurate. A device[1] known as a tangentimeter will give better results.

A procedure for calculating tangents by the method of least squares has been described [2] and this article may be consulted if necessary.

Thermometry

Since temperature is one of the variables that chemists must frequently measure, a brief word may be said about the use of the thermometer.

Thermometers are customarily designed by the manufacturers for either 75 mm. or complete immersion. Unless specifically guaranteed, a thermometer should always be calibrated by a method chosen in accordance with the accuracy required. A list of substances available for calibrating thermometers may be found in the various handbooks. When a standard thermometer or a previously calibrated thermometer is available for comparison, it should always be immersed to the same position in the heating vapor or bath.

Whenever the mercury thread of a thermometer projects above the closed system, a correction should be applied because of the cooling or heating effect of the surroundings (exposed stem correction). The mean stem temperature is measured by placing another thermometer adjacent to the mean position of the mercury in the exposed stem. The exposed stem is the difference in degrees from the temperature reading to the point where the thermometer leaves the closed system (the under side

[1] See Latshaw, *J. Am. Chem. Soc.*, **47,** 793 (1925)
[2] See Gucker and Brenner, *ibid.*, **54,** 886 (1932)

of a cork, etc.). It is also necessary to know the relative expansion of the glass and mercury; the temperature coefficient for the relative expansion is generally taken to be 1.6×10^{-4}. To obtain the corrected temperature, the following formula is applied

$$t_{corr.} = t_0 + 1.6 \times 10^{-4} \Delta t_e (t_0 - t_m) \tag{49}$$

where Δt_e is the length expressed in degrees of the exposed mercury column, t_0 is the observed temperature, and t_m is the mean temperature of the exposed portion of the mercury as recorded by the second thermometer.

To avoid error due to parallax, a thermometer should always be read with the eye at the same level as the top of the mercury column. A thermometer should never be used in a cold bath immediately after it has been heated; there may be a considerable time lag in the expansion and contraction of the glass.

When a large number of corrections are to be made, a nomograph [1] may be found to be of assistance in obtaining the emergent stem correction.

Manometers and Barometers

When a manometer is employed to measure pressure, certain qualifications and corrections are necessary in order to obtain the true pressure. For example, in a **U**-tube manometer, both arms should have approximately the same internal diameter so that the capillary effect will be the same in each arm. Since both the mercury column and the scale increase in length as temperature increases, it is desirable to refer the length of the column to some chosen reference temperature, generally 0°C.

The effect of an increase of temperature upon the scale length is to make the length of the mercury column appear smaller than it really is. Suppose L is the observed length of a column at $t°$, then its length L', measured with the scale at 0°C., would be

$$L' = L(1 + \beta t) \tag{50}$$

where β is the linear coefficient of expansion of the scale. To correct for the expansion of a mercury column of length L' so that its length L_0 at 0°C. is obtained, the mean cubical coefficient of expansion (α) of mercury is used. Thus

$$L' = L_0(1 + \alpha t) \tag{51}$$

[1] See Somerville, *Ind. Eng. Chem., Anal. Ed.* **17**, 675 (1945)

Solving equations 50 and 51 for L_0, one obtains

$$L_0 = \frac{(1 + \beta t)L}{1 + \alpha t} \tag{52}$$

The value of α is taken equal to 1.818×10^{-4} between 0 and 35°C., and β is equal to 1.84×10^{-5} for a brass scale. Obviously, β has a different value for scales made of different materials.

In many experimental arrangements, wooden meter sticks are employed. Since wood is a poor instrument of construction due to warpage, varying moisture content, and probably a variable linear coefficient of expansion β, it is clear that measurements requiring a high degree of accuracy cannot be obtained. Hence, when wooden scales are employed, it is even questionable whether or not to apply the correction for the expansion of the mercury, and the usual procedure is to omit it.

However, the above described corrections apply to the barometer, which is generally constructed with a brass scale. In addition, there are several other corrections which may be applied.

In reading a barometer of the Fortin type, which is the usual laboratory precision type, first obtain the temperature of the case from the small thermometer attached midway between the top and bottom of the instrument. Then adjust the mercury in the reservoir to the fixed point (an ivory pin), so that the tip of the pin and its image upon the mercury surface coincide. Tap the barometer case gently to be sure that the mercury is not stuck in the tube and verify the zero setting. Now bring the vernier down until the white background is cut off at the highest point of the meniscus. The reading is the uncorrected barometric height.

The barometric reading is generally corrected for the temperature expansion of the brass scale and mercury column. Equation 52 may be employed or tables in the various handbooks may be consulted.

In addition, for very precise work, several other corrections are necessary, such as the altitude-gravity, capillary depression, and vapor pressure of the barometric liquid. For most purposes, the expansion correction is sufficient; however even it may be neglected when wooden meter stick manometers are employed in the experimental procedures. Indeed, a simple wooden meter stick barometer will be found to be of comparable accuracy in this connection.

Other Apparatus

It is desirable that apparatus such as volumetric glassware and balance weights be calibrated or at least be of such quality as to meet the specifications for quantitative analysis. The procedures for calibrating volumetric glassware may be found in textbooks on this subject.

Every chemist should have some proficiency in glass blowing[1] since a simple mending operation can often save hours of lost time. It is not necessary that every student become an expert glass blower but merely that he can make straight seals, side arms, bends, and closures on the end of tubing. Proficiency in glass blowing results only through practice.

There is available to all students and teachers an elementary descriptive brochure published by the Laboratory and Pharmaceutical Division of the Corning Glass Works, Corning, N. Y., which gives an excellent description of simple glass blowing practice.

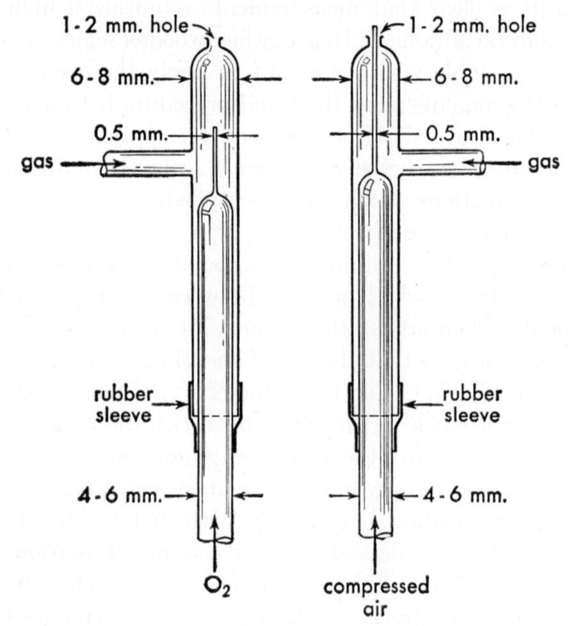

FIGURE 2

Simple blast lamps for glass blowing may be readily constructed from ordinary tubing and a glass **T** tube. The accompanying diagrams (Fig. 2) are self-explanatory. The lamps may be used for working with tubing up to 10-mm. diameter. Larger lamps may be made from larger tubing. It is advisable to employ Pyrex glass for all lamps.

REFERENCES

Brownlee, K. A., *Industrial Experimentation*, Chemical Publishing Company, New York, **1946**

[1] Heldman, *Techniques of Glass Manipulation*

Crumpler, T. B., and Yoe, J. H., *Chemical Computations and Errors,* John Wiley & Sons, Inc., New York, **1940**

Curtiss, D. R., and Moulton, E. J., *Elements of Analytic Geometry,* D. C. Heath & Company, Boston, **1947**

Daniels, F., *Mathematical Preparation for Physical Chemistry,* McGraw-Hill Book Company, Inc., New York, **1928**

Gucker and Brenner, *J. Am. Chem. Soc.,* **54,** 886 (1932)

Heldman, J. D., *Techniques of Glass Manipulation in Scientific Research,* Prentice-Hall, Inc., New York, **1946**

Latshaw, *J. Am. Chem. Soc.,* **47,** 793 (1925)

Margenau, H., and Murphy, G. M., *Mathematics of Physics and Chemistry,* D. Van Nostrand Company, Inc., New York, **1943**

Mellor, J. W., *Higher Mathematics for Students of Chemistry and Physics,* Chap. 9, Longmans, Green & Company, New York, **1926**

Sherwood, T. K., and Reed, C. E., *Applied Mathematics in Chemical Engineering,* McGraw-Hill Book Company, Inc., New York, **1939**

Somerville, *Ind. Eng. Chem., Anal. Ed.,* **17,** 675 (1945)

"Symposium on Statistical Methods," *Anal. Chem.,* **19,** 943–959 (1947); **20,** 1241 (1948)

Experiment 1

Molecular Weight by the Method of Dumas

The molecular weight of any gas or vapor may be determined with the aid of the ideal equation of state

$$PV = nRT = \frac{g}{M} RT \tag{53}$$

if the weight of a known volume, at known temperature and pressure, is measured. In this equation g is the weight in grams of vapor, M is the molecular weight; the pressure P may be expressed in atmospheres and the volume V in liters, while T is the absolute temperature. R is then expressed in liter-atmosphere units. However, other consistent units may be employed.

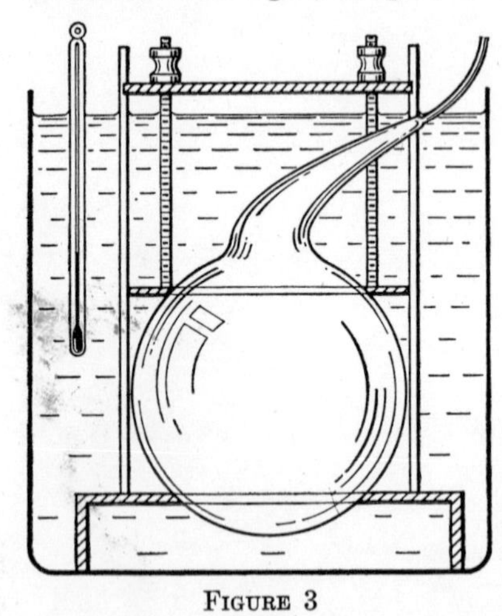

FIGURE 3

The Dumas method was designed to measure the molecular weight of substances which are liquid at room temperature but may be vaporized on heating to some easily controlled temperature, such as the boiling point of water.

Apparatus Dumas bulb (Fig. 3) of 200-ml. capacity; special clamp or wire rack to hold bulb under the surface of boiling water; thermometer graduated in whole degrees; barometer; large beaker or small pail for water bath; extra burner or torch (p. 18) to seal tip of bulb.

Instead of the usual Dumas type bulb, elongated bulbs of thin glass may be especially made or one end of a 100-ml. pipet may be sealed off as shown in Fig. 4. The bulb is suspended in a 51-mm. jacket through which steam may be passed.

Carbon tetrachloride is a good sample to be used in this experiment, though other liquids boiling 20° or more below the boiling point of water may be used.

Procedure The Dumas bulb should be cleaned and dried before the tip is drawn out. The neck is heated near the open end and is pulled out with tweezers, or a glass handle may be temporarily sealed to the end for the same purpose. A capillary tip about 1 mm. in diameter and 2 cm. long is required.

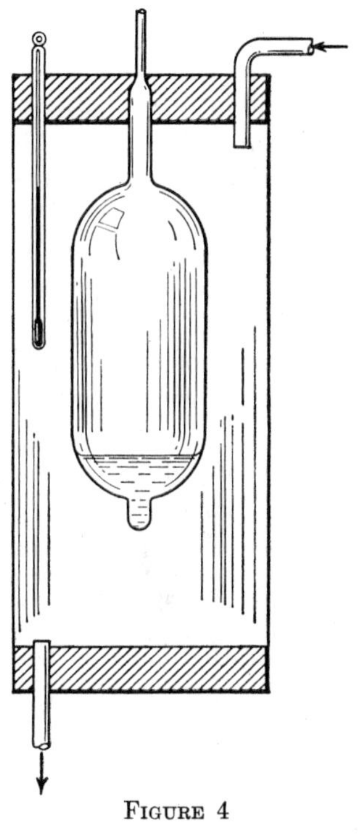

FIGURE 4

The bulb is weighed to the nearest milligram. Then 10–20 ml. of the sample is introduced by warming the bulb gently and holding the tip under the surface of the liquid while the bulb cools. The bulb is placed in a water bath which should be at the boiling point, or in the steam jacket through which steam is rapidly passed. The tip of the bulb should not project more than 2–3 cm. in either case.

The tip is to be sealed when all the liquid is vaporized and the bulb is filled with vapor. A small sealing flame held near the tip will be blown aside by the out-rushing vapor which may burn if flammable. The burning vapor should be promptly extinguished. In the meantime, care must be taken to maintain the bath at boiling temperature. When it is evident that no more vapor is escaping, carefully warm the projecting tip with the torch and seal by melting the end of the capillary together. Obtain the barometric pressure. The bulb is removed, allowed to cool, dried, and weighed to the nearest milligram.

To determine the volume of the bulb, the tip is immersed under water at room temperature and scratched near the end with a sharp file, the end being snapped off and saved. If the bulb was properly filled with vapor, it will fill almost completely with water. Otherwise, some air was not displaced or diffused in before the tip was sealed. If the remaining bubble is not larger than 5 ml., it will not invalidate the determination, since the volume of water closely approximates the volume of vapor actually present. The finger is placed over the tip; the bulb is removed, dried on the outside, and weighed along with the small piece of glass broken from the tip. The weighing should be done on a platform balance, and the result need not be more accurate than 0.1 g. Why?

Calculations The volume of the bulb, or of the vapor in it, is obtained with sufficient accuracy by subtracting the original weight of the bulb filled with air (to the nearest 0.1 g.) from the final weight filled with water. This weight in grams is a close approximation to the volume in cubic centimeters. The student may try the effect of correcting this value by first subtracting from the original weight the weight of air in the bulb (1 cc. air at 20°C. = 0.0012 g.) and finally dividing the weight of water by its density at the temperature of filling the bulb.

To obtain the corrected weight of the vapor, it is necessary to obtain the weight of air in the bulb accurately (to the nearest milligram) and subtract from the original weight of the bulb filled with air. This is equivalent to weighing an evacuated bulb initially. The weight of air may be found by using the density (or specific gravity) of air at the original balance-case temperature as found in a handbook, or by correcting the volume found above at room temperature to S.T.P. and using the standard density (1 cc. = 0.001295 g.). The true weight of the vapor is then calculated.

If the thermometer was not calibrated beforehand, it is advisable to find the true boiling point of water from the existing barometric pressure (B). This may be read from a graph, taken from tables, or calculated from the following equation, which is accurate near 760 mm.:

$$t(^\circ\text{C}) = 100.0 + 0.0367(B - 760). \qquad (54)$$

The molecular weight is calculated by substituting the data in equation 53 and the percentage error calculated, if a known sample has been used.

Discussion The Dumas method as described above is not highly accurate, but it can be refined in various ways and has, in general, certain advantages over other methods. For instance, it can be used over a wide range of temperatures, even at 1000°C. or more, by using porcelain or platinum vessels and suitable heating baths or furnaces.

Any impurity present in the sample may cause considerable error in the result. If the impurity has a higher boiling point than the liquid used, the vapor sealed off in the glass bulb may contain a greater proportion of it than the original liquid. This will usually give too high a value for the calculated molecular weight.

An error may result from condensation of vapor in the part of the tip exposed above the water or steam bath. This can be minimized by warming the end of the tube with the sealing flame just before sealing the tip. Of course, an incomplete seal, with even a tiny pinhole opening, will lead to considerable error. Also, it is assumed that all the vapor has reached the bath temperature at the moment of sealing, which may not be true.

An error, not of experiment but of theory, lies in application of the ideal equation of state to such vapors. The closer a gas is to the temperature and pressure at which it will liquefy, the greater the deviation from the simple gas laws. Partly for this reason, it is suggested that the sample should boil at least 20° below the temperature of the heating bath, although this is also meant to insure rapid and complete vaporization of the liquid.

If the critical temperature and pressure of the liquid are known, the molecular weight may be calculated, using the Berthelot equation (which will be more accurate than the simple gas law) to find how much the two values differ. As a general rule the experimentally determined molecular weight is larger than that calculated from the formula. One reason for this is that the PV product of vapors is less than that of an ideal gas at ordinary temperatures and pressures.

It was assumed above that even if the bulb did not completely fill with water, the volume of water was nevertheless equal to the volume of vapor. This is not always true and an error of 0.5 per cent or more may be easily introduced. The student might calculate the effect on the observed molecular weight if, for example, the measured volume of water were 2 ml. less than the actual volume of vapor.

The maximum error of the derived result may be calculated from the following assumed values:

Weight of bulb	$W_1 = 100.000 \pm 0.001$ g.
Weight of bulb and water	$W_2 = 200.0 \pm 0.2$ g.
Density of water	$d_w = 0.998 \pm 0.001$ g./ml.
Weight of bulb and sample	$W_3 = 100.500 \pm 0.001$ g.
Absolute temperature	$T = 373.0 \pm 0.2°$
Atmospheric pressure	$P = 760.0 \pm 0.2$ mm. or 1.0000 ± 0.0003 atm.
Density of air at 20°	$d_a = 0.00120 \pm 0.00001$ g./ml.

The molecular weight as calculated by equation 53 contains several composite quantities, such as g and V which are obtained from several other measurements. It is simpler to calculate the maximum error of these composite quantities first, and then obtain the maximum error of the entire result.

The mass g is the result of the calculation

$$g = W_3 - \left\{ W_1 - \left(\frac{W_2 - W_1}{d_w}\right) d_a \right\} \tag{55}$$

Upon substituting the above data in equation 55, there is obtained

$$g = 100.500 \pm 0.001 - 100.000 \pm 0.001$$
$$+ \frac{(200.0 \pm 0.2 - 100.000 \pm 0.001)(0.00120 \pm 0.00001)}{0.998 \pm 0.001}$$

Since the errors of some of the quantities in the parenthesis are much smaller than others, they may be dropped without serious error. Thus

$$g = 0.500 \pm 0.002 + \left(\frac{100.0 \pm 0.2}{0.998}\right)(0.00120 \pm 0.00001)$$
$$g = 0.620 \pm 0.0034$$

The volume of the bulb, and hence of vapor is equal to:

$$V = \frac{W_2 - W_1}{d_w} = \frac{200.0 \pm 0.2 - 100.000 \pm 0.001}{0.998 \pm 0.001}$$

Again neglecting the smaller errors in comparison to the larger

$$V = 100.0 \pm 0.2 \text{ ml.}$$

The student should carry out a similar calculation with his data and obtain the maximum error of the derived result by Method 2, page 9. The magnitude of the various errors may be taken from the illustration.

It should be realized that the precision illustrated would only be obtained by an experienced investigator who has a perfected technique. Errors of incorrect manipulation, such as sealing the bulb at the wrong time, cannot be estimated.

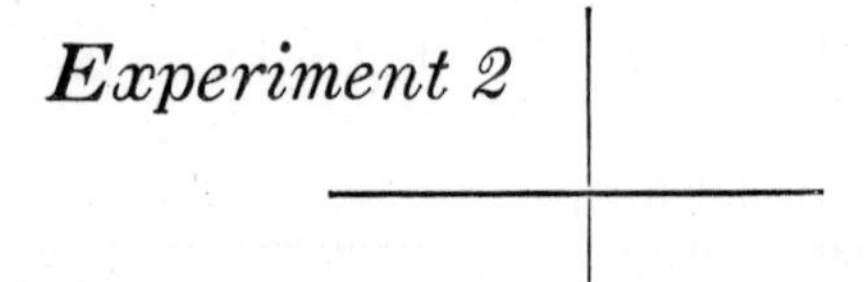

Experiment 2

Molecular Weight by the Method of Lumsden

In the Dumas method (Expt. 1) the molecular weight of a liquid was determined by allowing its vapor at a known pressure to fill a container whose volume was measured. In the Lumsden method, a weighed amount of liquid is vaporized in a closed container of known volume equipped with a manometer; the excess pressure created by the vapor at known temperature is measured. The molecular weight is calculated as before, by substitution in the equation of state

$$PV = \frac{g}{M} RT \tag{56}$$

where P is the excess pressure developed, g is the weight of sample, V is the known volume of the container, and T is the absolute temperature.

Any liquid having a boiling point at least 20° below that of water may be used in this experiment.

Apparatus A 10 or 25 ml. pipet or a tube with a similar bulb which has a mark (A) scribed on the lower end with glass marking ink (Fig. 5). Short sections of 6–8 mm. tubing are sealed to the upper and lower stems of the pipet to accommodate the stopper and the pressure tubing. The heating chamber is made from 32–51 mm. tubing. Rubber stoppers are used to hold the pipet in place, and the lower end is mounted in a split cork (C) which is pushed into the rubber stopper. The stopper S may be fitted, if necessary, by placing it in the chuck of a lathe or electric hand drill and cutting to size with coarse sandpaper.

The leveling bulb holder should be equipped with a screw adjustment to aid in fixing its height accurately. A meter stick (M) is employed to measure this height. A steam generator prepared from a 1-liter Florence flask is also required. The thermometer T need only be graduated in whole degrees.

A 3-in. magnifying lens will be needed so that the ordinary analytical balance may be converted to a semimicro balance. Small Victor Meyer bulbs (D) that will drop into the pipet, are also needed (see Expt. 3). If desired, the apparatus may be constructed with a 100-ml. pipet, and the entire experiment may be carried out as described, except that the sample need not be weighed by the micro procedure. A disadvantage is the larger quantity of mercury [1] required. A centrifuge is desirable though optional.

Procedure The volume of the pipet is obtained by first weighing it with the stopper and a rubber policeman. The pipet is inverted and distilled water, of known room temperature (t) is sucked up almost to the mark A, and the rubber stopper is then placed in position. The volume is adjusted so that the lower part of the meniscus is just above the mark A, when the pipet is in the inverted position. A capillary medicine

[1] If mercury is accidentally spilled, it should be immediately collected. Continued inhalation of the vapor is hazardous.

dropper will be of aid in adjusting the level. Slip the policeman over the free end and weigh to the nearest 0.01 g. From the known weight, temperature, and density of water filling the pipet, calculate the volume V_i. The volume V_f of the pipet at 100°C. is calculated with the following

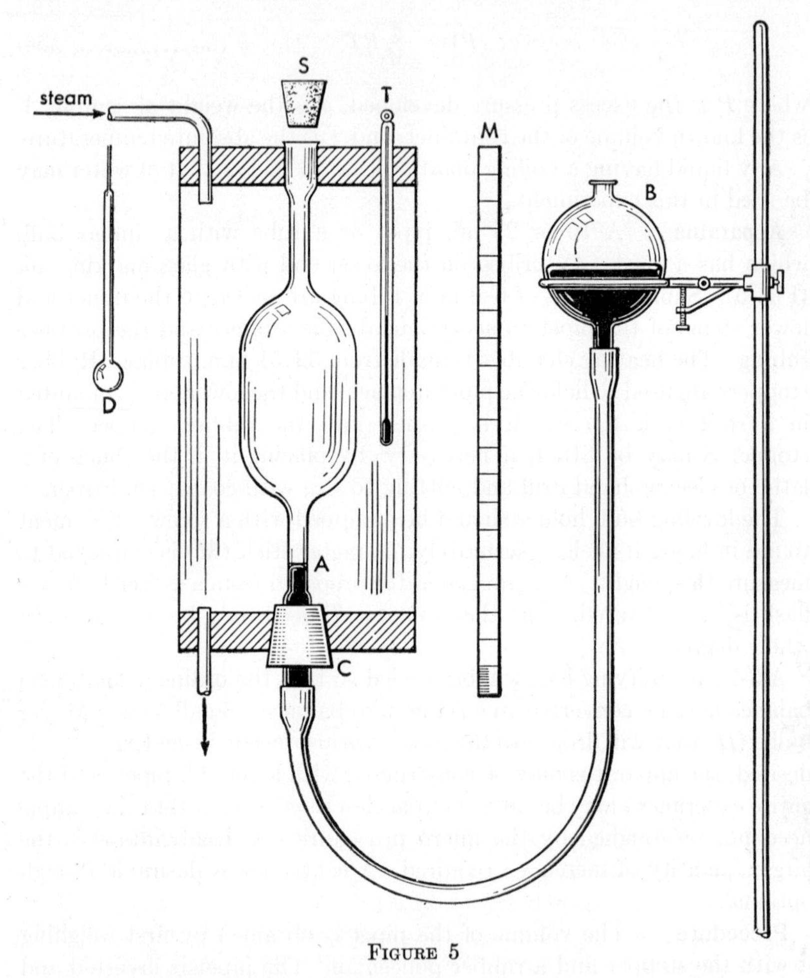

FIGURE 5

equation, where C is the cubical coefficient of expansion of glass and t is the temperature (°C.) of the water:

$$V_f = V_i[1 + C(100 - t)]; \quad C = 2.5 \times 10^{-5}$$

The pipet may be dried by rinsing with methanol and sucking air through it.

The ordinary analytical balance will serve as a semimicro balance; if a 3–4 in. hand lens is placed in front of the central scale, the scale may easily be read to ± 0.1 division. Obtain four successive readings for the rest point of the balance, estimating the pointer swings to the nearest tenth of a division. Record the average. Place the rider on the 1-mg. position, and obtain the new point of rest by taking the average of four readings. For example, if a displacement of 2.5 divisions per milligram was obtained, then the weight that corresponds to 0.1 scale division is given by

$$2.5:1 = 0.1:x$$

and $x = 0.04$ mg. Obtain and record the sensitivity of the balance for 0.1 scale division.

Weigh several Victor Meyer bulbs, using the method of sensitivity, and record the exact weight to the hundredth of a milligram. Be careful not to mix the bulbs; place them in separate test tubes.

The bulbs may be filled by placing them in an inverted position in a small side arm test tube containing the sample. Repeated evacuation and release of the vacuum will fill the bulbs. Place in a small hand centrifuge and spin for a few seconds so that the sample is driven into the bulb, or shake down vigorously. It is advisable to make a preliminary weighing, in order to adjust properly the weight of the sample. For CCl_4, the sample taken should weigh about 0.05 g., as this develops a pressure of about 30.0 cm. when a 25-ml. pipet is used. If less weight is taken, add more sample as previously described; if it is overweight, the excess can be removed by shaking the liquid down into the capillary tip and removing with filter paper. Seal the capillary, weigh, and record the weight to 0.01 mg.

Connect the steam generator to the inlet tube of the heating chamber, and pass steam through for at least five minutes while the mercury level in the pipet is at A. Raise the leveling bulb so that the mercury comes to about 2–3 mm. above the mark A, and then insert the stopper S. The mercury should be depressed to the mark A. It might be necessary to change the initial position of the mercury slightly in order that its surface coincide with the mark A on inserting the stopper. Measure the distance from the table top or a fixed point to the level of the mercury in the bulb B, and record this reading as h_1. The stopper may now be removed.

Place a scratch mark near the tip of the Victor Meyer bulb and break off a small section. Drop the bulb into the pipet and immediately insert the stopper firmly into position. Raise the leveling bulb slowly so that the mercury remains close to the mark A. Continue to pass steam through the heating chamber for 5–10 min., or until the mercury level does not change when adjusted at the mark *A*. Measure and record the height h_2 of the mercury level from the chosen fixed point, and the temperature. Record the temperature of the mercury in the leveling bulb. If the thermometer (*T*) has not been calibrated, obtain the barometric pressure.

Lower the leveling bulb and carefully remove the stopper so that the pressure is slowly reduced. Raise the leveling bulb carefully so that the small bulb may be retrieved.

The original vapors may be removed from the apparatus by raising and lowering the leveling bulb several times, meanwhile passing steam through the chamber. The apparatus is then ready to be used for a subsequent determination.

Calculations The pressure is the difference between the final height h_2 and initial height h_1 of the mercury in the leveling bulb. Correct this to the height that the mercury would be, if it were cooled to 0°C. HINT: Look up table of relative densities of mercury. This corrected height is the true pressure in centimeters of mercury. Is the correction important?

The volume should be corrected for the volume of air displaced by the sample bulb, with the aid of the equation $v = m/d$. The density of soft glass is 2.6 g./cc., and that of Pyrex is 2.25 g./cc. Is this correction important?

Since the thermometer is almost completely immersed in the steam, it is not necessary to apply any correction for the exposed stem. However, the thermometer should have been previously calibrated; otherwise the temperature is obtained from vapor pressure tables and the barometric pressure (see also eq. 54, p. 22).

The molecular weight is calculated by substituting the data in equation 56.

Calculate the estimated error of the derived result from the data. A similar problem is shown on page 23 and the numerical values for the errors of the individual quantities (or other suitable values) employed in the illustration may be used.

REFERENCES

Linhorst, *J. Am. Chem. Soc.*, **51,** 1165 (1929)
Lumsden, *J. Chem. Soc.*, **83,** 342 (1903)

Experiment 3

Molecular Weight by the Method of Victor Meyer

In the vapor density method described in this experiment, a weighed sample of liquid is vaporized, displacing a corresponding volume of air which is collected and measured in a gas buret over water at room temperature. The Victor Meyer method is widely used because of its simplicity. Numerous modifications of the apparatus have been designed to increase the accuracy and ease of manipulation, and the method has been adapted to the measurement of vapor densities up to very high temperatures. Micro and semimicro designs have been made for use when only small amounts of sample are available. The method described below is not highly accurate, but the apparatus and procedure have been kept as simple as possible. Liquids boiling at least 20° below the boiling point of water may be used.

Apparatus Victor Meyer tube about 80 cm. long; larger tube about 60 cm. long equipped as a steam jacket or vapor bath; steam generator; 50 or 100 ml. gas buret; leveling tube; thermometer; barometer; T stopcock (optional). The heating chamber may be modified by sealing a tube on the lower bulb and introducing a steam inlet tube in the split stopper. The Victor Meyer tube is then heated by passing steam through the jacket instead of using water in the boiling chamber.

Victor Meyer bulbs (M) can be made by heating and drawing 6-mm. tubing out so as to produce a 10-cm. length of 1-mm. capillary tubing. Cut into two equal pieces leaving part of the 6-mm. tubing attached to the capillary ends. A rubber tube with a mouthpiece is attached to the large end and the capillary end is heated in the flame to produce a small globule of molten glass. Remove from the flame and blow a 3–5-mm. bulb on the end. The other end is then drawn out to a fine capillary tip (0.2 mm.). Cut so that the total length is 4–5 cm.

Procedure The apparatus is assembled as shown in Fig. 6; the split stopper D holds the inner tube in placc. The buret G and leveling tube H should stand as shown, at the beginning of the experiment; as air collects in G, H can be lowered without overflowing. Sufficient water is added to the boiling chamber F so that it is three fourths filled, and it is heated to boiling with the stopper A removed; or steam is passed

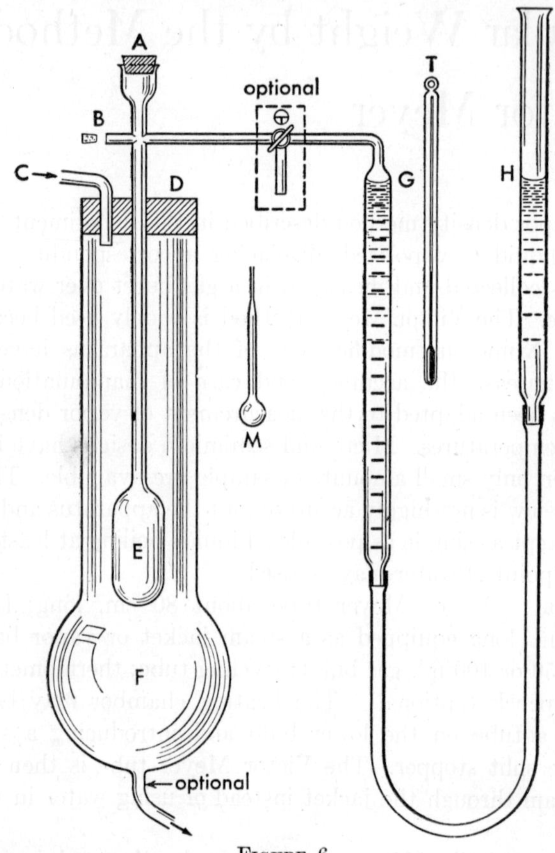

FIGURE 6

through the jacket if the modified design is employed. If the tube is not dry or contains vapor from a previous experiment, air is drawn or blown through with the aid of a glass tube which reaches into the lower part of the bulb E. A small amount of dry asbestos fiber or mercury may be placed on the bottom of E to break the fall of the bulbs.

The buret reading is noted and the stopper A is pushed firmly into place. This will cause a slight displacement of the water level in G, but if temperature equilibrium has been attained there will be no further movement of the meniscus. The levels of *G* and *H* are readjusted and the new reading taken. The difference will be used later to correct the volume of air displaced. This procedure is omitted if a three way **T** stopcock is employed as shown and no correction need be made. The apparatus should be tested for leaks by lowering the leveling tube *H* as far as possible, and the buret reading should not change with time.

The liquid is introduced into a previously weighed bulb *M* by placing the latter in an inverted position in a small side arm test tube containing the sample. Repeated evacuation and release of the vacuum will fill the bulb. A preliminary approximate weighing is made. The amount should be sufficient to displace about 30 ml. of air (0.1–0.15 g. of sample). Excess sample is shaken down into the capillary tip and removed with filter paper; if an insufficient quantity has been taken, fill as before. The bulb is sealed and accurately weighed.

The stopper *A* is removed, the water in *G* is brought near the top of the scale and the buret reading is obtained. The tip of the bulb *M* is snapped off (after being scratched with a file), the sample bulb *M* is dropped into *E*, and the stopper *A* is quickly and firmly inserted. If the three-way **T** stopcock is used, it is turned to the inverted **T** position immediately after inserting the stopper. As the sample vaporizes, the leveling tube *H* is lowered to avoid a pressure difference which might cause a leak to appear. When the volume no longer increases, the levels are carefully adjusted and the buret reading is obtained. If the reading is not steady, it may indicate an insufficient flow of steam or alternatively the water is boiling too slowly. After some time, vapor may reach the upper parts of the tube and condense causing the water in the buret to rise again. Record the temperature of the air in the buret and the barometric pressure.

The experiment should be repeated with another sample after drawing or blowing air through the tube to remove all traces of the previous liquid.

Calculations The data are inserted in the equation of state:

$$PV = \frac{g}{M} RT \tag{57}$$

Since the displaced air is measured over water at atmospheric pressure and is saturated with water vapor, the pressure should be corrected for the aqueous tension. However, the air in the tube originally contained some water vapor, the partial pressure depending on the humidity of the laboratory air. If some means of measuring the humidity is available, the difference between the saturated vapor pressure and the measured vapor pressure of the water should be subtracted from the barometric pressure. Otherwise, it is sufficiently accurate to subtract one-half the aqueous tension or vapor pressure of water at room temperature.

The values of P and R must be in consistent units. The temperature of the air in the buret was measured by a thermometer hanging nearby. While the vapor is formed at near 100° and hot air is displaced, it is cooled to room temperature before being measured. In estimating the volume V, the amount of air displaced by inserting stopper A is subtracted from the difference of the buret readings. This correction is not made if the three-way **T** stopcock is used. The molecular weights obtained are averaged and if a known liquid has been used the per cent error is calculated.

Discussion Some improvements in the apparatus can be made rather easily. A thin glass rod, with one end flattened, can be mounted in stopper B to support the weighed sample bulb while the stopper A is put in place and the water level is adjusted. A small movement of B will allow the bulb to drop. Sometimes, a magnetic release is mounted in the tube B to serve the same purpose. The bulb may be left sealed, and if it does not break upon falling, it will burst on heating because of the expansion of the liquid, provided the glass is thin enough and the bulb and capillary tip are nearly full. Sometimes the apparatus is equipped with a mechanical device to break the bulb. The gas buret may be equipped with a water jacket in order to prevent temperature changes of the collected air.

The student should make a list of the more important sources of error, estimate the error of each, and discuss methods of avoiding them or making corrections for them.

Suppose it is desired to obtain the molecular weight (assumed to be equal to 123.1) with a maximum error of ± 1.5 and it is required to know whether or not the humidity of the air in the apparatus should be accurately measured or whether a simple estimate, such as used in this experiment, will suffice. The procedure is to calculate the maximum error of the derived quantity P and compare it with the possible experimental variations.

Assume the following values and their possible errors:

$M = 123.1 \pm 1.5$ $\quad T = 300.0 \pm 0.2$ $\quad P = 760$ mm.
$V = 30.00 \pm 0.2$ $\quad g = 0.1500 \pm 0.0002$

Employing equation 18 (p. 6) and making all terms positive we may calculate the relative error $\dfrac{\Delta P}{P}$:

$$\pm\frac{\Delta P}{P} = (1)\left(\frac{\Delta g}{g}\right) + (1)\left(\frac{\Delta T}{T}\right) - (-1)\left(\frac{\Delta M}{M}\right) - (-1)\left(\frac{\Delta V}{V}\right)$$

$$\pm\frac{\Delta P}{760} = (1)\left(\frac{0.0002}{0.1500}\right) + (1)\left(\frac{0.2}{300}\right) + (1)\left(\frac{1.5}{123.1}\right) + (1)\left(\frac{0.02}{300}\right)$$

$$\pm\frac{\Delta P}{760} = 0.014$$

The variation permitted in pressure, while retaining the required precision of 1.5 units, is thus $\pm 760 \times 0.014$ or ± 10.6 mm. At 27°C., the aqueous tension is 27 mm. and if a correction of 13.5 mm. is used, it is extremely unlikely to be in error by as much as 10.6 mm.

Calculate the allowable error in the humidity from the experimental data. The errors illustrated in the above problem may be used in the calculation.

REFERENCE

Weiser, *J. Phys. Chem.*, **20,** 532 (1916)

Modified Victor Meyer apparatus.

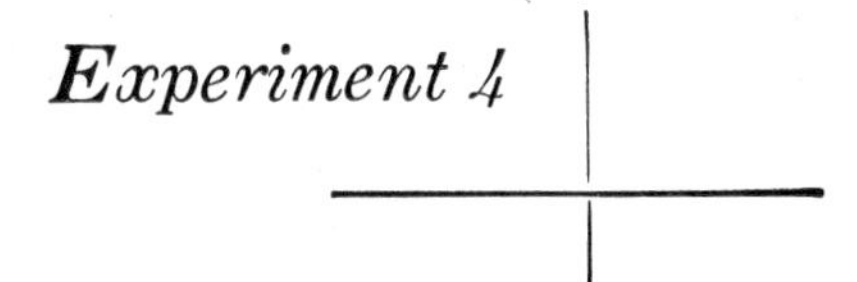

The Molecular Weight of Gases by Effusion

While the molecular weight of a gas may be found by direct measurement of its density, indirect methods of finding relative densities, such as the one described in this experiment, may also be used. It was found empirically by T. Graham (1829) that the rates of effusion of gases through a small orifice under a given pressure gradient, are inversely proportional to the square roots of the densities. This principle was used by R. Bunsen (1857) to measure relative gas densities, and the experimental apparatus is sometimes called the "Bunsen effusiometer."

In deriving the equation known as Graham's law, it is generally assumed that the gas is effusing through an orifice whose diameter and length are small compared to the mean free path of the gas molecules. While this is seldom, if ever, true in experimental practice, the apparatus is ordinarily calibrated with a gas similar in type and molecular weight to that being studied, and the small correction terms largely cancel.

Imagine a gas sample under low pressure enclosed in one compartment of a vessel, streaming through a very small hole in a very thin partition into another completely evacuated compartment. From kinetic theory, the number of molecules (n) striking the area (A) of the hole per second is

$$n = \frac{ANP}{\sqrt{2\pi MRT}} \tag{58}$$

where N is the total number of molecules per cubic centimeter, P the pressure, and M the molecular weight. If the dimensions of the hole are small enough, no molecules will be returned because of intermolecular collisions and kinetic energy will not be lost to the edge of the hole (the viscosity effect of a longer tube). Equation 58 then gives the number of molecules escaping through the orifice.

For two different gases at the same temperature and pressure, all terms of equation 58 except n and M will be the same, and

$$n_1 = k/\sqrt{M_1} \quad \text{and} \quad n_2 = k/\sqrt{M_2}$$

where k represents the constant terms. Dividing the first of these expressions by the second

$$\frac{n_1}{n_2} = \sqrt{\frac{M_2}{M_1}} \tag{59}$$

Since the number of molecules escaping through the orifice per second is inversely proportional to the time required for a fixed number of molecules to escape

$$\sqrt{\frac{M_2}{M_1}} = \frac{t_2}{t_1} \tag{60}$$

where t_1 and t_2 are the time intervals for the same volume of two gases to flow through the orifice under the same pressure gradient.

Apparatus The apparatus shown in Fig. 7 is used. This may be made from glass bulbs or pipets of the size shown in the diagram. Thermometer; stopwatch or other timing device; large beaker to serve as constant temperature bath; source of gases; calcium chloride drying tube; orifice tube (F) 2.5-cm. long made of 6-mm. tubing. To make a suitable orifice, a small piece of 0.001-in. aluminum foil is punctured with a needle. The foil is pressed flat with a piece of glass tubing and cemented on the tube F with a low melting point wax. This may be done by warming the end of the tube, touching to the wax, centering over the orifice and pressing to the foil (laid on a flat surface), until the wax hardens. The orifice must be tested and unless the time of efflux with air is greater than 300 sec., it will not be satisfactory. Consult the literature [1] for a commercially prepared orifice.

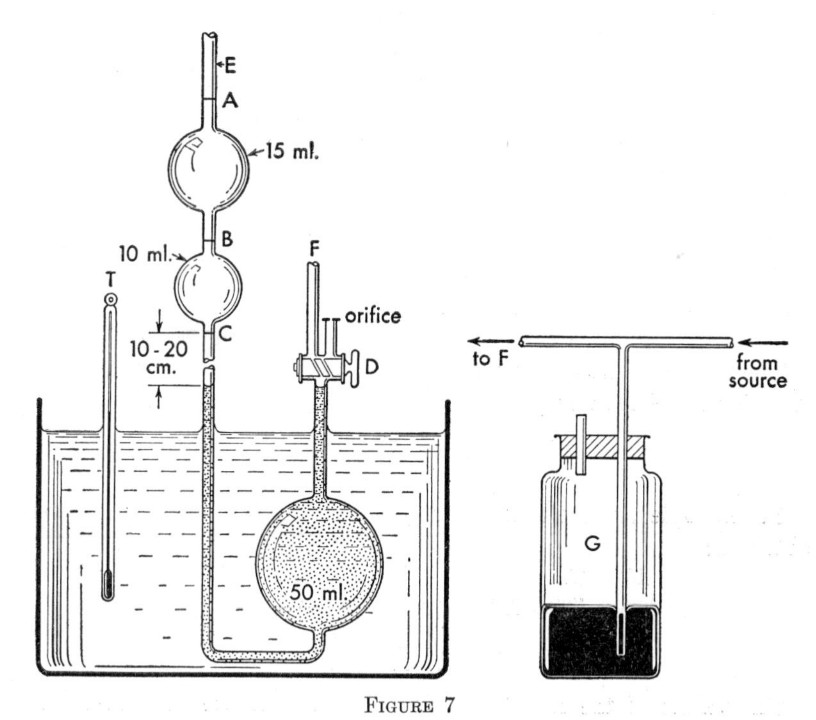

FIGURE 7

Procedure Sufficient dibutyl phthalate, or No. 0 motor oil, is placed in the apparatus to bring the liquid level slightly below the stopcock *D*. Dried filtered air (calcium chloride tube) is drawn into the apparatus through the inlet *F* by applying suction at *E* until the liquid level is above *A*. Alternatively, air may be pumped in through *F*.

After temperature equilibrium has been attained, stopcock *D* is opened to the orifice, and the time for the liquid to pass between the marks *A* and *C* is determined. The experiment is repeated four or more times, care being taken to maintain the water bath constant to 1° or better and to allow time for temperature equilibrium between the thermostat and sample to be attained.

[1] See Drake, *Ind. Eng. Chem., Anal. Ed.*, **15**, 647 (1943).

The air is displaced from the apparatus by passing in dry carbon dioxide or other gas through F. It is necessary to empty and fill the apparatus several times in order to remove the gas previously employed. If the new sample of gas is obtained from a steel cylinder, the gas flow must be regulated carefully and a pressure release bottle G should be included. The time of efflux is obtained with the new sample of gas and the average of four or more runs is obtained.

If hydrogen is used, the gas should be quite pure and extra care must be taken to eliminate all air from the apparatus and orifice tube. Since the molecular weight of hydrogen is small, even minor amounts of other common gases mixed with it will lead to a large percentage error in the results. It is essential that the time of outflow be long (at least 120 sec.), as otherwise a large kinetic flow error is introduced.

Calculations Obtain the *A.M.* of the time of effusion for each different sample employed.

Calculate the probable error of a single observation (eq. 9, p. 4).

The molecular weight and the estimated error are calculated by substituting the *A.M.* and probable error r in equation 60, thus

$$M_2 = M_1\left[\frac{(t_2 \pm r_2)^2}{(t_1 \pm r_1)^2}\right]$$

For example, assume that the following data and probable errors were obtained:

$$M_1 = 28.96 \qquad t_2 = 400.0 \pm 5 \text{ sec.}$$

$$t_1 = 300.0 \pm 6 \text{ sec.}$$

$$M_2 = 28.96\left[\frac{(400.0 \pm 5)^2}{(300.0 \pm 6)^2}\right]$$

The values of the numerator and denominator are computed from equation 30, page 8:

$$M_2 = 28.96\left[\frac{160{,}000 \pm 4000}{90{,}000 \pm 3600}\right]$$

The estimated error of dividing $A \pm e_1$ by $B \pm e_2$ is calculated by equation 29, page 8, and

$$M_2 = 28.96[1.78 \pm 0.084]$$

Since in the last product only one error is involved, equation 28, page 8, reduces to simple multiplication.

$$M_2 = 51.5 \pm 2.4$$

The student should calculate the molecular weight and estimated error of this quantity by the procedure illustrated, or by using equation 20, page 7.

Discussion The effusion method offers a rapid and easy means of obtaining molecular weights or densities of pure or mixed gases. It can be used for routine analysis [1] of gaseous mixtures, since the apparatus can be calibrated with known mixtures. Various improvements can be made, such as automatic and accurate temperature control, electrical timing,[2] protection of the orifice from air currents, calibration with a gas of the same molecular type and similar density to the unknown sample. As the size of the orifice may change, the apparatus must be calibrated frequently.

The student should calculate, or discuss the effect of, each of the following on the calculated molecular weights:

1) The presence of 1 per cent oxygen in hydrogen if this gas were used.
2) The presence of 1 per cent air in carbon dioxide if this gas were used.
3) An error of 1 per cent in timing.
4) A temperature difference of 1° in two runs.
5) Using air saturated with water vapor, instead of dry air.
6) Deviation of the gases from the ideal laws.

REFERENCES

Drake, *Ind. Eng. Chem., Anal. Ed.*, **15**, 647 (1943)
Eyring, *J. Am. Chem. Soc.*, **50**, 2398 (1928)
Nash, *Anal. Chem.*, **20**, 258 (1948)

Micro-effusiometry.

Satterthwaite and Wallace, *ibid.*, **20**, 555 (1948)

Frequency error in timing with electric clocks.

Steinbach and Conery, *J. Chem. Ed.*, **21**, 216 (1944)

[1] Drake, *loc. cit.*
[2] Satterthwaite and Wallace, *Anal. Chem.*, **20**, 555 (1948)

Experiment 5

The Viscosity of Gases

A stream of gas flowing at very low pressure may exhibit molecular flow in which viscosity has no significance, because molecular collisions and frictional resistance are not present. At ordinary pressures, gases behave very much like liquids and are sometimes called highly compressible fluids. Fluids exhibit two well-known types of flow, namely, viscous or streamline (Poiseuille) flow, and turbulent flow. Viscosity is an important factor in both types, but the viscosity coefficient η is most easily defined and measured in terms of the frictional loss of energy in viscous or streamline flow.

A fluid does not move like a plug of solid material through a tube with all the frictional effect at the edges, because it offers comparatively little resistance to shear. It behaves, rather, as if it consisted of a very large number of thin concentric tubes, with the tube next to the solid wall practically motionless, and the speed of flow increasing from layer to layer away from the wall. Friction between layers arises because the molecules do not remain in their original tubes. In addition to their net movement in the direction of flow (x), they possess the normal random thermal motion with components in x, y, and z directions. Molecules moving away from the solid wall tend to slow down the faster layers into which they move. Molecules moving toward the wall lose some of their extra flow velocity by collision with other molecules and with the wall.

The viscosity coefficient η is expressed in terms of the force per unit area, f/A, required to maintain a definite gradient of velocity (∂w), with distance (∂d) from the solid wall. In differential form this may be written:

$$\frac{f}{A} = \eta \frac{\partial w}{\partial d} \tag{61}$$

or

$$\eta = \frac{f/A}{\partial w/\partial d} \tag{62}$$

The coefficient η is expressed in dyne sec./cm.^{2}, as it is the result of dividing a pressure (force per unit area) by the velocity gradient (cm. per sec.)/cm. The unit is called the "poise" (from Poiseuille).

The absolute viscosity of a fluid is usually determined by observing the rate of flow through tubes, under such conditions that the equation of Poiseuille applies. In one of its forms, this may be written:

$$\eta = \frac{\pi(P_1 - P_2)r^4t}{8VL} \tag{63}$$

This equation applies to a fluid moving with viscous flow through a cylindrical tube of radius r and length L, under the pressure gradient $(P_1 - P_2)$, where t is the length of time for the volume V to flow through the tube. The coefficient of viscosity η increases with rising temperature in the case of gases, because the increased thermal motion results in a larger loss of energy to the wall, but decreases with liquids because of other factors. Theoretically $(P_1 - P_2)$ should be very small, and L very large for equation 63 to apply accurately.

If the absolute viscosity of one gas has been established in a properly designed apparatus, a simpler apparatus can be calibrated with this gas and used to measure the viscosity of other gases. For two gases, equation 63 may be written

$$\eta_1 = kt_1 \quad \text{and} \quad \eta_2 = kt_2$$

where k includes all the constant terms. It follows that

$$\frac{\eta_1}{\eta_2} = \frac{t_1}{t_2} \tag{64}$$

That is, the viscosity coefficients are directly proportional to the times of outflow of a given volume of the gases. If the same gas is used in two experiments with outflow tubes of different lengths but of the same diameter, equation 63 may be written

$$\eta_1 = \frac{k't_1}{L_1} \quad \text{and} \quad \eta_1 = \frac{k't_2}{L_2}$$

where k' includes all the constants, except L. This gives

$$\frac{t_1}{L_1} = \frac{t_2}{L_2} \tag{65}$$

The outflow times are, according to equation 65, directly proportional to the tube lengths.

Apparatus The apparatus illustrated in Fig. 7 is employed, the orifice tube being replaced by a glass capillary tube. A suitable capillary tube 10–20 cm. in length may be obtained from the stem of a broken thermometer. Stopwatch; thermometer; 3-liter beaker to serve as a thermostat; dibutyl phthalate for use in the apparatus; source of CO_2.

Procedure The apparatus is filled with dry air ($CaCl_2$ tube at F) by applying suction at E or pressure at F, until the liquid is slightly above mark B. When temperature equilibrium has been established, stopcock D is opened and the time of fall of the liquid between marks B and C is carefully measured. The procedure is repeated at least twice with air. The individual values are recorded and the average calculated.

The length of the capillary is measured accurately, about one-fourth of it is cut off, and both remaining lengths measured. The efflux time of two samples of air is measured with the shorter segment, and four measurements are made with the longer piece.

The air is replaced with dry carbon dioxide, or any other gas which is available, provided it is insoluble in the dibutyl phthalate. At least four values are obtained for each new gas, using the longest remaining capillary, after one or two trial runs to displace the preceding gas from the capillary and connecting tube. Enter data in a table similar to Table 3.

Calculations To evaluate the effect of the tube length, the values of t_1, L_1, and L_2 are substituted in equation 65, and t_2 is calculated for each of the shorter capillaries. The percentage difference between observed and calculated values is obtained.

The absolute viscosity coefficient of air, in micropoises, is given between 10° and 40°C. by the equation

$$\eta \times 10^6 = 171.2 + 0.48t \tag{66}$$

where t is the temperature in °C. Using this relation and equation 64, the viscosity of the second sample (carbon dioxide) is calculated, and the result compared with values given in the literature.

The data collected in this experiment may also be used to calculate the mean free path (l) and the molecular diameter (σ). The equations below are derivable from the kinetic theory:

$$l_1/l_2 = (\eta_1/\eta_2)(M_2/M_1)^{\frac{1}{2}} \tag{67}$$

$$\sigma_1/\sigma_2 = (\eta_1/\eta_2)(M_2/M_1)^{\frac{1}{4}} \tag{68}$$

To calculate l and σ for one gas, the values for the standard gas must be known. For air in the neighborhood of 20°C., the following approximate values may be used: $l = 1.05 \times 10^{-5}$ cm., and $\sigma = 3.0 \times 10^{-8}$ cm. The average molecular weight (M) of air is 28.96.

Calculate the estimated error of the viscosity of carbon dioxide, using a procedure similar to that illustrated in Expt. 4.

TABLE 3 t ____ °C.

SAMPLE	LENGTH OF SEGMENT (cm.)	TIME (sec.)	MEAN (A.M.)	t_2 (calc.)	$\eta \times 10^6$ (calc.)	PER CENT ERROR

REFERENCES

Eyring and Van Valkenburgh, *J. Am. Chem. Soc.*, **52,** 2619 (1930)

Glasstone, S., Laidler, K. J., and Eyring, H., *The Theory of Rate Processes,* McGraw-Hill Book Company, Inc., New York, **1941**

Melaven and Mack, *J. Am. Chem. Soc.*, **54,** 888 (1932)

Sperry and Mack, *ibid.*, **54,** 904 (1932)

Steinbach and Conery, *J. Chem. Ed.*, **21,** 216 (1944)

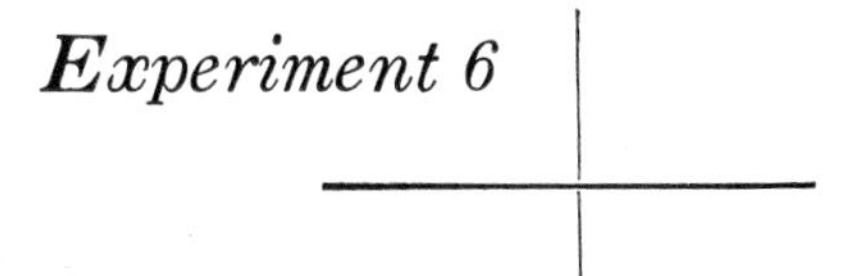

Experiment 6

The Ratio of the Heat Capacities of Gases

The determination of the heat capacity or specific heat of gases is not easy experimentally, but comparatively simple methods are available for measuring the ratio of heat capacities. The method of Clement and Désormes is one such procedure and is described in this experiment. The ratio γ of specific heat capacities and of molar heat capacities is, of course, the same:

$$c_P/c_V = C_P/C_V = \gamma \tag{69}$$

The volume of a gas may undergo a change in three different ways, namely, isothermally, isopiestically or isobarically, and adiabatically.

The relation between P and V for an isothermal change is given by Boyle's law

$$PV = k_1 \tag{70}$$

while for isobaric changes the relation between V and T is given by Charles' law. For adiabatic changes the relation between P and V is given by the following equation:

$$PV^{\gamma} = k_2 \tag{71}$$

Assume two identical samples of gas, one in a perfectly insulated container in which adiabatic changes may be studied, the other in a container of the same dimensions but arranged so that the gas may be kept at constant temperature; initially both samples of gas have the same volume, temperature, and pressure (point A in Fig. 8). If each sample

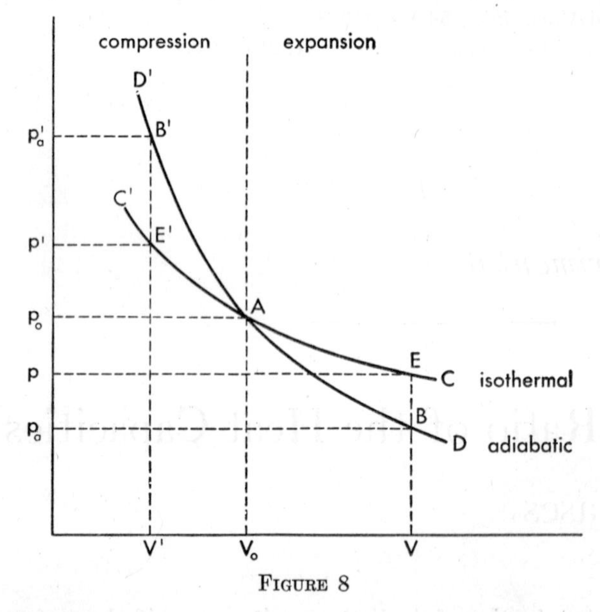

FIGURE 8

of gas is allowed to expand to the same new volume, from V_o to V, the pressure of the sample undergoing adiabatic expansion will be the smaller. The adiabatic expansion follows the curve AD while the isothermal expansion follows the curve AC. If each sample of gas is compressed to the same new volume, from V_o to V', the pressure after the change will be larger for the adiabatic process as shown by considering the curves AC' and AD'.

It can be shown from equations 70 and 71 that the ratio of the slope of the adiabatic change to the isothermal one is γ:

$$
\begin{aligned}
&PV^{\gamma} = k_2 && PV = k_1 \\
&\log P + \gamma \log V = \log k_2 && \log P + \log V = \log k_1 \\
&\frac{1}{P}\,dP + \frac{\gamma}{V}\,dV = 0 && \frac{1}{P}\,dP + \frac{1}{V}\,dV = 0 \\
&\frac{dP}{dV} = \frac{-\gamma P}{V} && \frac{dP}{dV} = \frac{-P}{V}
\end{aligned}
$$

$$
\frac{\dfrac{dP}{dV}\ \text{(adiabatic)}}{\dfrac{dP}{dV}\ \text{(isothermal)}} = \gamma \tag{72}
$$

If the volume and pressure changes were very small, the curves AD and AC might be considered as approaching straight lines whose slopes have the ratio AB/AE. Then

$$
\frac{AB}{AE} = \frac{P_o - P_a}{P_o - P} \tag{73}
$$

and it will be shown that this ratio is approximately equal to γ.

In this experiment, a sample of gas (air or carbon dioxide) is allowed to expand adiabatically through a known pressure interval with a consequent fall in temperature, and then to absorb heat from the surroundings until the initial temperature is restored, giving the final pressure of an isothermal expansion. The differences $P_o - P_a$ and $P_o - P$ are measured, from which γ may be calculated; if the relation

$$
C_p - C_v = R \tag{74}
$$

is assumed, both C_p and C_v may be calculated.

Apparatus A 5-gal. bottle; hand bellows or atomizer bulb; manometer containing dibutyl phthalate or similar liquid, equipped with a meter stick; glass stopcock; short section of $\frac{1}{2}$-in. glass tubing (cut from test tube and retaining the lip end); rubber stoppers to fit; calcium chloride drying tube; two celluloid buret readers (useful for obtaining the manometer readings).

Procedure It is assumed that the room temperature will remain constant throughout the experiment. Air is pumped into the bottle until a pressure difference of 10–20 cm. of dibutyl phthalate is obtained. When temperature equilibrium with the surroundings is attained, the manometer readings will not change; record these values. The rubber stopper A is now pulled out and immediately reinserted tightly. The gas expands from pressure P_o to atmospheric pressure P_a so quickly that practically no heat is gained from the surroundings (adiabatic). However, in a short time (3–5 min.) the gas returns to room temperature, and the final manometer levels are obtained and recorded. Obtain the barometric pressure.

Five to ten readings should be made with air, in this manner. Carbon dioxide, obtained from a steel bottle or Kipp generator, may then be substituted. If the gas is obtained from a steel bottle it is advisable to insert a pressure release trap between the tank and the inlet (Fig. 7).

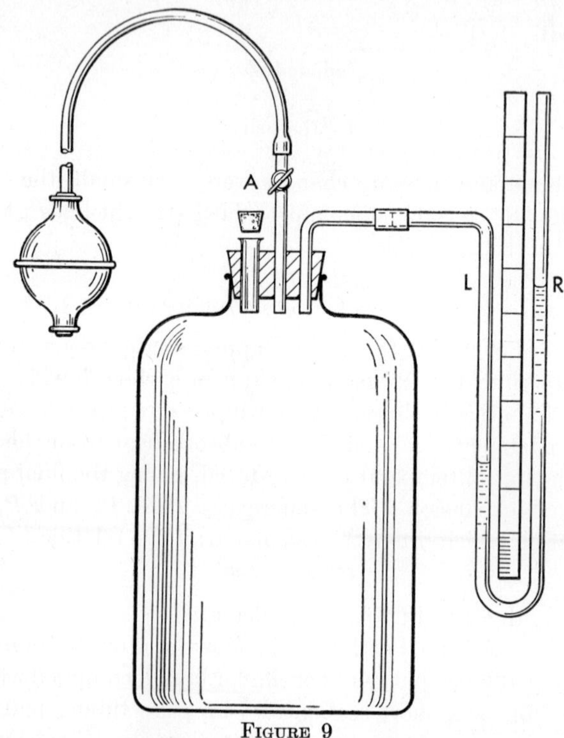

FIGURE 9

The gas should be dried by passing through calcium chloride. As a large amount of gas is necessary to displace all the air from the bottle, it is more convenient to use a duplicate outfit which is left filled with carbon dioxide. Arrange the data as illustrated in Table 4.

bar. press. —— cm. TABLE 4 t —— °C.

TRIAL	R_o INITIAL (cm.)	L_o INITIAL (cm.)	$R_o - L_o = h_o$ (cm.)	R FINAL (cm.)	L FINAL (cm.)	$R - L = h$ (cm.)	CALC. γ
1							
2							
3							
4							
5							
6							

Calculations In equation 73 it is evident that $P_o - P_a = h_o$, the initial manometer difference. Also, since $P_o - P$ is the difference between initial and final pressures, $P_o - P = h_o - h$, and equation 73 becomes

$$\gamma = \frac{h_o}{h_o - h} \tag{75}$$

Since a ratio is involved, the measured quantities are expressed directly in centimeters of dibutyl phthalate, rather than changing into centimeters of mercury. The student should calculate and tabulate values of γ and the average (arithmetical mean) for each gas. The average error of a single observation (average deviation) is also computed; any values showing a deviation as much as four times the average are discarded, and a new average and average deviation are computed (see page 5). Calculate the average error of the arithmetical mean. Finally, the percentage deviation from the accepted value is determined. C_p and C_v are calculated by simultaneous solution of equations 69 and 74, and are compared with values from the literature.

Discussion It was mentioned that the pressure ratio of equations 73 and 75 is only approximately equal to γ. The exact equation is obtained as follows: the P-V relation for the adiabatic change for one mole of gas (eq. 70) becomes in this case:

$$P_oV_o^\gamma = P_aV_a^\gamma,$$

This may be written

$$(V_a/V_o)^\gamma = P_o/P_a \tag{76}$$

For the isothermal change

$$P_oV_o = PV_a \quad \text{or} \quad V_a/V_o = P_o/P \tag{77}$$

Pa = atm pressure
Po = ho
P = h.

Inserting this value of V_a/V_o in equation 76

$$(P_o/P)^\gamma = P_o/P_a,$$

and taking logarithms

$$\gamma(\log P_o - \log P) = \log P_o - \log P_a$$

or

$$\gamma = \frac{\log P_o - \log P_a}{\log P_o - \log P} \tag{78}$$

Equation 78 is the more exact equation for the specific heat ratio. The student should recalculate one or two of his best results using this equation, and compare with the value obtained using equation 75. It is advisable to employ seven place logarithms for this calculation. The pressures are expressed in centimeters of mercury or dibutyl phthalate. However the units should be consistent.

That equation 78 reduces to equation 73 as an approximation is shown by expanding each logarithm as a series

$$2.303 \log x = (x - 1) - \tfrac{1}{2}(x - 1)^2 + \tfrac{1}{3}(x - 1)^3 - \cdots \approx (x - 1) \quad (79)$$

and dropping all but the first term of each series. It is evident that conditions used in this experiment are ideal for using the approximate equation; *i.e.*, the pressure changes are very small compared to the total pressure.

The maximum error of the derived result may be calculated by assuming that the manometer readings L and R may be estimated to ± 0.05 cm. This is not an unreasonable assumption since it represents the average error that attends the observation with a simple meter stick.

Assume that the following values were obtained:

Initial	$R_o = 25.0 \pm 0.05$	$L_o = 15.0 \pm 0.05$
Final	$R = 21.4 \pm 0.05$	$L = 18.6 \pm 0.05$

Then

$$h_o = R_o - L_o = (25.0 \pm 0.05) - (15.0 \pm 0.05) = 10.0 \pm 0.1$$
$$h = R - L = (21.4 \pm 0.05) - (18.6 \pm 0.05) = 2.8 \pm 0.1$$
$$\therefore h_o - h = (10.0 \pm 0.1) - (2.8 \pm 0.1) = 7.2 \pm 0.2$$

Employing Method 1, page 9, to calculate the maximum (or minimum) and normal values of the function (eq. 75)

$$\pm \Delta\gamma = \frac{10.1}{7.0} - \frac{10.0}{7.2}$$
$$= 0.05$$

Thus it may be concluded that $\gamma = 1.39 \pm 0.05$. Any experimental result that does not fall within this range is probably caused by incorrect observations of L and R or by errors of manipulation. Since certain experimental procedures do not readily lend themselves to evaluation, the actual error of γ may be different from the calculated one. Compare the maximum error as calculated above with that obtained from the experiment.

Calculate the maximum error of γ using the arithmetical mean of all L and R readings obtained with one gas. The error of L and R may be that suggested in the illustration.

If the student calculates the maximum error of the derived quantities C_P and C_V, it will be observed that the error is quite large. This indicates that the method cannot be used to evaluate these quantities with any degree of accuracy.

REFERENCES

Crouthamel and Diehl, *Anal. Chem.*, **20,** 515 (1948)

Gas analysis apparatus employing the velocity of sound.

Glasstone, S., *Textbook of Physical Chemistry,* 2d ed., Chap. 3., D. Van Nostrand Company, Inc., New York, **1946**

Rundle, *J. Am. Chem. Soc.*, **66,** 1797 (1944)

The van der Waal's constant a from C_p/C_v measurements.

Stuckey and Saylor, *ibid.*, **62,** 2922 (1940)

Density of dibutyl phthalate.

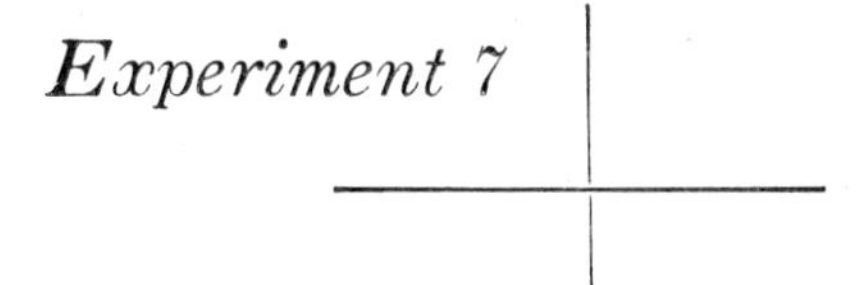

The Density of Liquids

The density d of any solid, liquid, or gas is defined as the mass M per unit volume, thus

$$d = \frac{M}{V} \tag{80}$$

Density is a dimensional quantity and is expressed in various ways, such as g./ml., lb./cu. ft., etc.

Equation 80 may be expressed in a more fundamental way. The total mass of any given quantity of material is equal to the product of the mass m of each molecule and the number n of molecules present. Placing this in equation 80

$$d = \frac{n \cdot m}{V} \tag{81}$$

When two liquids (or solids) are compared, since equal volumes do not necessarily contain equal numbers of molecules, it follows from equation 81 that

$$\frac{d_1}{d_2} = \frac{n_1 \times m_1}{n_2 \times m_2} \tag{82}$$

Thus the density of two liquids may be and probably will be different, even though the molecules have the same mass. This is illustrated by isomeric organic compounds, such as normal and isopropyl alcohol. The density of a liquid is proportional to the mass of the molecules and the closeness of packing in a given volume. The latter is dependent upon the size of the molecules, their shape, and the specific attractive forces.

Another quantity frequently used is specific gravity. This term is defined as the relative density of two substances, one of which is selected as the standard. Thus, specific gravity, when d_b is taken as the standard, is

$$\text{sp. gr.} = d_a/d_b \qquad (83)$$

Specific gravity, in contrast to density, is a dimensionless quantity.

Since the substances a and b do not usually have the same temperature coefficient of volume expansion, the ratio changes with temperature. If d_b is taken as unity by choosing water at 4°C. as the standard, the specific gravity becomes numerically equal to the density.

In this experiment several methods of measuring density, of different degrees of accuracy and precision, will be illustrated.

The direct weighing of a known volume of liquid Weigh a clean dry 50-ml. graduated cylinder upon an ordinary platform balance. The cylinder is filled to the 50-ml. mark with a 5 per cent sugar solution (or any other substance designated by the instructor) and it is again weighed. Since the mass of liquid occupying a known volume has been determined, the density may be obtained by substituting the data in formula 80.

The above procedure can be used to obtain the density with a maximum error of approximately ± 2 per cent. This can be shown if it is assumed that the volume is known to ± 1 ml. and the mass is obtained to ± 0.1 g.

Specific gravity by the hydrometer method The specific gravity of a liquid may be measured by a hydrometer, which is based upon Archimedes' principle of floating bodies. The commercial hydrometer is a centrally loaded float which sinks in a liquid until the mass of the liquid displaced equals that of the float. It follows that in liquids of different densities the depth of immersion of the hydrometer will not be the same, and accordingly it may be designated as a variable immersion instrument.

While one hydrometer could be designed to indicate specific gravity over a large range of values, practically it is found desirable to construct hydrometers which are useful over short intervals. In this way, greater accuracy is obtainable.

The hydrometer scale reads specific gravity directly because the manufacturer locates the scale in the stem so that when the instrument is placed in water at the specified temperature the scale reading is unity

($d_a/d_b = 1$, in eq. 83). When the hydrometer is placed in a second liquid at the specified calibration temperature $t°$, the scale reading corresponds to sp. $gr._{t°}^{t°}$. This permits the calculation of density to be made since the density of water at the calibration temperature is known; that is, sp. $gr._{t°}^{t°} \times d_b^{t°} = d_a^{t°}$.

When the temperature of the second liquid is different from the specified value $t°$, the specific gravity should be recorded as sp. $gr._{t°}^{t°_1}$ where $t°_1$ is the new temperature. Conversion to density is limited in this case to those liquids whose volume coefficient of expansion is known.

Determine the specific gravity of various designated liquids. Calculate the density of the samples. If the volume coefficient of expansion for the liquids is known, calculate the density at 25°C. See handbooks for specific details.

The Westphal balance The Westphal balance is capable of measuring the specific gravity or density of liquids with an accuracy of about one part in 1000. Like the hydrometer, its use is based upon the principle of Archimedes for submerged bodies. The balance, shown in

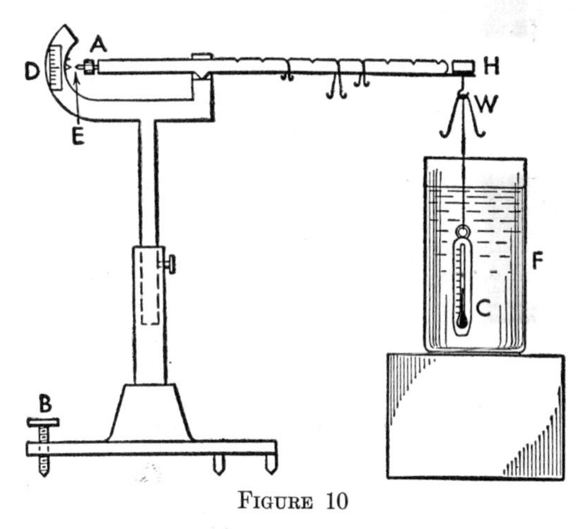

FIGURE 10

Fig. 10, is first adjusted to equilibrium with the plummet C suspended in air, with the use of screw B and counterpoise A until the pointer is opposite zero on the scale. When the plummet is immersed in pure water at the temperature specified by the manufacturer and the unit weight W is placed on the hook H, the pointer should again read zero.

If the instrument is properly adjusted and the temperature of the water is correct, we may write

$$W = Vd_{H_2O} \tag{84}$$

where V is the volume of the plummet and d_{H_2O} is the density of water at the specified temperature. Corrections for the buoyant effect of air on the weight W and the plummet are omitted since they are negligibly small. If the plummet is immersed in a second liquid (x) at the same temperature, a new weight W_x is necessary to re-establish equilibrium, and for the new condition we have

$$W_x = Vd_x \tag{85}$$

Equations 84 and 85 may be combined, and assuming that the specified temperature is 18°, the following equation results:

$$\frac{W_x}{W} = \frac{d_x^{18°}}{d_{H_2O}^{18°}} = \text{specific gravity}_{18°}^{18°} \tag{86}$$

The absolute magnitude of the weights W and W_x need not be known since only their ratio is involved. Further, since $d_{H_2O}^{18°}$ is known, the density of x may be calculated.

The Westphal balance should only be used at the specified calibration temperature. This limitation results because a definite numerical ratio (unity) between the mass of the unit weight W and the mass of water displaced by the plummet has been selected.

Since the density of a given sample and water vary unequally with change of temperature, the numerical values of specific gravity will likewise be different. In order to obtain specific gravity at any other temperature the following method may be employed: The plummet of the Westphal balance is suspended from the left pan support of an analytical balance and its weight W_a is obtained in air. It is then immersed in water, at the desired temperature, contained in a cylinder which is placed on a special support which bridges the balance pan. The special support is generally supplied by the balance manufacturer. The new weight W_2 is obtained; since the balance swings are so strongly damped, the original rest point must be restored entirely by the removal of weights.

The procedure is repeated with the liquid sample and the weight W_3 to establish the same rest point is determined. Neglecting the correction for the buoyancy of air upon the weights and plummet (which are small), the specific gravity is calculated using the equation

$$\frac{W_a - W_3}{W_a - W_2} = \text{sp. gr.}_{t°}^{t°} \tag{87}$$

An accuracy of 0.01–0.02 per cent can be obtained if the temperature is adequately controlled.

Procedure The balance is assembled as shown in Fig. 10, with the plummet suspended in air at H. The indicator point E, attached to the balance arm, is brought into coincidence with the zero point D of the scale by adjusting the leveling screw B (which is placed in line with the central post and balance arm) and the threaded counterpoise weight A, if necessary.

The glass cylinder F is filled to the indicated mark with distilled water at the specified calibration temperature. The large unit weight W is placed on the hook H and the plummet is completely submerged by raising the glass cylinder and sliding the wooden block under it. The plummet must hang free and should not touch the walls of the cylinder. If the points D and E do not coincide, either the temperature is not correct or the weight and plummet are not correctly calibrated.

When the density or specific gravity of some other liquid is to be measured, the cylinder and plummet should be rinsed with distilled water and dried before the cylinder is filled with the sample. If the new substance is miscible with the water or old sample, the cylinder and plummet may be rinsed with the new sample and the drying process may be dispensed with. The sample should be at the specified calibration temperature. The plummet should be immersed to the same depth to avoid changes in surface tension and buoyancy upon the platinum wire.

The beam of the balance is divided into ten equal parts, and the rider weights are made in multiples of ten. The balance is ordinarily equipped with the following riders: 1.0000, 0.1000, 0.0100, and 0.0010. With the unit weight 1.0000 on the hook H, the 0.1000 rider on the fifth, the 0.0100 rider on the sixth and the 0.0010 rider on the third notch, the specific gravity is, by the principal of moments, equal to

$$1.0000 + 5/10 \times 0.1000 + 6/10 \times 0.0100 + 3/10 \times 0.0010 = 1.0563$$

The weights for the Westphal balance may be calibrated by the methods used for analytical weights. The plummet may be calibrated for use at its specified temperature ($t°$) by weighing it when suspended from an analytical balance, first in air and then submerged in water at $t°$. The difference of these weights represents the weight W_1 of water displaced by the plummet. Obviously, the weight of water displaced and the unit weight W should be equal. If the weights do not agree, all specific gravity calculations should be corrected using the following equation

$$\text{sp. gr.}_{t°}^{t°} = \text{sp. gr.}_{1\,t°}^{t°} \times \frac{W}{W_1} \qquad (88)$$

where sp. $\text{gr.}_{t°}^{t°}$ is the true specific gravity and sp. $\text{gr.}_{1\,t°}^{t°}$ is the experimentally measured value.

The student should measure the specific gravity of various samples designated by the instructor at the specified calibration temperature. The density of the sample may also be calculated with the use of equation 86.

The specific gravity and density might also be obtained by employing the Westphal plummet and the analytical balance as described.

Density by the use of pycnometer or specific gravity bottle The graduated cylinder method for determining density is an approximate method at best, for the results are impaired by the relatively poor sensitivity of the balance, the inaccuracy of the calibrations of the graduated cylinder, and the poor temperature control. Any method designed to measure density with a high degree of precision must utilize accurate temperature control and exact duplication of the volume. There are many types of pycnometers and the student should acquaint himself with them by consulting catalogues.

The first task that must be accomplished is to establish the exact volume of the pycnometer. This can be done by filling it with distilled water at a known temperature, weighing, and then calculating the volume from the known density of water. The pycnometer should ordinarily contain from 10 to 25 milliliters, since in this range the error of weighing will be vanishingly small. However, with careful filling and weighing much smaller pycnometers can be used.[1]

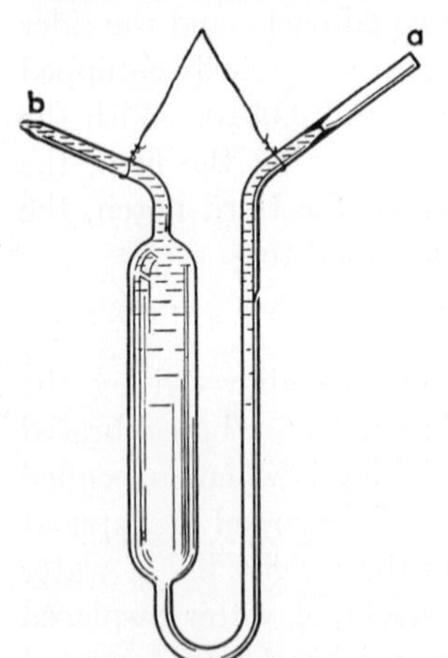

FIGURE 11

The pycnometer is washed with warm soap solution, rinsed with water several times, filled with dichromate cleaning mixture, and allowed to stand for one-half to one hour. It is emptied, rinsed several times with distilled water, and allowed to drain by standing inverted on filter paper, and finally dried by drawing air through it.

The dry pycnometer is carefully weighed to ±0.0001 g. Call this weight W_1. It is then filled with recently boiled and cooled distilled water whose temperature is slightly less (1–3°) than the temperature of the measurement. If the pycnometer shown in Fig. 11 is to be used, the sample is sucked into the pipet by attaching a piece of rubber tubing at *a*, while the tip *b* is held under the surface of the liquid. The pyc-

[1] Anderson, *Anal. Chem.*, **20**, 1241 (1948); Schneider, *Qualitative Organic Microanalysis*, page 98.

nometer is then placed in either a large beaker or thermostat, with temperature regulation maintained at 25.0 ± 0.1°C. or better. The pycnometer may be suspended in the bath by a wire hook hung upon a support above the beaker or bath.

After the pycnometer or specific gravity bottle has been in the thermostat for 15–20 minutes, the volume is adjusted. A piece of filter paper is used to remove the excess drop on the stopper of the specific gravity bottle (Fig. 12), leaving the capillary completely filled. If the pycnometer is used, it is tilted to withdraw excess liquid by placing a piece of filter paper against the tip *b*. If too much is withdrawn, a stirring rod carrying a drop of liquid is touched to the tip *b* to readjust it to the mark. It is replaced in the constant temperature bath for 15 minutes and the meniscus readjusted if necessary. The pycnometer is removed from the bath, dried with a cloth, and accurately weighed after it has attained the temperature of the balance case. Call this weight W_2. The more often the above procedure is repeated, the better the technique the student acquires, and hence the smaller will be the error of measurement.

FIGURE 12

The specific gravity and density of another sample, such as a 5 per cent sugar solution, is determined by first rinsing the pycnometer or specific gravity bottle with distilled water, draining, and drying as described above. It is again weighed, dried, and the weight is recorded as W_3. W_1 and W_3 should agree to ±0.0002 mg. Any greater difference may be due to water adsorbed on the weighing vessel, caused by inconsistent procedures in drying or to extraneous materials acquired by careless handling. The sample is introduced into the pycnometer which is then thermostated, adjusted to the mark, and accurately weighed. Call this weight W_4. The temperature of the thermostat should be recorded, especially if it is different from the original calibration temperature.

Calculations The specific gravity may be obtained with a reasonable degree of accuracy by use of the following formula:

$$\frac{W_4 - W_3}{W_2 - W_1} = \text{sp. gr.}_{t^\circ}{}^{t^\circ} \tag{89}$$

For many purposes this result is sufficiently accurate. In order to express the specific gravity at $t°$ relative to water at another temperature, say $t_1°$, the following equation should be employed

$$\text{sp. gr.}_{t_1^\circ}{}^{t^\circ} = (\text{sp. gr.}_{t^\circ}{}^{t^\circ}) \times (d_{t^\circ}/d_{t_1^\circ}) \tag{90}$$

where $d_{t°}$ and $d_{t_1°}$ are the densities of water at the temperatures $t°$ and $t_1°$. Note that if $t_1° = 4°$C., then the sp. gr.$_{4°}^{t°}$ is numerically equal to the density of the sample at $t°$.

To obtain a higher degree of accuracy, corrections are made for the weight of air displaced from the pycnometer when it is filled and for the additional air displaced by the brass weights from the right-hand balance pan when the filled pycnometer is weighed. The approximate volume is

$$V = \frac{W_2 - W_1}{d} \tag{91}$$

where d is the density of water. The weight of the pycnometer emptied of air is

$$W_1 - d_a V \tag{92}$$

where $d_a = 0.001177$, the density of air which has a relative humidity of 50 per cent at 25° and 760 mm. The weight of the filled pycnometer, corrected for the air displaced by the additional brass weights is

$$W_2 + d_a\left(\frac{W_2 - W_1}{d_b}\right) \tag{93}$$

where d_b, the density of brass, is 8.4. Then the vacuum weight of the water is

$$W_{\text{vac.}} = W_2 + d_a\left(\frac{W_2 - W_1}{d_b}\right) - (W_1 - d_a V) \tag{94}$$

The volume of the pycnometer is obtained by the usual method, that is

$$V_o = \frac{W_{\text{vac.}}}{d} \tag{95}$$

The student should calculate the true volume of the pycnometer at 25°C.

If the pycnometer is to be used at a different temperature, t_1, from that at which it was calibrated, t_o, the volume V_o must be corrected by the use of the general interpolation formula 96:

$$V_1 = V_o[1 + 2.6 \times 10^{-5}(t_1 - t_o)] \tag{96}$$

The density d_L of the sample is obtained by first calculating the vacuum weight of the sample using equation 97, and finally using equation 95 and the known volume V_o to calculate the density.

$$W_{\text{vac.}} = W_4 + d_a\left(\frac{W_4 - W_3}{d_b}\right) - (W_3 - d_a V) \tag{97}$$

If the volume of the pycnometer need not be known, the following formula may be used to compute d_L:

$$d_L = \frac{(W_4 - W_3)d}{W_2 - W_1} - \frac{0.001177(W_4 - W_3 - W_2 + W_1)}{W_2 - W_1} + \frac{(W_4 - W_3)d}{W_2 - W_1} \times 2.6 \times 10^{-5}(t_1 - t_o) \tag{98}$$

The student may calculate the density of the liquid sample, using this formula. Note that the last term drops out if $t_1 = t_o$, as it is the correction term for the volume expansion of the pycnometer.

It should be possible to obtain the density to approximately ± 0.0001 units by the procedure of this experiment. If better temperature control and a more exact estimation of the density of the air at the existing temperature and humidity are obtained, it is possible to estimate the density to ± 0.00001 units. The greatest possible accuracy is obtained when the above factors are known and the duplication of the volume is carefully controlled. The latter factor is obtained with pycnometers of special design.

REFERENCES

Anderson, *Anal. Chem.*, **20,** 1241 (1948)

Dreisbach, *Ind. Eng. Chem., Anal. Ed.*, **12,** 160 (1940)

Schneider, F., *Qualitative Organic Microanalysis,* John Wiley & Sons, New York, **1946**

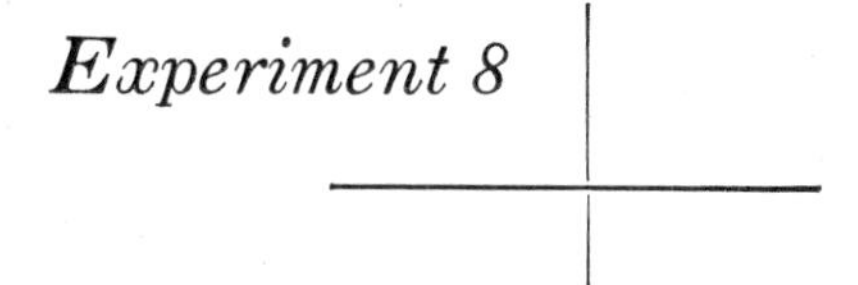

The Viscosity of Liquids

In an investigation of the flow of liquids through glass capillary tubes, Poiseuille found that the viscosity coefficient could be expressed by the following equation

$$\eta = \frac{P\pi r^4 t}{8LV} \qquad (99)$$

where V is the volume of liquid delivered in time t, through a capillary of radius r and length L, with a hydrostatic head or pressure P; η is the coefficient of viscosity, a specific constant characteristic of each substance.

The measurement of the absolute coefficient of viscosity is not easy because of the difficulty of measuring the terms in equation 99. In an apparatus designed so that equal volumes of liquid can flow through the same capillary of length L and radius r, equation 99 may be written

$$\eta = k'hdgt \tag{100}$$

hdg being substituted for P. The gravitational unit g remains constant in any given location. If then the height h through which the liquid falls is kept constant, equation 100 becomes

$$\eta = kdt \tag{101}$$

By employing a liquid of known viscosity and density, and measuring the time t that it takes for the given volume to pass through the capillary, it is possible to evaluate k, the dimensional constant of the apparatus. Then the viscosity coefficient of any other liquid can be obtained if the time of outflow is measured with the same apparatus. The density d is, of course, determined separately.

The same result can be obtained from slightly different considerations. If two liquids are compared in the apparatus, it follows that

$$\frac{\eta_1}{\eta_2} = \frac{d_1t_1}{d_2t_2} \tag{102}$$

If η_2, the coefficient of viscosity of one of the substances, is known from a previous measurement, then η_1, the viscosity of the other liquid, can be calculated from the measured quantities, d_1, d_2, t_1, t_2. It should be observed that the quantity d_1/d_2 in equation 102 represents "specific gravity" when d_2 refers to water. Hence specific gravity, which is easily determined with a Westphal balance or specific gravity bottle, may be used in calculating the coefficient of viscosity.

It is necessary to maintain good temperature control since a change of 1°C. produces a variation of about 2 per cent in the measured viscosity. The viscosity decreases with an increase of temperature, and the relation between η and T for many liquids may be expressed by an empirical equation such as

$$\log \eta = A/T + B \tag{103}$$

where A and B are empirical constants.[1]

Another quantity frequently employed is known as "fluidity," and is defined as the reciprocal of the viscosity:

$$\phi = 1/\eta$$

In general, for mixtures of nonpolar liquids it is found that fluidities are additive; this fact is expressed by the following equation

$$\phi = x_a\phi_a + x_b\phi_b \tag{104}$$

[1] Souders, *J. Am. Chem. Soc.*, **59**, 1252 (1937)

where ϕ is the fluidity of the mixture whose components in the pure state have fluidities of ϕ_a and ϕ_b respectively, and x_a and x_b may represent the volume fraction or mole fraction of the components.

It is known that no general relation exists between the viscosity of a solution and its composition, and most of the results obtained by various investigators are expressed by empirical formulas. It might be supposed that if the two components of a solution formed a compound, say of equimolecular proportions, the viscosity-composition curve should indicate a maximum. This is approximately true, though the maximum does not ordinarily occur at the composition corresponding to the compound, but is more often shifted in the direction of the component of greater viscosity. Experience has further shown that the existence of a maximum does not necessarily indicate that the formation of a compound has occurred. Likewise, the absence of a maximum in the viscosity-composition curve does not insure that a compound has not been formed.

The unit of viscosity is called the poise, and has the dimensions of dynes $\times$ seconds/cm^2. This can be shown by substituting the dimensions for the quantities P, r, t, L, and V in equation 99. The poise is a rather large unit, so that frequently the millipoise, $\frac{1}{1000}$ of the poise, is used. For expressing the viscosity of gases the micropoise, one millionth of a poise, is sometimes used. Occasionally the centipoise, a unit which is $\frac{1}{100}$ of the poise, is useful.

Apparatus Ostwald viscometer (100 second); 5-ml. pipet; stop-watch or electric timer; thermometer graduated in 0.1 or 0.2°C.; large beaker; rubber tubing; pinch clamp; 2.5-cm. piece of 6-mm. glass tubing with fire polished end; air or motor stirrer (slow speed); Westphal balance or specific gravity bottles. In selecting mixtures for study, the viscosity of the various components should not differ by more than two or three fold.

Procedure The viscometer (Fig. 13) is washed thoroughly with a warm soap solution, which should be filtered since suspended particles might clog the capillary. The viscometer is rinsed thoroughly with water and clamped upon a stand with an empty beaker under it. It is filled with a freshly prepared warm cleaning mixture and allowed to stand for at least one-half hour before emptying and rinsing with distilled water.

Pipet 5 or 10 ml. of water into the right arm of the viscometer, the quantity depending upon the size of the bulb D. Place the viscometer in a thermostat at 25.0 $\pm$ 0.1°C., and mount it as nearly vertical as possible. Suck the liquid up into the left arm above the mark A by attaching a piece of rubber tubing. Release the finger from the end of the mouthpiece, and allow the liquid to flow back; do this several times to be sure that no air bubbles remain on the wall of the capillary. Again suck the liquid up into the left arm above *A* and, using a stopwatch, determine the time it takes the liquid to pass between marks *A* and *B*. Repeat this procedure so that at least four readings are obtained. The viscometer should have a time of outflow of about 100 seconds for water.

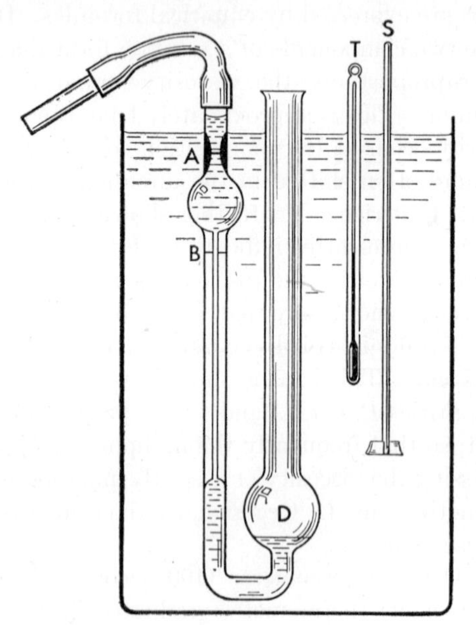

FIGURE 13

The observations should not deviate more than ±0.2 second among themselves; any greater deviation is due to a dirty capillary or lack of timing practice.

Rinse the apparatus first with pure methanol and then with pure benzene. Pour the rinsing liquid into the large arm of the viscometer, and work it back and forth through the capillary several times. Mixtures of the following volume proportions are prepared:

	(1)	(2)	(3)	(4)	(5)
C_6H_6	100	75	50	25	0
CCl_4	0	25	50	75	100

The density of each sample is obtained either by a Westphal balance or a specific gravity bottle, at 25°C. or at the temperature of the thermostat.

The viscometer should be rinsed out three times with each new sample, and four observations of the time of efflux obtained. The data should be entered in a table with headings like those in Table 5.

The viscosity of mixtures of isopropyl alcohol and water may be measured. The density of these mixtures is measured and the composition is obtained by reference to a prepared graph which relates density and composition. Consult various handbooks for the composition-density relationships.

TABLE 5 t ___ °C.

SAMPLE	TIME OF OUTFLOW	DENSITY	CALC. η EQ. 102	ACCEPTED η	% ERROR	$\frac{\eta_x}{\eta_{H_2O}}$	ϕ OBS.	ϕ CALC.

Calculations Calculate the *A.M.* of the time of efflux for each sample. Calculate the probable error of a single observation for each sample.

Calculate the absolute viscosity and the probable error for each sample, employing the known viscosity of water as the standard of comparison. In order to obtain the viscosity of water at the temperature of the experiment, it may be necessary to interpolate[1] the data in the tables. The absolute viscosity of H_2O at 25°C. is 8.93 millipoise. When substituting the quantity "time" in equation 102, employ the *A.M.* and probable error as illustrated in Expt. 4.

Plot the fluidity of the samples as ordinate against the mole fraction as abscissa, and draw a line (or curve) through the points. Prepare another graph of absolute viscosity (ordinate) and mole fraction (abscissa). Repeat, substituting volume fraction for mole fraction. Interpret the curves.

The relative viscosity of the different liquids is calculated with respect to water assuming the viscosity of H_2O to be unity in equation 102. This is another way in which the results may be expressed.

Discussion The student will notice that certain errors are inherent in every experimental procedure. For example, there may be a short interval between the time that the liquid passes the marks *A* and *B*, and the starting and stopping of the stopwatch. If these intervals are not the same, the error is included in the recorded time of outflow. Is it the same for a person at all times?

There is, of course, the variation of viscosity with temperature: if the temperature changes by 0.1°C., the viscosity may vary by about 0.2 per cent. Another error is the result of not mounting the viscometer in the vertical plane. How much error is realized if the instrument is mounted

[1] A graphical procedure may be used.

one degree from the vertical? Will it cause the time of outflow to be greater or less? How will this in turn affect the observed viscosity? To what per cent does the pipet used to deliver the measured volume of liquid reproduce its delivery? How will the observed viscosity be affected if slightly differing quantities of liquid are introduced into the viscometer?

The student may also inquire about the design of the viscometer. Is any turbulent flow present at the lower end of the capillary, and if there is, to what extent will the results be affected? Can the same viscometer be used for the measurement of mobile and viscous liquids? What liquid should be employed for the standard of comparison for very viscous substances? How do thixotropic liquids differ from normal liquids? These are questions which are important, and whose answers should be known if one is to carry out extended measurements of viscosity.

Actually, the equation of Poiseuille should be employed only when the velocity of the liquid leaving the capillary approaches zero; otherwise a suitable kinematic correction factor should be made. If the velocity is small, the correction factor is small.

The precise determination of viscosity involves the elimination or at least the reduction of the possible errors which have been mentioned.[1]

REFERENCES

Chadwell and Asnes, *J. Am. Chem. Soc.*, **52,** 3493 (1930)
Hurd, *ibid.*, **68,** 364 (1946)
Souders, *ibid.*, **59,** 1252 (1937)
Van Wazer, *Ind. Eng. Chem.*, **41,** 189 (1949)

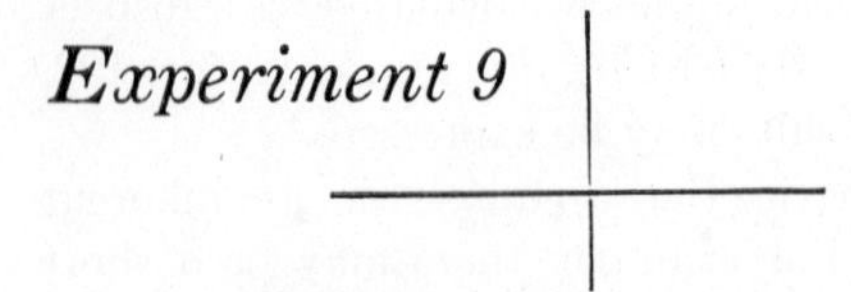

Experiment 9

The Surface Tension of Liquids

The Capillary Rise Method

When a capillary tube is dipped into a liquid, the latter will rise above the outer plane surface if it wets the tube walls. Let the upward force

[1] Chadwell and Asnes, *J. Am. Chem. Soc.*, **52,** 3493 (1930)

per centimeter of contact be γ_1 (Fig. 14); the total upward force in the round tube is $2\pi r\gamma_1$, where r is the radius of the tube. This is balanced by a downward force, which equals the volume of liquid in the tube above the outside surface multiplied by its density (d) and the gravitational constant (g):

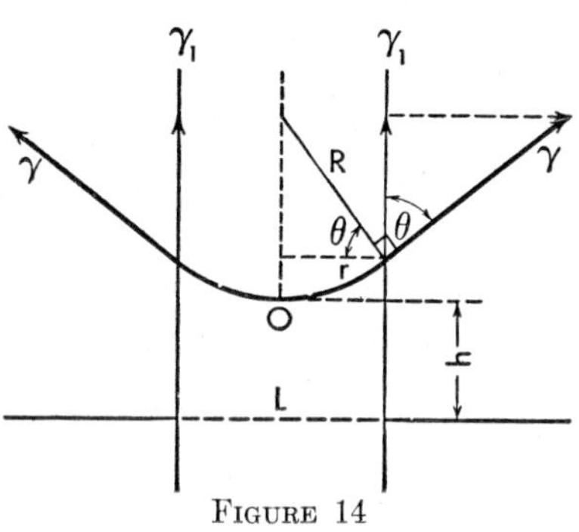

FIGURE 14

$$2\pi r\gamma_1 = \pi r^2 hdg$$

or

$$2\gamma_1 = rhdg \qquad (105)$$

Surface tension γ is defined as the force per centimeter required to extend the surface in its own plane. From Fig. 14 the relationship between γ, the true surface tension and γ_1, the upward force is $\gamma_1 = \gamma \cos\theta$. Substituting and rearranging

$$2\gamma = \frac{hdgr}{\cos\theta} \qquad (106)$$

If the wetting angle θ is zero or very nearly so, $\cos\theta \approx 1$ and this equation may be written:

$$\gamma = \frac{hdgr}{2} \qquad (107)$$

The radius r can be measured with a microscope micrometer, or by weighing the mercury necessary to fill a known length of the tube. Often the tube is calibrated with a liquid of known surface tension whereupon it may be used to measure the surface tension of another liquid. In this case

$$\frac{\gamma_a}{\gamma_b} = \frac{h_a d_a}{h_b d_b} \qquad (108)$$

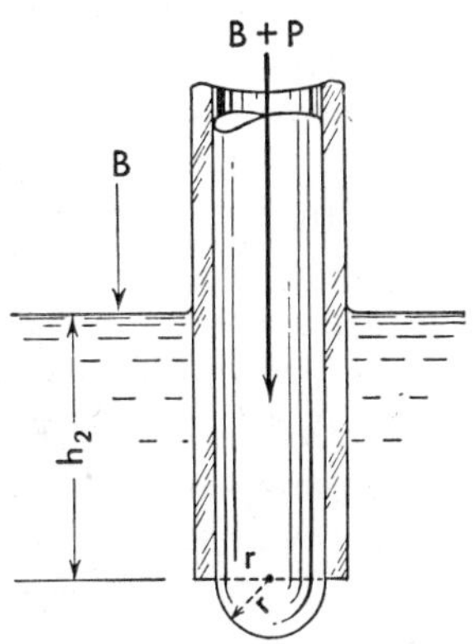

FIGURE 15

THE BUBBLE PRESSURE METHOD

In order to form a hemispherical gas bubble of radius r on the end of a capillary tube located h_2 cm. below the surface of a liquid (Fig. 15), the pressure acting upon the liquid in the capillary will have to be increased by an amount equal to P above atmospheric (B). When the bubble is formed, the total force acting to detach it is $\pi r^2(B + P)$. The opposing force is equal to the sum of $\pi r^2 B$, the hydrostatic force $\pi r^2 h_2 dg$, and the force of surface tension acting on the inner circumference of the capillary tip $2\pi r\gamma$. When all upward and downward forces are balanced, then

$$\underbrace{2\pi r\gamma + \pi r^2 h_2 dg + \pi r^2 B}_{\text{upward forces}} = \underbrace{\pi r^2(B + P)}_{\text{downward forces}}$$

Upon canceling equalities, dividing by πr, and rearranging

$$\gamma = \frac{r}{2}(P - h_2 dg) \tag{109}$$

It is to be observed that the pressure P is that recorded by the manometer, that is, it is the excess above atmospheric pressure.

Upon comparing two liquids as before

$$\frac{\gamma_a}{\gamma_b} = \frac{P_a - h_a d_a g}{P_b - h_b d_b g} \tag{110}$$

Since the pressures P_a and P_b are measured on a manometer, each may be substituted by its equivalent $\Delta L_m d_m g$, where ΔL_m is the manometer rise and d_m the density of the manometer liquid. Upon substituting in equation 110 there is obtained

$$\gamma_a = \gamma_b \left\{ \frac{\Delta L_m{}^a \cdot d_m - h_a d_a}{\Delta L_m{}^b \cdot d_m - h_b d_b} \right\} \tag{111}$$

Apparatus Manometer, short arm 15 cm., long arm 30 cm.; 250-ml. side-neck flask; 50-ml. buret; capillary tubing; large test tube or bottle 5-10 cm. in diameter; large beakers to serve as constant temperature baths, etc.; dibutyl phthalate; two celluloid buret readers; Westphal balance or pycnometer.

Procedure Obtain a 20–30 cm. length of capillary tubing graduated in millimeters for surface tension measurements, or the stem of a broken thermometer (the 110° range is quite suitable). Place the thermometer stem between two meter sticks and with the aid of a white card and a hand lens, calibrate the degree markings in terms of centimeters. Take at least four readings, at least 10 cm. apart, at various points along the scale; the average will give the best value for the relation between the scale readings in degrees and length (cm.). Select a prominent marking 1–2 cm. from the end and determine exactly how far this is from the end. Take at least four different readings and calculate the average. This fixed point is chosen to locate the position of the capillary tip under the liquid surface.

The capillary should be thoroughly cleaned. Freshly prepared cleaning mixture is drawn into the tube and allowed to remain for at least one-half hour or, better yet, over night. A water aspirator connected to a safety trap through old rubber tubing is very useful for this purpose.

Rinse the capillary several times by drawing distilled water through it while connected to the safety trap and aspirator.

Clean the large test tube and fill it to the desired depth with a sample of distilled water. Then place the tube in a constant temperature water bath maintained at 20° ± 0.1°C. Mount the capillary in a rubber

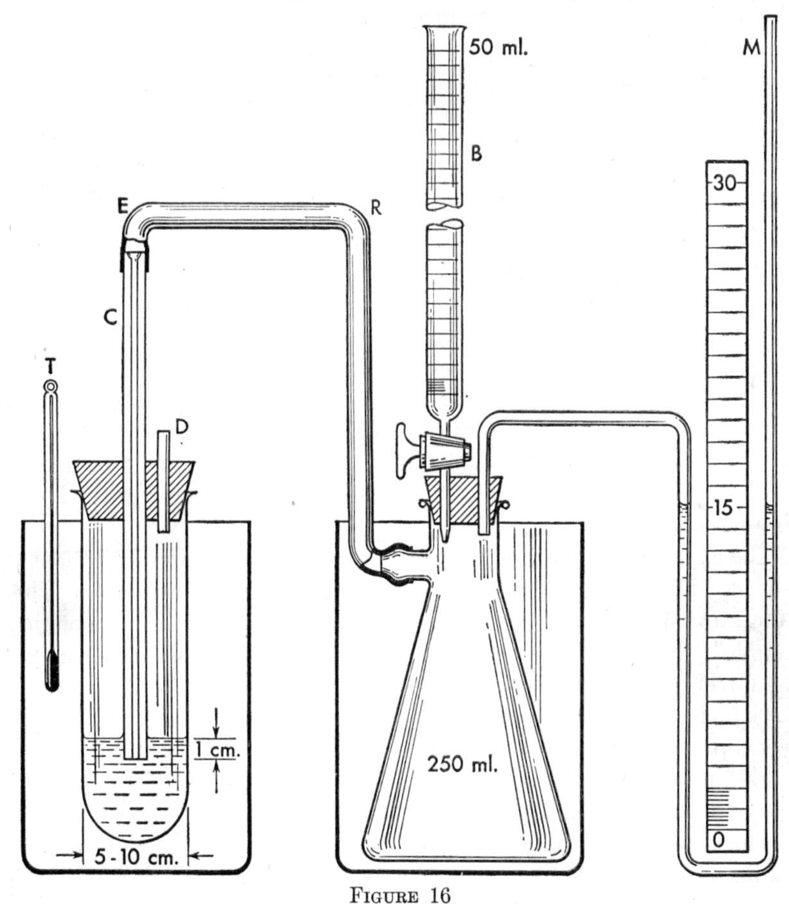

FIGURE 16

stopper and assemble it in the apparatus as shown in Fig. 16 so that it is vertical. The tube should be located so that the selected mark coincides with the surface of the liquid. The capillary can always be adjusted to the same position if it is viewed from the under side of the liquid surface. Disconnect the rubber tubing at *E* (Fig. 16) and attach a small piece of rubber tubing with a glass mouthpiece to *D*. Apply gentle pressure to force the liquid about 1 cm. above the point of maximum rise in the capillary. Release the pressure and obtain the height of rise, after waiting about three minutes for the liquid to recede. Then apply gentle suction so that the liquid is depressed about 1 cm.; release the pressure and again obtain the height of rise after waiting three minutes. A hand lens should be used to observe the meniscus; care should be taken not to introduce a parallax error of reading. If the difference in the readings amounts to more than one division on the scale, the capillary is dirty and should be recleaned. The average of the two readings is taken to be the height of rise and is recorded in Table 6.

To obtain the surface tension by the bubble pressure method, the rubber tubing R is connected to the capillary tube at E and dibutyl phthalate is admitted into the flask. The buret stopcock is adjusted so that air bubbles are formed slowly on the end of the capillary tube at the rate of one every two to five seconds. Upon closing the stopcock the formation of bubbles should stop, otherwise the pressure is in excess of that required to form them; if the manometer levels should change, look for leaks. With liquids of high surface tension, the manometer levels will be observed to rise during the formation of the bubble and fall as it is detached. The maximum difference in the levels is recorded in Table 7. Two celluloid buret readers are useful for observing the levels simultaneously.

The capillary is removed, connected to a water aspirator and the end is placed in a small sample of methanol, which is drawn through it. This procedure should be used for rinsing the capillary for the remaining samples; the only precaution to be observed is that the new sample should be miscible with the previous one. Rinse the test tube with methanol and fill to approximately the same level as before. Replace the capillary, being sure that it is vertical, adjust to the selected mark, and obtain the height of rise for the new sample. The pressure required to form bubbles is then obtained. It is advisable to repeat the measurement several times to obtain an average for the pressure readings.

The surface tension of benzene, which is used as the standard of comparison in this experiment, should now be obtained by both methods. Various other liquids, such as toluene, carbon tetrachloride, aniline, and nitrobenzene should also be measured. It is necessary to know the densities of the liquids at the temperature of the thermostat. They are measured with a Westphal balance or a specific gravity bottle. The densities may also be obtained from a handbook, the small error for any differing temperatures being neglected.

Calculations *Capillary rise method.* The accepted value for the surface tension of benzene at the temperature of the experiment is obtained from a handbook or from the following interpolation formula:

$$\log \gamma = 1.85689 + 1.23 \log \left(1 - \frac{T\,°A}{561.6}\right) \tag{112}$$

TABLE 6 t ____ °C.

	RISE IN DEGREE MARKS	RISE IN cm.	CALC. EQ. 108 γ	AC-CEPTED γ	% ERROR	$2\gamma/r$ EQ. 107	r CALC.
Benzene							
Water							
Methanol							
Toluene							

Calculate the surface tension of the various liquids, using the surface tension of benzene as a standard, with the aid of equation 108.

Calculate the value of $2\gamma/r$ with the aid of equation 107.

Calculate the value of r from the above quantity using the measured values of γ (Table 6, col. 3).

Bubble pressure method. Calculate the surface tension of the various liquids using the surface tension of benzene as a standard with the aid of equation 111.

Calculate the value of $2\gamma/r$ with the aid of equation 109.

Calculate the value of r from the above quantity using the measured values of γ.

TABLE 7 t ____ °C.

	ΔL_m	CALC. γ EQ. 111	ACCEPTED γ	% ERROR	$2\gamma/r$ EQ. 109	r CALC.
Benzene						
Water						
Methanol						
Toluene						

Discussion *Capillary rise method.* Perhaps the greatest difficulty in the measurement of surface tension is caused by the adsorption of surface active substances. These impurities are generally firmly adsorbed and are therefore difficult to remove. They are especially noticeable when the surface tension of an aqueous solution is measured, as they lower it considerably even though present in infinitesimal quantities, since they collect at the interface glass-water-air or vapor.

When greater accuracy is desired, a cathetometer should be used to obtain the height of rise. In the present method, an error of 1 mm. in a measured height of rise of 10 cm. will lead to an error of about 1 per cent. The surface tension is also a function of the temperature; a change of 1° may alter its value by about 0.5 per cent.

The radius of a capillary may vary along its entire length. For example, Harkins examined 500 ft. of tubing to find several suitable lengths of uniform diameter. Probably an error of 3 per cent is a reasonable minimum to expect with an uncalibrated tube. Two other possible errors are that the diameter of the container is too small and that the capillary is not mounted in a truly vertical position. For results of greater accuracy, it is customary to correct the height of rise for the amount of liquid above the bottom of the meniscus. As this correction is small, it has been neglected in the above calculations.

Bubble pressure method. The errors which are present in the capillary rise method are also inherent to the bubble pressure method, in addition to other possible factors. For example, the error of the manometer readings enters into the calculation of surface tension. The hydrostatic pressure on the bubble is not quite correctly given by h_2dg; it is slightly larger than this, for the lower part of the bubble is located a finite distance below the tip of the capillary. For precise results, the wall thickness at the tip of the capillary should be very small and the end surface should be flat and at right angles to the bore.

General discussion The maximum error of the surface tension by the capillary rise method may be obtained by applying the usual procedures of error analysis to equation 108. The method of normal and maximum values will be used although there is one factor, namely the change of surface tension with temperature, which is not accounted for. Hence it should be realized that the calculated error will itself be inexact because of the failure to make this correction. If the temperature coefficient of surface tension and the variation of the thermostat were known, a more accurate evaluation of the maximum error could be obtained.

Assume the following quantities (and their possible errors) were obtained in order to calculate γ_a, the surface tension of a given sample:

$$\gamma_b = 72.75 \pm 0.05 \qquad d_a = 0.9000 \pm 0.0002$$
$$h_a = 7.0 \pm 0.1 \text{ cm.} \qquad d_b = 0.9970 \pm 0.0002$$
$$h_b = 14.0 \pm 0.1 \text{ cm.}$$

Since the relative error of the density is so much smaller than the others, it may be neglected; then:

$$\pm\Delta\gamma_a = \left(\frac{\gamma_b h_a d_a}{h_b d_b}\right)_{\text{max.}} - \left(\frac{\gamma_b h_a d_a}{h_b d_b}\right)_{\text{normal}}$$
$$= \left(\frac{(72.80 \times 7.1 \times 0.9000}{13.9 \times 0.9970}\right) - \left(\frac{72.75 \times 7.0 \times 0.9000}{14.0 \times 0.9970}\right)$$
$$= 33.57 - 32.84$$
$$\pm\Delta\gamma_a = 0.73$$

It can therefore be concluded that the surface tension is 32.84 ± 0.73.

Calculate the maximum error for one of the samples used in this experiment. Assume that the surface tension of benzene, to be used as the standard, is known within ±0.03 units.

REFERENCES

Cupples, *J. Am. Chem. Soc.*, **67,** 987 (1945)
Davis and Bartell, *Anal. Chem.*, **20,** 1182 (1948)
Surface tension of molten materials.
DeWitt and Roper, *J. Am. Chem. Soc.*, **54,** 444, 455 (1932)
Gans and Harkins, *ibid.*, **52,** 2287, 2289 (1930)
Holmes, H. N., *Laboratory Manual of Colloid Chemistry,* Chap. 8, John Wiley & Sons, Inc., New York, **1934**
Steinbach, *J. Chem. Ed.*, **21,** 582 (1944)

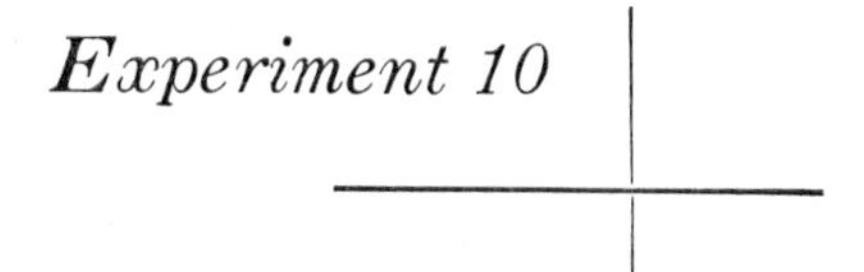

Refractometry

The principle of refraction of light was discovered by Snell in 1621 and is sometimes stated as follows: The ratio of the sines of the angles of incidence and of refraction of a beam of light is a constant for a given liquid, that is $\sin i/\sin r = n$ (a constant). Since the index of refraction is a specific constant for each substance, its determination furnishes a method of identification. The angle of refraction varies with the wave length of the light employed, but not necessarily in the same manner for different liquids, since dispersive power (the ability to spread white light into a spectrum) may differ from one liquid to another. For this reason, the measurement of refractive index requires that light of known wave length be employed, and the yellow sodium light which has a wave length of 5890 Angstrom units (the D line) is often selected.

The refractive index of a substance decreases with an increase of temperature, since the density (d) decreases, there being fewer molecules present per unit volume at the higher temperature to refract or deviate the light. A quantity, known as the specific refraction (r), is independent of temperature and may be calculated by the following equation:

$$r = \frac{1}{d}\frac{n^2 - 1}{n^2 + 2} \tag{113}$$

The refractive index of a liquid is not affected by ordinary changes in barometric pressure; the density is only slightly changed by large increments in pressure.

To compare the refractive power of pure liquids, a quantity known as the molar refraction (R) is also employed. This is equal to the product of the specific refraction (r) and the molecular weight (M), thus

$$R = r \cdot M \tag{114}$$

Since the refraction of light is an additive property of the atoms and partly a constitutive one of the molecules, it is possible to assign numerical values of atomic refraction to the various functional groups present in organic compounds. In this way, the molar refraction of a compound can be calculated on the basis of an assigned structure and compared with the experimental value.

There are several simple methods [1] for measuring the refractive index of a liquid with an accuracy of about one per cent. With present-day apparatus, such as the Abbé refractometer, a precision of about two parts in ten thousand can be obtained; the Pulfrich instrument gives a precision of one part in a hundred thousand. In many industrial laboratories, the Abbé refractometer is used for routine determinations as it is simple and rapid to operate. The Pulfrich instrument is more suitable for precise research work. For further information, consult Gibb, *Optical Methods of Chemical Analysis*.

In this experiment it will be assumed that the Abbé refractometer is to be used. This instrument is designed to give, by direct scale reading, the index of refraction for the sodium D line when white light is used as the source of illumination. Details of construction may be found in the bulletins issued by the manufacturers; the operation is indicated diagrammatically in Figs. 17 and 18.

[1] Edwards and Otto, *Ind. Eng. Chem., Anal. Ed.*, **10**, 225 (1938)

White light reflected from the mirror M enters the lower prism P_i, and is scattered in all directions at its upper ground surface. Rays passing through the liquid film into the upper prism P_r at an angle near 90° to its surface will be bent the least on entering prism P_r; rays entering P_r at an angle near 0° will be bent the most. The latter will constitute the edge of the bright field observed when the telescope is moved to the proper position, since, of course, no rays can enter P_r at a smaller angle.

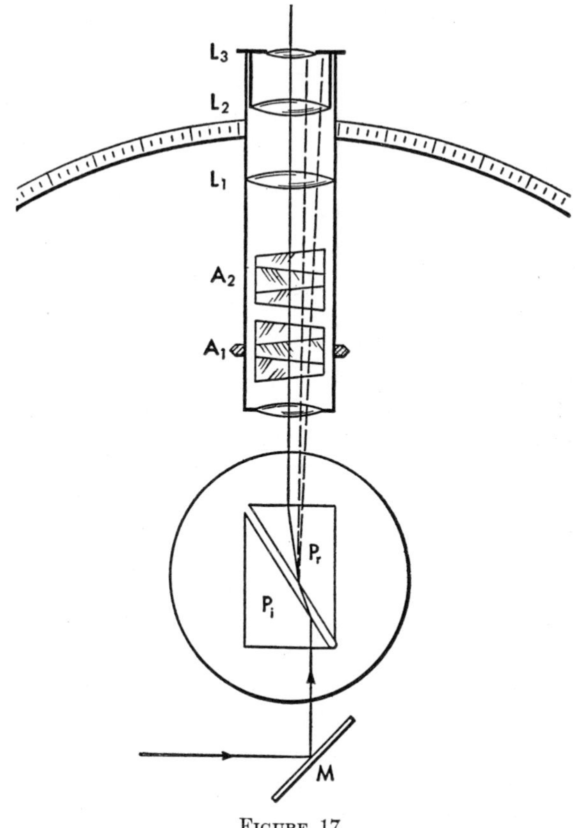

FIGURE 17

The boundary between light and dark fields will ordinarily be fringed with color because both the liquid and the upper glass prism refract light of different wave lengths to different extents (optical dispersion). The Amici prisms in the telescope barrel (A_1 and A_2) correct for this dispersion. They are direct vision prisms made by cementing a wedge of flint glass between two prisms of crown glass. If A_1 spreads white light into a spectrum, A_2 reverses this dispersion when it is set at an angle of 180° to A_1. When set at a somewhat different angle, it will correct for the dispersion caused by the liquid and prism P_r as well.

The Amici prism adjustment is made by turning the knurled ring on the telescope barrel until the color fringe disappears, and the sharpest possible light-dark boundary is seen in the eyepiece. The reading on the compensator then gives the dispersive power of the liquid.

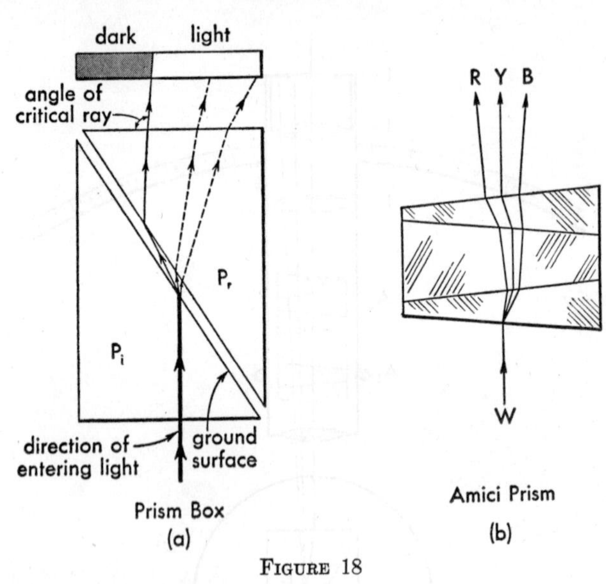

FIGURE 18

A new type of Abbé refractometer does not have built in Amici compensating prisms and illumination is obtained from a sodium vapor lamp or other monochromatic source instead of white light.

Apparatus Abbé refractometer; medicine droppers; two burets; silicone grease or phosphoric acid to lubricate stopcocks of burets.

Procedure The instructor should be sure that the instrument is correctly adjusted. A glass test piece of known refractive index is provided by the manufacturer, and pure liquids of known refractive index can also be used to check the scale reading.

The mirror is illuminated with a microscope lamp, a suitably placed electric lamp with a frosted surface or shield, or with daylight from a north window. Measurements may be made at room temperature, or better, with water of controlled temperature flowing through the water jackets on the instrument. This may be siphoned from a large thermostat or recirculated by a small pump.

The refractive index of a relatively nonvolatile liquid is determined by placing a few drops on the ground glass surface of the lower prism with a medicine dropper and then closing and clamping the prism box. The telescope is focused upon the cross hairs in the field by turning the eyepiece (L_3). Bring the edge of the dark band to the intersection of the cross hairs, and adjust the compensator until the colored fringe disappears and a sharp dark-white contrast is obtained. The dark field [1] should be uniformly gray. Carefully adjust the instrument until the intersection of the cross hairs and the dark edge of the band coincide. Obtain the refractive index on the scale with the aid of the reading telescope, estimating to the fourth place.

When volatile liquids or mixtures are used, the sample is introduced through the groove provided in the prism box, as this procedure reduces the error caused by evaporation of the more volatile component. Since the dispersive power of a solution varies with its composition, it is necessary to readjust the compensator for each sample.

The refractive index of the following compounds is determined: acetone, toluene, bromobenzene, ethyl alcohol, normal and isopropyl alcohols. Enter the data in Table 8.

The refractive index of a mixture of two liquids in varying proportions is determined. Any one of the following pairs may be selected: methanol–carbon tetrachloride, ethanol–water, carbon tetrachloride–benzene, ethanol–benzene, isopropyl alcohol–benzene, methanol–benzene, isopropyl alcohol–water, chloroform–acetone, and carbon tetrachloride –methyl acetate. Burets are used to make up the various mixtures and the following ratios are suggested:

A (ml.)	20	18	16	14	12	10	8	6	4	2	0
B (ml.)	0	2	4	6	8	10	12	14	16	18	20

The containers are securely stoppered to prevent loss by evaporation. Enter the data in Table 9. It is interesting to place one of the mixtures in a shallow dish and determine the refractive index as evaporation progresses.

TABLE 8

Sample	n_D^t	Density	Specific Refraction	Molar Refraction	*R* Calc.	% Error

[1] If the light and dark fields appear splotchy in the eyepiece, there is probably not a uniform film of liquid between the prisms. If both fields appear gray with little contrast, the eyepiece may be out of focus or the illumination inadequate.

TABLE 9

MOLE PER CENT OF A	VOLUME PER CENT OF A	n_D^t

Calculations The specific refraction of each pure liquid sample is calculated, the necessary density values being obtained by measurement or from tables in the various handbooks or the *International Critical Tables*. The molar refraction of each sample is also calculated.

The atomic refractions are obtained from a handbook and the molar refractions of the compounds selected for measurement are calculated. The known structural formulas are used. Determine the per cent of error between observed and calculated values.

Prepare a plot of the refractive index of the mixtures employed as ordinate and mole per cent (mole fraction) as abscissa.

Prepare a plot of refractive index of the mixtures employed as ordinate and the volume per cent as abscissa.

REFERENCES

Dreisbach, *Ind. Eng. Chem.*, **40,** 2269 (1948)

Correlation of density and refractive index by the Eykman equation.

Edwards and Otto, *Ind. Eng. Chem., Anal. Ed.*, **10,** 225 (1938)

Gibb, T. R. P., *Optical Methods of Chemical Analysis*, McGraw-Hill Book Company, Inc., **1942**

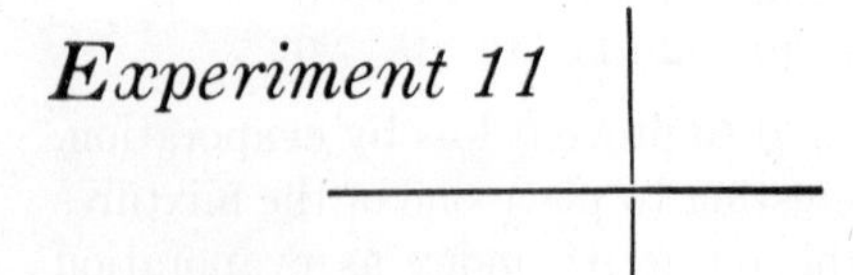

Polarimetry

The ability to rotate the plane of polarized light through a definite angle is possessed by a number of solids, liquids, and solutions. The rotation of the plane of polarization takes place if molecular or structural asymmetry is present. Accordingly, solids may be optically active as either of the above conditions may be present; however, liquids (with the exception of liquid crystals) cannot have structural asymmetry, and they rotate the plane of polarization only because of molecular asymmetry. The plane of polarization may be rotated to the left or right; in the former case a substance is said to be levorotary while in the latter it is called dextrorotary.

The angle of rotation is characteristic of the substance; it also depends upon other factors such as the wave length of the polarized light, the temperature, and the number of molecules per unit volume. These conditions must be carefully controlled if measurements of a high degree of accuracy are desired.

The polarimeter is constructed with two Nicol prisms which are made of calcite (Iceland spar). The fixed one, located at the front of the instrument, produces plane polarized light; the second prism is mounted in a movable graduated circular scale and is known as the analyzer. The observation tube, which holds the sample, is placed between the polarizer and the analyzer. The angle through which the incident beam of plane polarized light is turned by the sample is measured by rotating the analyzer.

In some precision polarimeters, the optical system is arranged so that the incident light is divided into two fields. This is accomplished by placing another small Nicol prism N at a small angle behind the polarizer, so that it covers one half the field. The resulting two beams of polarized light, which are slightly out of phase, are then matched for intensity of grayness in the analyzer. This type of instrument, known as the Lippich half shadow polarimeter, is illustrated diagrammatically in Fig. 19. For further information, consult Gibb.[1]

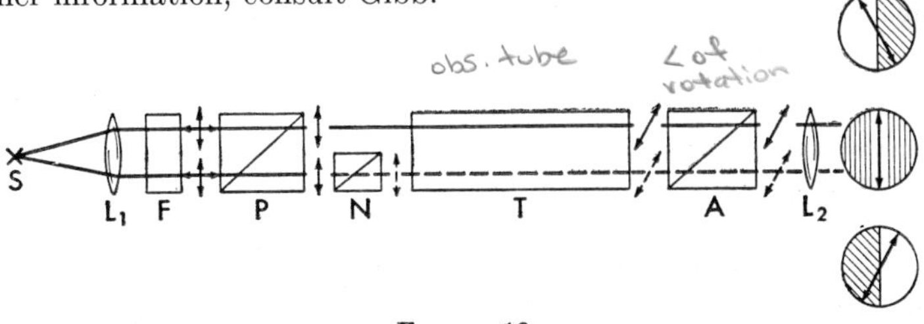

FIGURE 19

The angle of rotation (A) of a liquid is proportional to the number of optically active molecules and the latter is equal to the product of the length of the observation tube (L) and the number of molecules per unit length, or to the density, d. Then

$$A = [A]_D{}^t \cdot L \cdot d \tag{115}$$

[1] *Optical Methods of Chemical Analysis*

where $[A]_D{}^t$, the proportionality constant, is known as the specific rotation and is dependent upon the chemical nature of the sample. Practically it is found that L should be expressed in decimeters, otherwise the constant $[A]_D{}^t$ becomes a rather small number. The subscript D indicates that the measurement was made with sodium light of wave length equal to 5890 Å.

Since the angle of rotation depends upon the number of optically active molecules between the prisms, it is necessary to specify the concentration when solutions are employed. Then

$$A = [A]_D{}^t \cdot \frac{L \cdot C}{100} \tag{116}$$

where C is the number of grams of solute per 100 ml. of solution. The factor 100 is used to divide C to obtain the grams of solute per milliliter, an equivalent density term. Occasionally the concentration is expressed in terms of weight and density of solution

$$A = [A]_D{}^t \cdot \frac{L \cdot g \cdot d}{100\,w} \tag{117}$$

where w is the weight and d the density of solution containing g grams of solute per 100 g. of solution.

Another term employed to express the optical activity of a substance is the molar rotation, which is the product of the specific rotation and the molecular weight M:

$$[M]_D{}^t = [A]_D{}^t \cdot M \tag{118}$$

The angle of rotation is affected by temperature changes, though usually to a small extent. This may be partly ascribed to the change in the density of the sample with temperature, partly to changes in molecular association, solvation, or other molecular interaction. The temperature coefficient is characteristic of the chemical identity of the sample. For example, the specific rotation of sucrose at different temperatures is given by

$$[A]_D{}^t = [A]_D{}^{t=0°} + 0.0144t$$

where t is the temperature in centigrade degrees.

The specific rotation of a dissolved substance generally decreases somewhat at higher concentrations for similar reasons; equation 116 is quite accurate for dilute solutions.

Apparatus Polarimeter; cane sugar; 100-ml. volumetric flasks. A sodium vapor lamp [1] may be used as a source of the yellow D line.

[1] A 100-watt electric light bulb may be substituted for the sodium vapor lamp if the latter is not available. The results with a single pure substance are comparable, but the value of the specific rotation cannot be compared with those in the literature for monochromatic light.

If such a lamp is not available, asbestos which has been treated with a saturated solution of sodium chloride, dried, and wrapped with platinum or nichrome wire and held in a Meker burner is used. The source is placed 10–15 cm. in front of the polarimeter to avoid a heat strain in the condensing lens. In order to obtain more nearly monochromatic light, a glass absorption cell F containing a 9 per cent solution of $K_2Cr_2O_7$ is placed in front of the condensing lens L_1 or in the space provided. If the mercury arc lamp is used as a source of monochromatic light, a suitable glass filter is used to isolate the line of wave length 5461 Å.

The polarimeter tube should be kept at constant temperature if the instrument is so designed. While the experiment may be performed at room temperature, the precision will not be as great as when the temperature is controlled; nevertheless, the accuracy is sufficient for most purposes.

The end caps of the observation tubes should be firmly screwed in place; but they should not be screwed on so tightly that the glass plates are optically strained (change in angle of rotation). Accurate results are obtainable only when the solutions are clear, as cloudy ones may contain particles of colloidal dimensions which produce polarized light by scattering. Be certain to fill the observation tube completely so that there will be no air bubbles in the light path. For best results, the polarimeter should be located in a dark room and the observer should not be subjected to any bright light.

Procedure Several solutions of cane sugar are made by dissolving accurately weighed amounts (± 0.001 g.) of oven dried samples in a total volume of 100 ml. (volumetric flask). Suggested approximate weights are 5, 10, 15, and 20 gram samples.

The observation tube is filled with distilled water and placed in the polarimeter. The zero point of the scale is obtained by rotating the analyzer A until half of the field appears black. The eyepiece L_2 is adjusted until the line dividing the dark and light fields appears sharp. The analyzer is now turned until the two fields are darkened and are of equal grayness. Record the setting to the 0.01 degree. Obtain a total of eight readings, approaching the zero point alternately from the left and right. The average of these readings, A_o, is the zero point of the scale.

The lever which adjusts the setting of the small auxiliary nicol N (located at the front of the polarimeter) should never be disturbed during any series of readings, otherwise it will be necessary to relocate the zero point of the scale. This prism is generally set at an angle of 10–15 degrees for clear solutions but for cloudy or colored ones, it should be made larger.

The observation tube is rinsed with several small portions of the sugar solution and then filled completely. The angle of rotation is obtained from four independent observations, the setting being approached alternately from the left and right. The angle of rotation of the remaining sugar samples is determined in the same way. Determine the angle of rotation of a sugar solution of unknown concentration.

TABLE 10 A_o =

Sucrose g/100 ml.	A Obs.	A Corr.	$[A]_D^t$	$[M]_D^t$

Calculations Plot the observed angle of rotation, corrected for the zero point reading, as ordinate against the concentration in grams per 100 ml. of solution as abscissa. A line (or curve) should be drawn through the points and the origin. Obtain the slope of the line. What does the slope correspond to? Obtain the concentration of the unknown sample.

The specific rotation of each sample is calculated (eq. 116). The molar rotation of each sample is calculated (eq. 118).

Calculate the probable error of a single observation and of the arithmetical mean. The results should enable one to make some conclusion regarding the precision of the polarimeter.

REFERENCES

Gibb, T. R. P., *Optical Methods of Chemical Analysis*, McGraw-Hill Book Company, Inc., New York, **1942**

Noller, *J. Chem. Ed.*, **24,** 600 (1947)

Experiment 12

Colorimetry

When a colored solution is illuminated with white light, part of the light is absorbed by the solute molecules and converted ultimately into heat (providing chemical reaction does not occur) and the remainder is transmitted. It is assumed that the solvent molecules do not absorb any of the wave lengths present in white light. Only those wave lengths of light absorbed by the solute are of use in colorimetric analysis.

The relationship between the intensity I_o of the incident light and that portion I which is transmitted is given by the Beer-Lambert law

$$\log \frac{I}{I_o} = -\frac{kLC}{2.303} \tag{119}$$

where k is the absorption coefficient, L is the thickness of the solution, and C is the concentration of the solute. Using this relationship, it is possible to determine the concentration of the solute providing the terms I_o and L can be made constant and I is measurable.

The measurement of I or I/I_o may be made either by visual methods or, with much greater precision, by means of photoelectric cells. It is a difficult task to obtain light of constant intensity and of the requisite wave lengths. The former has been accomplished to a certain extent by operating a lamp source from a special constant voltage transformer. However, many instruments rely upon a rapid interchange of unknown sample and a blank, or a standard sample, to obtain the ratio of I/I_o.

In the spectrophotometer, nearly monochromatic light is obtained by means of a prism or a ruled reflection grating to spread the white light source into a spectrum, any desired narrow spectral band being passed through a slit to the solution cells. Some photoelectric colorimeters employ a grating in a similar manner, but others rely upon filters which transmit a rather wide band of wave lengths. Most colored substances in solution absorb in a similarly wide region in the spectrum, and a filter or combination of filters may be chosen whose maximum transmission corresponds to the maximum absorption of the solutions to be used.

The concentration of solute may be obtained by comparing the intensity of the transmitted light with that from solutions of known concentration, the same light source being incident upon samples of equal thickness. This is the principle of the photoelectric colorimeter. Equation 119 may be written as

$$\log \frac{I}{I_o} = -k'C, \tag{120}$$

a linear equation if Beer's law is valid.

The visual colorimeter is always used to compare an unknown with a standard and it is usually unnecessary to use filtered light. The eye automatically compensates, to a certain degree, for light outside of the absorption band of the colored substance. Equal intensity of transmitted light, from solutions of known and unknown concentration, is obtained by varying the length of the column of one liquid; then

$$L_1C_1 = L_2C_2 \tag{121}$$

Photoelectric Colorimeter

Procedure A standard 0.1 *M* solution of $CuSO_4$ is prepared by weighing clear crystals of the pentahydrate; or more accurately, electrolytic copper may be dissolved in nitric acid and the excess acid fumed off with concentrated sulfuric acid. Solutions of varying concentration are prepared as shown in Table 11, by pipetting the requisite amount of copper sulfate into 100-ml. volumetric flasks, adding ammonia with a cylinder and diluting to the mark with water. The concentrations are given for a cell that is 1 cm. thick. If cells of greater thickness are employed, the concentration will have to be reduced proportionally.

TABLE 11

ml. 0.1 *M* $CuSO_4$	ml. 15 *M* NH_3	ml. 0.1 *M* $CuSO_4$	ml. 15 *M* NH_3
1	5	6	5
2	5	7	5
3	5	8	5
4	5	9	5
5	5	10	5

The actual procedure of making the measurements will not be described as it depends upon the type of instrument available. Consult the directions before making the measurements. Generally the colorimeter is calibrated by measuring the intensity of the transmitted light in terms of the galvanometer reading, using the appropriate filter for known samples. A calibration curve is prepared by plotting log *I* or galvanometer reading as ordinate and concentration as abscissa, and drawing a smooth curve through the points.

If the calibration curve deviates from a straight line, several possibilities are indicated. It may be that Beer's law does not apply to the system, the proper color filters have not been selected, the colored component may be undergoing dissociation or hydrolysis, or that some other type of chemical change is taking place as the concentration is varied.

The Visual Colorimeter

Procedure Prepare a 0.01 per cent solution of $KMnO_4$ either by weighing the necessary amount of solid salt or preferably by diluting a standard solution. A series of solutions from 0.01 per cent to 0.004 per cent in steps of 0.001 per cent is then prepared by dilution.

A quantity of the standard 0.01 per cent solution is introduced into one of the colorimeter cups until the mark is reached. The glass plunger is lowered until it is approximately three-fourths immersed in the solution, the plunger being set at some whole numbered graduation. See Fig. 20. Place the necessary amount of a 0.01 per cent solution in the other cup and adjust the plunger until both half fields have the same intensity. The setting of the standard cup and the second one should agree closely; otherwise, the instrument should be adjusted and special attention should be given to see that both samples receive equal illumination.[1] Repeat the procedure until eight readings have been obtained, alternately approaching the setting four times from above and four times from below the matching position. Calculate the arithmetical mean, the probable error of the *A.M.*, and the probable error of a single observation. This is done so that the precision measure of the determinations may be estimated.

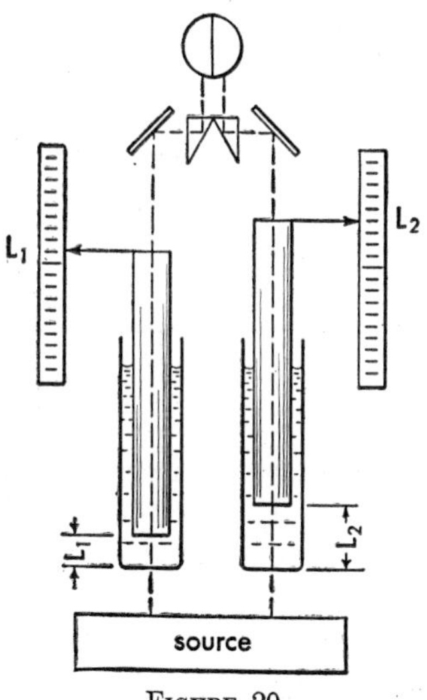

FIGURE 20

Place the 0.009 per cent solution in the second cup after rinsing it out several times, and compare it with the cup containing the 0.01 per cent solution. Do not change the setting of the cup containing the standard solution once it has been fixed in position. Obtain four readings when the fields are matched in the eyepiece. The average of these readings is the accepted value.

Repeat this process for each of the remaining solutions, obtaining four readings for each solution.

Obtain an "unknown" and determine the concentration. Prepare a table and enter all observed data in it.

Calculations Plot the instrument reading as abscissa against the concentration of $KMnO_4$ as ordinate and draw a smooth curve through the points.

From the reading of the instrument and the prepared calibration curve, obtain the concentration of the unknown solutions furnished by the instructor.

From the data obtain the estimated error of C_2 for any one of the known samples; equation 16 (p. 6) will be a suitable function to use.

[1] If the instrument is one wherein the illumination cannot be adjusted, the left cup is adjusted to the arithmetical mean of the values obtained for the right cup. This is equivalent to employing a fixed color standard for a standard concentration.

Note that $L \times C$ = constant. Test this relation with the data for each sample. Obtain the *A.M.* of the constants, the probable error of the mean, and the probable error of a single observation. What can you conclude about the precision of the visual colorimeter?

Determination of the Indicator Constant of a Neutralization Indicator

A neutralization indicator can be used to determine the *p*H of a solution, as it may exist in two forms of different color. One of the forms is generally a nonelectrolyte; the other form may either be an acid or a base. In any case, the following type of equilibrium must be present

$$\underset{\text{acid color}}{H_2O + HIn} \rightleftharpoons H_3O^+ + \underset{\text{base color}}{In^-}$$

and the equilibrium constant for this change, using activities (*a*), is

$$K = \frac{a_{H_3O^+} \times a_{In^-}}{a_{HIn}} \qquad (122)$$

When excess hydrogen ions are present, the indicator exists almost entirely as HIn or the acid form. If an excess of base is present, the indicator exists almost completely as In^- or the base form.

Taking logarithms of the above equation and inserting the relations

$$pH = -\log a_{H_3O^+} \quad \text{and} \quad pK = -\log K$$

we get

$$pK = pH - \log \frac{a_{In^-}}{a_{HIn}} \qquad (123)$$

If the solution is dilute, the activity and concentration are approximately equal and the latter may be used as a first approximation. Equation 123 furnishes a means of determining the indicator constant *K* or *pK* from the ratio of the base color to the acid color in a solution of known *p*H.

Apparatus Block comparator or colorimeter of the Gillespie, Hastings, or Bjerrum wedge type. Various indicators listed in Table 12

TABLE 12

Indicator	*p*H Range	Concentration
Methyl orange	3.1–4.4	0.02 g./100 ml. H_2O
Brom phenol blue	3.0–4.6	0.40 g./100 ml. 95% ethanol
Brom cresol green	3.8–5.4	0.50 g./1.45 ml. 0.1 *N* NaOH, 100 ml. H_2O
Methyl red	4.2–6.3	0.10 g./100 ml. 95% ethanol
Chlor phenol red	4.8–6.4	0.05 g./2.35 ml. 0.1 *N* NaOH, 100 ml. H_2O

may be selected and the practical working range of each is given. Twenty-five matched test tubes (4 in. × ½ in.) whose diameters are within 2–3 per cent. The comparator block is made by drilling six holes to accommodate the test tubes with a close fit. Three small holes (¼ in.) are drilled at right angles through the holes which hold the test tubes. The holes are painted with a flat optical black paint. See Fig. 21. Several burets; medicine dropper; 0.2 *M* Na_2HPO_4; 0.1 *M* citric acid. Approximately 0.001 *M* NaOH and 0.01 *M* HCl.

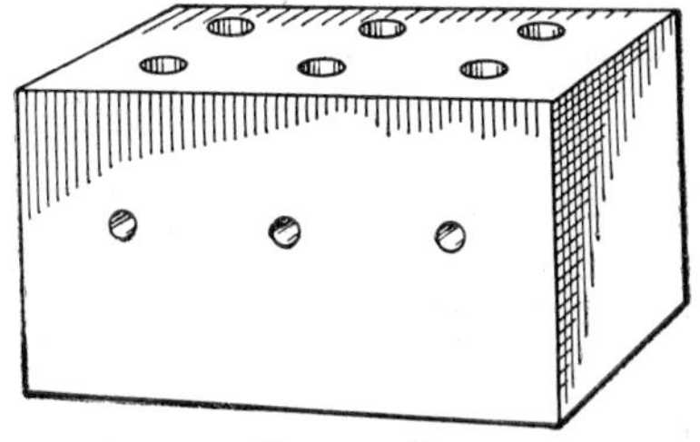

FIGURE 21

The indicator brom cresol green is recommended as the colors are readily matched in a block comparator.

Procedure Use of the block comparator only will be described here. Prepare two series of nine test tubes, each marked from *A* to *I*, and arrange them in test tube racks as shown in Table 13. To each test tube add the number of drops of indicator (a medicine dropper may be used) shown in the circle in the diagram. Add 1 ml. of 0.001 *M* NaOH to each of the test tubes in the base series and 1 ml. of 0.01 *M* HCl to those in the acid series. Add 9 ml. of recently boiled, cooled distilled water from a buret to each and stopper with corks. Invert several times to insure uniformity.

TABLE 13

	A	*B*	*C*	*D*	*E*	*F*	*G*	*H*	*I*
% neutralized	10	20	30	40	50	60	70	80	90
Base series	①	②	③	④	⑤	⑥	⑦	⑧	⑨
Acid series	⑨	⑧	⑦	⑥	⑤	④	③	②	①
$\log \frac{In}{HIn}$	−0.95	−0.60	−0.37	−0.18	0	0.18	0.37	0.60	0.95

The acid and base are added in sufficient amount to change the indicator completely to the base or acid color as the case may be. Upon looking through any two test tubes placed as in Table 13, the same amount of indicator is always present. The color perceived by the eye is, however, determined by the ratio of the acid and base color present.

Select a series of six or seven buffer mixtures from Table 14, whose *p*H range lies within the working range of the indicator. Prepare the buffer solutions by carefully measuring the solutions from a buret into test tubes. Add 10 drops of indicator to each prepared buffer solution, cork and invert several times to mix. Place the test tube in the front middle hole of the comparator block. Another test tube containing distilled water is placed in the hole back of it. The comparator block should be placed at some distance from a source of light, such as a frosted electric light bulb.

TABLE 14

pH	0.2 M Na_2HPO_4	0.1 M Citric Acid
3.0	2.06 ml.	7.94 ml.
3.2	2.47	7.53
3.4	2.85	7.15
3.6	3.22	6.78
3.8	3.55	6.45
4.0	3.86	6.14
4.2	4.14	5.86
4.4	4.41	5.59
4.6	4.68	5.32
4.8	4.93	5.07
5.0	5.15	4.85
5.2	5.36	4.64
5.4	5.58	4.42
5.6	5.80	4.20
5.8	6.05	3.95
6.0	6.32	3.68
6.2	6.61	3.39
6.4	6.93	3.07
6.6	7.28	2.72

Match the color of this test tube with the various pairs of the previously prepared indicator solutions placed on either side of the unknown. For example, the final arrangement of the test tubes in the comparator block might be *CUD*, where *U* stands for the unknown sample. Suppose that the color of *U* is midway between that of *C* and *D*; then the observer would conclude that 35 per cent of the indicator is in the base form and the remaining 65 per cent is in the acid form. Estimate the per cent neutralized for each of the buffered samples containing indicator.

Calculations Using equation 123, calculate pK and K for the indicator, using the data for each of the buffered samples employed. Obtain the arithmetical mean and the probable error of the arithmetical mean for pK and K.

REFERENCES

Gibb, T. R. P., *Optical Methods of Chemical Analysis*, McGraw-Hill Book Company, Inc., New York, **1942**
Hirsch, *J. Chem. Ed.*, **18,** 7 (1941)
Kilpatrick, *J. Am. Chem. Soc.*, **63,** 2667 (1941)
Kolthoff and Guss, *ibid.*, **60,** 2516 (1938)
Mellon, *Ind. Eng. Chem., Anal. Ed.*, **11,** 80 (1939)
Smith and Sullivan, *J. Chem. Ed.*, **9,** 1461 (1932)

Experiment 13

The Measurement of Vapor Pressure

The change of vapor pressure with temperature is given by the differential form of the Clausius-Clapeyron equation, namely

$$\frac{d \ln P}{dT} = \frac{-\Delta H}{RT^2} \tag{124}$$

The equation is more useful when integrated either as an indefinite integral or between specified limits. It is generally used in the following forms:

$$\log P = \frac{-\Delta H}{2.303RT} + \frac{I}{2.303} \tag{125}$$

$$\log \frac{P_2}{P_1} = \frac{-\Delta H}{2.303R}\left(\frac{1}{T_2} - \frac{1}{T_1}\right) \tag{126}$$

The constant of integration I in equation 125 is related to the entropy of vaporization, for it can be demonstrated that when $P = 1$ atmosphere, $\log P = 0$, and

$$\frac{\Delta H}{T} = RI \tag{127}$$

The term on the left-hand side of equation 127 is, by definition, the entropy of vaporization. This term is also part of the relation used by Trouton, namely

$$\frac{\Delta H}{T_b} \approx 21 \tag{128}$$

Using Trouton's relation, the constant I is found to be equal to 10.571. Equation 125 may then be written as

$$\underset{\text{in atmospheres}}{\log P} = \frac{-\Delta H}{2.303RT} + 4.590 \tag{129}$$

Since ΔH may be estimated by Trouton's relation if the boiling point of a pure liquid is known, equation 129 can be used to calculate the approximate vapor pressure at other temperatures. The equation is useful in the absence of data and, of course, will apply more exactly the more closely a substance follows Trouton's relation.

The validity of the Clausius-Clapeyron equation depends upon several assumptions. It is assumed that the heat of vaporization is independent of temperature, that the specific volume of liquid is small compared to that of the vapor, and that the vapor obeys the simple equation of state for gases. Nevertheless, the equation fits experimental data reasonably well, as the approximations involved tend to cancel each other. Many equations have been suggested to give more accurate relations between vapor pressure and temperature.[1]

The latent heat of vaporization may be obtained by a graphical solution of equation 125. When $\log P$ is plotted as the ordinate against $1/T$ as the abscissa, the equation is of the form $y = mx + I$ and the slope m of the curve is given by the relation

$$m = \frac{-\Delta H}{2.303R} \tag{130}$$

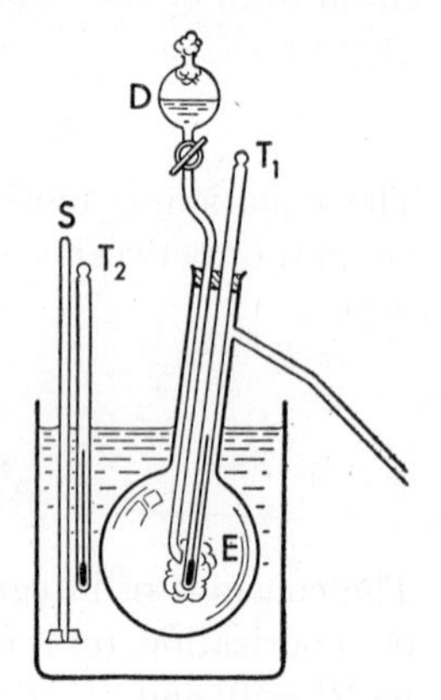

FIGURE 22

METHOD OF RAMSAY-YOUNG

Apparatus The Ramsay-Young apparatus is shown in Fig. 22. It consists of a 250–500 ml. side arm flask; dropping funnel; thermometer (T_1) which reads in tenths or fifths of a degree. The accessory apparatus is shown in Fig. 23. The 2–5 gal. ballast bottle is protected by a wooden box or wire screen. Also pressure tubing; large test tube trap; water aspirator pump; manometer; meter stick; mercury; thermometer (T_2) graduated in whole degrees; large beaker; silicone grease; three-way **T** glass stopcock.

When a water bath is used to heat the sample, liquids boiling below 85°C. must be used; for higher boiling liquids, an oil or glycerin bath is necessary.

Procedure Assemble the apparatus as shown in Figs. 22 and 23. It is advisable to test the apparatus before using to see if it will hold a vacuum. Evacuate with a pump, noting if the manometer remains steady. If the mercury level drops, a leak is present and must be "hunted out" and corrected. Coating the rubber-glass joints with various types of sealing compounds or rubber tape will eliminate the leaks. Always turn stopcocks counterclockwise to open and clockwise to close. Soft rubber stoppers are a good protection against leakages. Use silicone

[1] Thomson, *Chem. Rev.*, **38**, 1 (1946)

grease on the stopcock of the dropping funnel, since organic liquids will dissolve ordinary stopcock grease.

Place pure, redistilled benzene or other liquid boiling below 85°C. in the separatory funnel and evacuate the system until the pressure is 10 cm. or less. Close the **T** stopcock to disconnect the pump. The stopcock of the dropping funnel is opened slightly so that the cotton wrapping around the thermometer is kept moist with liquid, and so that 4–5 drops will fall off the thermometer into the flask each minute. The water bath is heated so that its temperature is 18–20°C. above that registered by thermometer T_1. The purpose of this is to supply heat to the thermometer bulb and to prevent liquid from collecting in flask *E*. The trap *G* is surrounded by a mixture of ice and water to condense the distilled vapor and so maintain a constant pressure at the manometer.

When the temperature and pressure readings have become steady, record them. Stopcock *B* is opened slightly so that the manometer reading is lowered by 2–3 cm.; the water bath is heated to maintain the

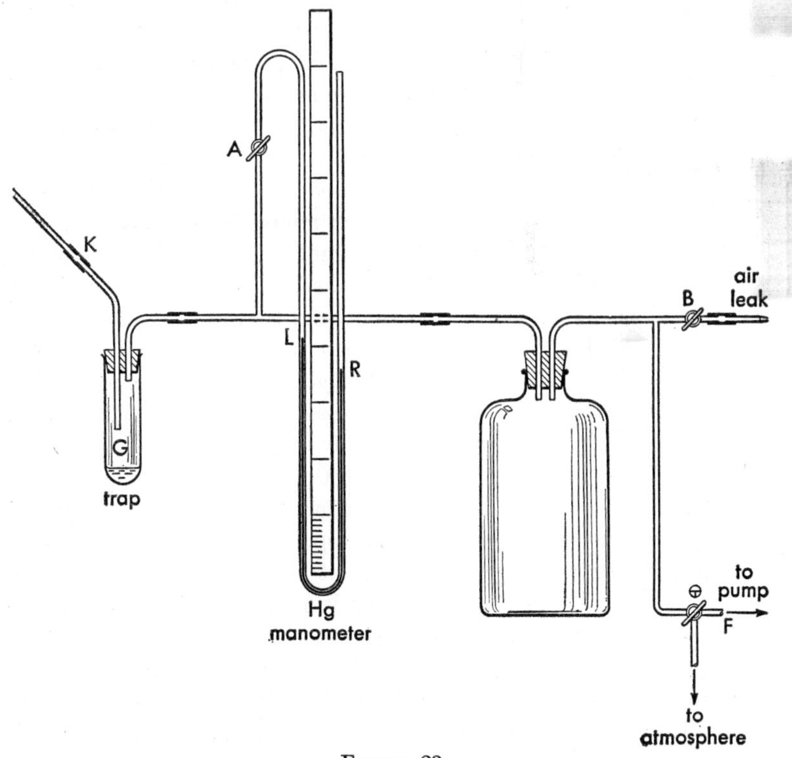

FIGURE 23

18–20° differential. When the temperature and pressure have again become steady, the new readings are recorded as above. Continue to increase the pressure in the flask 2–3 cm. at a time until the temperature of the vapor reaches about 50°C., whereupon the pressure is increased in increments of 10 cm. until atmospheric pressure is reached. The water bath is then allowed to cool and pressure readings are obtained at similar intervals. If sufficient time is available the experiment should be repeated or a different liquid sample employed.

The pressure in the apparatus is given by $B + R - L$ where B is the barometric pressure and R and L are the manometer readings. The data are entered in Table 15.

The Isoteniscope

Vapor pressures may also be measured with the apparatus devised by Menzies which is known as the isoteniscope. In the following paragraphs use of a semimicro isoteniscope is described but the experimental procedure with a larger instrument is identical. When the technique of adjusting the level of the isoteniscope manometer has been acquired, it will be found to be simple to operate.

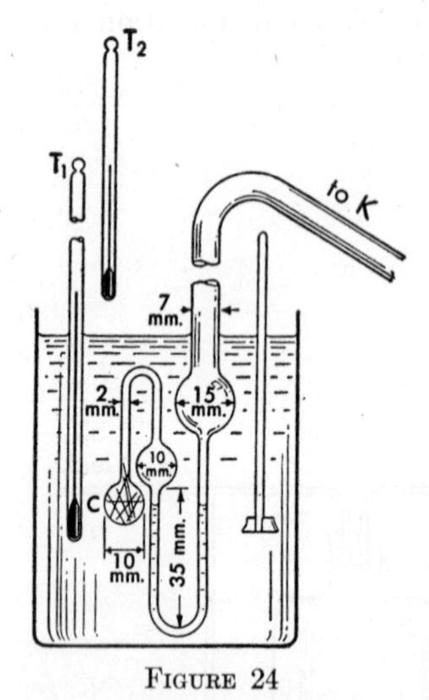

FIGURE 24

Apparatus The general dimensions of an isoteniscope are given in Fig. 24. The bulb C which holds the liquid sample is in a plane at right angles to the rest of the apparatus so as to increase its compactness. Just before bending the completely blown apparatus into its final shape, several pieces of very thin glass rod and some crushed glass are worked into the bulb C. This is then carefully heated to fuse the rough fragments to the bottom.

The apparatus is connected at K as shown in Fig. 23. The mercury manometer is constructed with a glass stopcock A so that the pressure and temperature readings can be made at the same time; closing the stopcock retains the levels. The air leak is made by drawing out 6-mm. glass tubing to a 0.5-mm. tip; the entrance of air may be governed by a glass stopcock, a Hoffman screw clamp, or a small metal needle valve.

The water bath should be stirred efficiently with a motor driven stirrer. The thermometer T_1 is graduated in fifths or tenths of a degree and is placed close to the bulb C. The volume of sample required is about 2 ml.

Procedure The isoteniscope is filled by placing a small amount of sample in it with a dropper, connecting to an aspirator pump, and evacuating for a few seconds. Upon breaking the vacuum the sample is forced into the bulb C and the bend which serves as a manometer. (The apparatus is emptied by the same procedure except that it is held in an inverted position.) The instrument is then connected at K (Fig. 23) and placed in a 2–3 liter beaker of hot water whose temperature is close to the normal boiling point of the sample.

The water aspirator pump is turned on at approximately half force, the stopcock B being wide open. The pressure in the system is reduced slightly by adjusting stopcock B in order to boil the sample and drive out the dissolved and trapped gases between the bulb C and the manometer. The air leak is carefully adjusted to allow the pressure to increase slowly. When the levels of the isoteniscope manometer are the same, close the stopcock A to retain the levels of the mercury manometer and read the temperature of the bath (T_1). Immediately after this, close the stopcock or air leak *slightly* to prevent air from entering the isoteniscope. If air is accidentally drawn back into it, reduce the pressure in order to boil the sample and drive the air out. Record the stem temperature and the reading of the mercury manometer. Open stopcock A so that the manometer again registers the pressure in the system.

As the temperature of the bath drops, it is necessary to adjust the air leak continuously. When the levels in the isoteniscope again become equal, close stopcock A, obtain the temperature T_1, and close the leak slightly once again. Record the stem temperature and manometer reading. At the start, readings should be made every 2–3°; later 5–8° intervals are sufficient. It will probably be necessary to turn the water aspirator on more fully in order that lower pressures may be obtained.

The rate of cooling of the heating bath should be about one degree every two to five minutes. This can be controlled by placing a small burner flame under the beaker. If the rate is too rapid, the temperature of the sample and bath will not be the same.

TABLE 15 B ____ mm.

t_1 °C.	Stem Temp. °C.	t_1 °C. Corr.	Manometer Reading R mm.	L mm.	Vapor Pressure	log P	T_1 °A.	$1/T$ °A.

Finally obtain the barometric pressure once again to determine if it has changed. If it has, assume that the rate of change is proportional to the time elapsed from the initial reading.

Calculations The temperature should be corrected for the exposed stem for each reading (see pp. 15–16).

Plot vapor pressure as ordinate against the corrected temperature in °C. as abscissa, and with the aid of a French curve draw a smooth line through the points. From the slope of the curve at any point, the reciprocal dT/dP may be obtained. This differential coefficient is useful for calculating the change in boiling point with pressure over a very small range.

Plot the log vapor pressure as ordinate against the reciprocal of absolute temperature as abscissa. Use graph paper which is at least $8\frac{1}{2} \times 11$ in. in size; larger paper may be used if warranted by the precision of the data.

Obtain the slope of the line using the method of average points (see p. 13). Derive an equation of the following form

$$\log P = -\frac{A}{T} + B$$

by also evaluating the constant B. Express this equation in the exponential form, *i.e.*

$$P = Ce^{-A/T}$$

Calculate the heat of vaporization from

$$-\Delta H = 2.303R \cdot \text{slope}$$

or

$$\Delta H = 2.303R \cdot A$$

Extrapolate the $\log P - 1/T$ curve to find the temperature at which $P = 760$ mm. Compare this value with the accepted boiling point.

With a given set of experimental points, the slope of a straight line may be obtained graphically with a precision of ± 1 per cent or better by different observers, depending on the smoothness of the points. Using the equation derived above, calculate $\log P$ for each experimental temperature and the deviation of the measured $\log P$ ($\Delta \log P$). The sum of the positive and negative deviations should be nearly zero; if not, the best line has not been drawn.

Examine the position of the points carefully to see if they might best be represented by a line of uniform curvature rather than a straight line. Since the heat of vaporization of common liquids varies 5–10 per cent over the range of temperatures which may have been used, careful measurements by a good method will show noticeable deviations from linearity. Values of ΔH may then be calculated from the slope at two or three temperatures.

An excellent test of the entire procedure is to compare the vapor pressure at several temperatures with the accepted values. In this way the actual accuracy of the method may be estimated.

If the chemical identity of the sample employed is known, compare the vapor pressure at various temperatures and also the heat of vaporization with published values. What is the per cent error?

REFERENCES

Felsing and Durban, *J. Am. Chem. Soc.*, **48,** 2885 (1926)
Kobe, Okabe, Ramstad, and Huemmer, *ibid.*, **63,** 3251 (1941)
Lane, Hammerschlag, and Roehl, *ibid.*, **54,** 1020 (1932)
Linhorst, *ibid.*, **51,** 3263 (1929)
Smith and Menzies, *ibid.*, **32,** 1427 (1910)
Steinbach and Devor, *J. Chem. Ed.*, **22,** 288, 496 (1945)
Thomson, *Chem. Rev.*, **38,** 1 (1946)

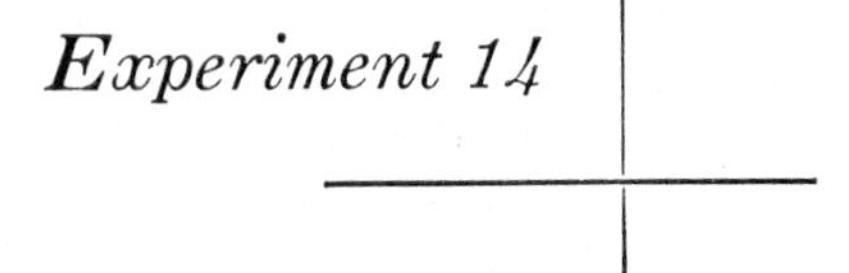

The Change of Solubility with Temperature

When a solid dissolves in a liquid to form an ideal solution, the process may be considered equivalent to the melting of pure solute at the lowered temperature where solution is taking place. Simultaneously, the addition of solvent molecules lowers the vapor pressure ($p_L°$) of undercooled liquid solute in accordance with Raoult's law. In a saturated solution the vapor pressure of solute must equal that of the pure solid solute p_s, and is also equal to the product of $p_L°$ and the mole fraction x

$$p_s = p_L°x \tag{131}$$

This may be expressed in logarithmic form as

$$\ln p_s = \ln p_L° + \ln x \tag{132}$$

Upon differentiating with respect to temperature

$$\frac{d \ln p_s}{dT} = \frac{d \ln p_L^\circ}{dT} + \frac{d \ln x}{dT} \tag{133}$$

and upon substituting the equivalent quantities from the Clausius-Clapeyron equation

$$\frac{\Delta H_s}{RT^2} = \frac{\Delta H_v}{RT^2} + \frac{d \ln x}{dT} \tag{134}$$

The difference between the molar latent heat of sublimation of the solid solute and the molar latent heat of vaporization of the undercooled liquid solute ($\Delta H_s - \Delta H_v$) is equal to the molar latent heat of fusion ΔH_f of pure solute, and

$$d \ln x = \frac{\Delta H_f}{RT^2} dT \tag{135}$$

The above equation may be integrated between the limits where $x = 1$ (pure solute) and T (the melting point of pure solute), and x_2 and T_2, the mole fraction of dissolved solute at the temperature of the solution

$$\ln x_2 = \frac{\Delta H_f}{R}\left(\frac{1}{T} - \frac{1}{T_2}\right) \tag{136}$$

This equation is known as the ideal solubility equation. In its derivation various simplifying assumptions are made, such as: (*a*) The latent heat of fusion of pure undercooled solute is constant and independent of temperature; (*b*) Raoult's law is obeyed; (*c*) the specific volumes or partial molar volumes of dissolved solute and of undercooled liquid solute are equal. These effects tend to cancel each other so that equation 136 often gives a good approximation to the experimental data. As the equation contains quantities relating only to the solute, the solubility of any substance should be the same in all ideal solutions at the same temperature.

Equation 135 may be integrated so that it applies to the solubility between two different concentrations by using as the limits $x = x_2$ and $x = x_2'$, $T = T_2$ and $T = T_2'$:

$$\ln \frac{x_2}{x_2'} = -\frac{\Delta H_f}{R}\left(\frac{1}{T_2} - \frac{1}{T_2'}\right) \tag{137}$$

The term ΔH is also known as the differential heat of solution for the solute whether or not it is equal to the molar latent heat of fusion.

Since the left-hand side of equation 137 contains a ratio, any consistent concentration units, such as molarity, normality, or grams of solute per 100 g. of solvent may be substituted, and in general

$$\log \frac{S_2}{S_2'} = \frac{-\Delta H}{2.303R}\left(\frac{1}{T_2} - \frac{1}{T_2'}\right) \tag{138}$$

Apparatus 1-liter beaker; motor driven stirrer; thermometer graduated in 0.1 or 0.2 degrees (0–50° range); 25-ml. pipet; standard 0.1 *M* NaOH; phenolphthalein indicator; wash bottle containing 95 per cent ethanol; six pieces of glass tubing 6 × 20 mm. to serve as sample withdrawing tubes. About 5 cm. from the lower end, a constriction is formed in the tube by heating uniformly and sucking in the walls slightly. A pressure-release tube is prepared from 6-mm. tubing, or a simple mechanical pipet filler may be used.[1]

Procedure Weigh 4.2–4.5 g. of benzoic acid on a platform balance and transfer to about 500 ml. of distilled water which has been heated to 50°C. in a 1-liter beaker. The motor stirrer is used to dissolve the solid rapidly and maintain equilibrium between solid and solution during the entire experiment. In order to prevent too rapid cooling of the solution, a small burner flame should be placed under the beaker so that a cooling rate of about one degree every three to five minutes is obtained.

A small plug of cotton is placed in the bottom of the sample withdrawing tube and pushed up to the constriction with the aid of a glass rod. A rubber policeman is placed over the upper end. The tubes are placed in the beaker containing the solution at the start and used when needed.

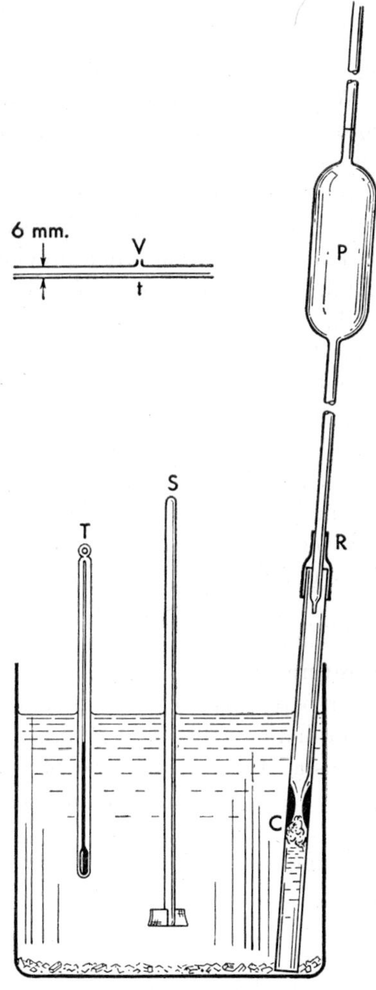

FIGURE 25

When crystals of benzoic acid appear and the temperature has dropped to about 45°, connect a sample withdrawing tube to a 25-ml. pipet using a 2.5-cm. length of rubber tubing. Remove a sample, employing suction, and transfer to a flask. The tube *t* (Fig. 25) is installed in the suction

[1] Brinton, *Anal. Chem.*, **20**, 186 (1948)

line and vacuum is applied or released by placing the finger over the vent V. Record the mean temperature during the withdrawing operation. Rinse the pipet free of solution with 10 ml. of ethanol from the wash bottle. Add a few drops of phenolphthalein indicator and titrate with standard 0.1 M NaOH. (The latter solution should be standardized against benzoic acid.) The end color should last 30–60 seconds.

When the temperature drops 3–5°C., withdraw another sample, record the mean temperature, and titrate as above. Secure five or more different samples at 3–5° intervals.

If it is desired to compare the measured solubilities with published values, the pipet may be calibrated. It is filled to the mark with water and allowed to drain into a previously weighed flask. Since content and not delivery is desired, the few drops which remain are blown out into the flask. The weighings are made to the nearest hundredth of a gram. The density of water is assumed to be 1.0 in making the calibration calculation.

Calculations From the molarity or the milliequivalence of the standard NaOH solution, calculate the amount of benzoic acid present in each sample, in grams. If the pipet has not been calibrated, obtain the molarity of each sample instead.

From the calibration value obtained for the pipet, calculate the weight or solubility of benzoic acid per 100 g. of water. For this purpose, it is sufficient to assume the solution has a density of 1.0. Prepare a plot of solubility (S) of the acid (grams per 100 g. H_2O or molarity) and temperature (°C.).

Prepare a plot of log solubility (grams per 100 g. of H_2O or molarity) as ordinate against the reciprocal of the absolute temperature ($1/T$) as abscissa. Obtain the slope of the curve and calculate the differential heat of solution ΔH, per mole, using the equation $2.303 \cdot R \cdot \text{slope} = -\Delta H$.

Using the above graph, obtain the equation of the line in the following form:

$$\log S = \frac{-\Delta H}{2.303RT} + B \qquad (139)$$

Evaluate the constant B.

Calculate several values of ΔH, by employing equation 138 and substituting data either from the graph or from the experimental results.

Obtain the latent heat of fusion of benzoic acid from a handbook and compare with ΔH.

Further experimental suggestions The solubility of oxalic, succinic, or salicylic acid may be measured.

TABLE 16

SAMPLE	t °C.	T(°A.)	ml. NaOH	g. ACID PER SAMPLE	g. ACID PER 100 g. H_2O	$\frac{1}{T}$	log S

REFERENCES

Brinton, *Anal. Chem.*, **20,** 186 (1948)
Chase and Kilpatrick, *J. Am. Chem. Soc.*, **53,** 2589 (1931)
Goeller and Osol, *ibid.*, **59,** 2132 (1937)
Hill and Distler, *ibid.*, **57,** 2203 (1935)
The solubility of ammonium oxalate

Experiment 15

Molecular Weight by the Freezing Point Method

The freezing point of a solution is the temperature at which solid solvent is in equilibrium with the solution. At the freezing point the solvent must have a definite solubility. The ideal solubility equation (Expt. 14) should be applicable to the solubility of the solvent as well as the solute and may be arranged in the form

$$T_1 - T = \frac{RTT_1 \ln x_1}{\Delta H_f} \qquad (140)$$

where T_1 and T are the freezing points of solution and pure solvent respectively. This equation is valid over a wide range of concentrations, provided that ΔH_f is constant. For application to dilute solutions it is generally used in the approximate form

$$\Delta T = \frac{RT^2M_1}{1000\,\Delta H_f} \cdot m_2 \qquad (141)$$

where ΔT is the freezing point lowering and m_2 is the molality of the solute.

The first term on the right contains constants which depend upon the specific properties of the solvent. Its numerical value may be calculated, and it is known as the molar freezing point constant K_f; then

$$\Delta T = K_f \cdot m_2 \tag{142}$$

Apparatus Freezing point apparatus consisting of inner and outer jackets; ice jar with cover and stirring rings; Beckmann thermometer preferably graduated for F.P. determinations; tablet press (optional). Benzene or cyclohexane and naphthalene or paradibrombenzene may be used for solvent and solute respectively.

The Beckmann thermometer generally has a range of 5–6°C. The scale is subdivided into tenths and hundredths, and with the aid of a magnifying lens the temperature may be estimated to approximately ±0.0015°. The Beckmann thermometer differs from the usual instrument in that it is possible to vary the amount of mercury in the lower bulb and thereby change the range of the thermometer.

To adjust a Beckmann thermometer so that it may be used in a desired range, the bulb is placed in a bath (large test tube) adjusted to the highest temperature expected. In this case, either partially frozen benzene (or other solvent selected) or water at a corresponding temperature (5.5°) may be used. If the mercury column remains above the scale markings, the thermometer is removed and warmed in another bath 10–20° higher in temperature until the estimated excess of mercury has risen into the reservoir above the point *a* in Fig. 26. The thermometer is quickly inverted and struck against the palm of the hand to separate the mercury at *a*. It is again placed in the cold bath to determine whether it is set in the desired range. Some thermometers have a capillary inseal at *a* which permits a few drops of mercury to be expelled without inverting.

If the mercury is too low or below the scale, more must be added from the reservoir above *a*. This is accomplished by tipping the thermometer so that the reserve mercury runs to the inseal at *a*; the lower bulb is then heated in a warm water bath until the thread rises and effects a junction with the reservoir mercury. The thermometer is placed in a somewhat cooler bath (10–20° above the desired range) for a few minutes; it is then inverted and struck against the palm to separate the thread at *a*. Finally it is tested in the cold bath.

Procedure Set the Beckmann thermometer so that the freezing point of the solvent is within 1.0–1.5° of the uppermost scale division.

In this experiment it should correspond to about 5.5°C. which is the freezing point of benzene.

Pipet 25 ml. of pure dry benzene, or a volume sufficient to completely cover the thermometer bulb, into the clean dry inner tube *A* (Fig. 26).

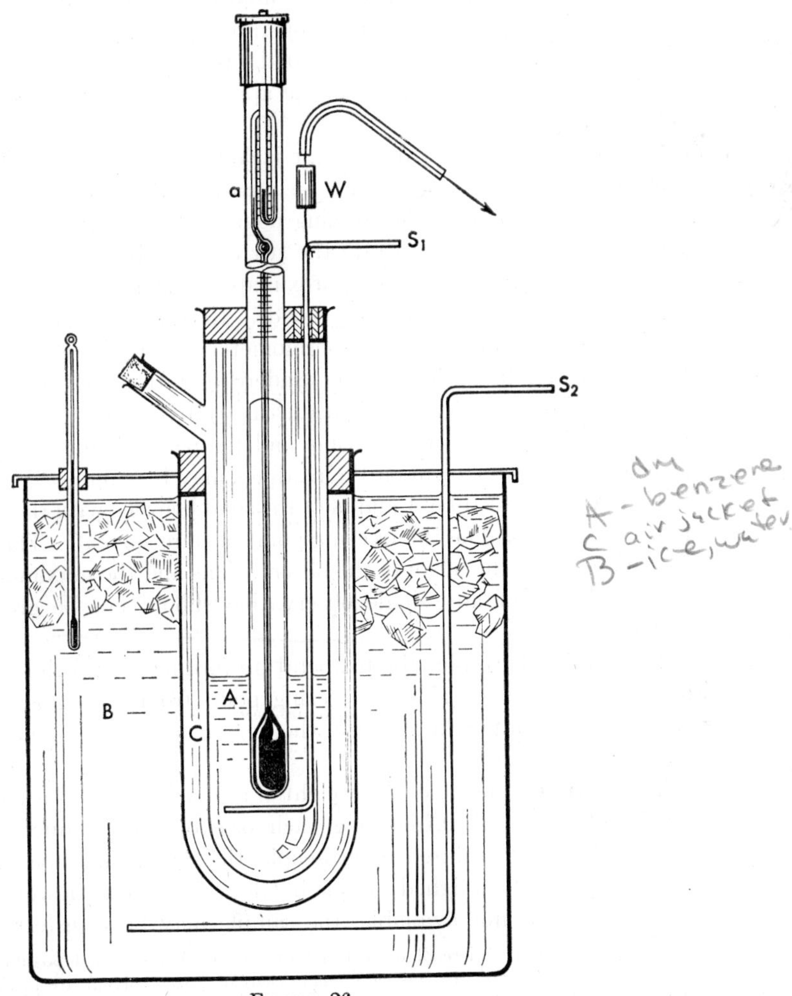

FIGURE 26

The thermometer is put in place and the ring stirrer is tested several times. It should operate freely and must not strike the thermometer bulb.

The cooling bath is an ice-water mixture and should be stirred frequently during the experiment; excess ice should always be present.

The temperature is satisfactory if it remains at 2°C. during this experiment. As a general rule, the temperature of the cooling bath should not be more than 3° below the expected freezing point. Place the tube *A* in the ice-water bath, meanwhile stirring until solid begins to form. Remove the test tube from the freezing mixture, dry thoroughly, and place it in the air jacket. Continue to operate the stirrer steadily so that it moves up and down once every second. When the temperature remains constant, record this reading as the approximate freezing point of the solvent.

Remove the tube *A* from the air jacket and melt the solid with the hand. The temperature should be raised in this operation not more than one degree above the freezing point. Place the tube *A* in the air jacket and continue to operate the stirrer steadily; when the temperature is 0.10–0.15° above the approximate freezing point, begin to read the thermometer every 20–30 seconds. Record the time (in seconds) and the temperature. Tap the thermometer gently with the finger before taking the reading. The liquid undercools[1] from 0.2–0.5° below its freezing point as a rule, and upon starting to freeze the temperature will rise. Continue to record the time and temperature for a few minutes after this occurs, whereupon the readings may be stopped.

Remove the test tube *A* and melt the solid benzene with the hand once more and redetermine the freezing point of pure solvent.[2] The accepted freezing point is the mean of the observations and the maximum acceptable deviation of any single observation should not be greater than ±0.002°.

It is advisable to plot the temperature (ordinate) and time (abscissa) for each run and obtain the freezing point from the smoothly drawn curve. The results will indicate whether or not it will be necessary to make another run.

To determine the molecular weight of a solute, the solid is compressed into tablets weighing 0.15–0.40 g. each, or enough to produce a lowering of 0.2–0.5°. If the solute is hygroscopic, the sample must be transferred from a previously weighed sample bottle which is then reweighed. If a tablet press[3] is not available, the sample may be transferred from a

[1] Certain solvents undercool to such a large extent that it is not possible to obtain accurate freezing points. In this case, small seeds of frozen solvent are introduced into the solution through the side arm when the temperature has been lowered 0.2–0.5° below the freezing point.

[2] If the solvent is not pure, the temperature will not remain constant during the initial stages of crystallization, and it will be necessary to purify the solvent until it meets these requirements.

[3] A cork borer with a snug-fitting glass rod and a cork to rest it on may be used as a substitute.

weighed glass tube which is inserted through the side arm. The tube is reweighed if any sample adheres to it.

The sample is dissolved by operating the stirrer. The test tube is placed in the outer freezing bath until the freezing point of the solvent is reached, whereupon it is removed, dried, and placed in the air jacket.

Continue to operate the stirrer; when the temperature drops to the freezing point of pure solvent, record the temperature every 20–30 seconds and the total elapsed time. The solution will undercool below its freezing point and when crystallization starts, the temperature will rise and reach a maximum; unlike pure solvent, it will not remain constant, but will begin to decrease.[1]

The freezing point of the solution is obtained by plotting the temperature (ordinate) against the time (abscissa) and drawing a smooth curve through the points. The maximum temperature reached after the undercooling period is passed is considered to be the freezing point.

The test tube is removed from the air jacket and allowed to warm about 0.2° above the observed freezing point. It is replaced in the air jacket and the above procedure repeated to obtain the freezing point of the solution. Obtain three observations of the freezing point.

Finally, a second similar weighed portion of solute is added and the freezing point is obtained by using the above procedure. Obtain a total of three observations for the freezing point. The temperature should not deviate from the mean more than $\pm 0.002°$ for the first run and not more than $\pm 0.003°$ for the more concentrated solution. It is assumed that a reading lens is available; if not, the best that can be expected is $\pm 0.005°$.

Calculations Assuming the density of benzene to be 0.879 g./ml., calculate the molecular weight of the solute with the aid of the following practical formula:

$$\text{Mol. wt.} = \frac{1000 \cdot \text{wt. of solute} \cdot K_f}{\text{wt. of solvent} \cdot \Delta T} \tag{143}$$

The accepted value of the molal freezing point lowering constant (K_f) for benzene is 5.12.

Assuming the molecular weight of the sample to be known, calculate (*a*) the freezing point constant and (*b*) the molar latent heat of fusion of benzene (solvent).

The estimated error of the molecular weight may be calculated from equation 143. Assume the following data and probable errors:

Weight of solute $g = 0.1000 \pm 0.0002$ $\quad \Delta T = 0.200 \pm 0.004$
Weight of solvent $G = 20.00 \pm 0.02$ $\quad K_f = 5.12$ (a constant)
Mol. weight $M = 128.0$

[1] The freezing out of pure solid solvent increases the concentration of solution and the temperature at which solid solvent and solution may exist in equilibrium is lowered.

Employing equation 20, page 7

$$\left(\frac{\Delta M}{M}\right)^2 = (1)^2\left(\frac{\Delta g}{g}\right)^2 + (-1)^2\left(\frac{\Delta G}{G}\right)^2 + (-1)^2\left(\frac{\Delta T}{T}\right)^2$$

and substituting the above values in this equation

$$\left(\frac{\Delta M}{128.0}\right)^2 = (1)\left(\frac{0.0002}{0.1000}\right)^2 + (1)\left(\frac{0.02}{20.00}\right)^2 + (1)\left(\frac{0.004}{0.200}\right)^2$$

$$\left(\frac{\Delta M}{128.0}\right)^2 = 4 \times 10^{-6} + 1 \times 10^{-6} + 4 \times 10^{-4} \approx 4 \times 10^{-4}$$

$$\pm \Delta M = 2.6$$

In examining the above calculations, it can be seen that the greatest error is contributed by the temperature measurements. The above estimated error may not correspond to the experimental one since it was assumed that K_f is a constant. Actually this constant is a derived quantity and its probable error should be included if a more accurate estimate were desired.

In order to illustrate this, calculate the estimated error of the molecular weight from the experimental data. Assume that the probable error of K_f is ± 0.02; the probable error of the other quantities may be taken as in the illustration.

REFERENCES

Batson and Kraus, *J. Am. Chem. Soc.*, **56**, 2017 (1934)

Freezing points of solutions in benzene.

Scatchard, Jones, and Prentiss, *ibid.*, **54**, 2676 (1932)

Twin apparatus, differential type.

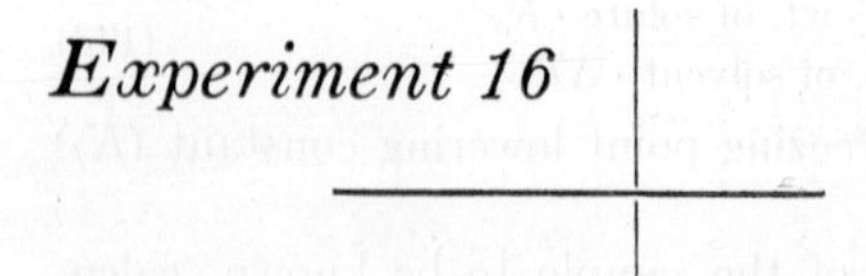

Molecular Weight by the Boiling Point Method

The relation between the vapor pressure and temperature of a solution containing a nonvolatile solute can be obtained by combining

Raoult's law and the Clausius-Clapeyron equation. The latter equation may be written for small finite changes as

$$\frac{1}{p} \cdot \Delta p = \frac{\Delta H}{RT^2} \cdot \Delta T \tag{144}$$

Raoult's law, expressed in terms of the relative lowering of the vapor pressure of solvent, moles solute n_2 and solvent n_1, is

$$\frac{\Delta p}{p} = \frac{n_2}{n_1} \tag{145}$$

Upon combining equations 144 and 145, there is obtained

$$\Delta T = \frac{RT^2}{\Delta H} \cdot \frac{n_2}{n_1} \tag{146}$$

Setting n_1 equal to 1000 g. of solvent ($1000/M_1$ moles), n_2 becomes molality of solute m_2:

$$\Delta T = \frac{RT^2 M_1}{1000 \cdot \Delta H} \cdot m_2 \tag{147}$$

The fraction in the right-hand term contains only constant quantities which depend upon the specific properties of the solvent. The numerical value may be calculated and is known as the boiling point constant K_b. Substituting this quantity for the constant terms in equation 147, there results

$$\Delta T = K_b \cdot m_2 \tag{148}$$

This equation may be used for calculating the molecular weight of a solute from the boiling point elevation produced when a known weight of solute is dissolved per 1000 g. of solvent.

Since liquids are easily superheated several hundredths of a degree above their boiling points, and equal superheating of solvent and solution cannot be assured, the apparatus must be designed to avoid this source of error. Shielding the boiling chamber from the hot gases of the Bunsen flame and the addition of boiling stones or sealing platinum wires into the bottom of the boiling chamber help to reduce superheating.

The Cottrell apparatus employs a pump to spray boiling liquid over the bulb of the thermometer and establish equilibrium between boiling liquid and vapor. However, the Cottrell pump requires some superheating in the liquid phase for it to operate.

Changing barometric pressure may introduce considerable error; large changes in pressure, such as occur when stormy weather is approaching, may produce a change of 0.1°C. in the course of a day's work. In fact, a boiling-point apparatus could be used to predict weather changes. Manostats have been suggested to overcome the difficulty caused by changing barometric pressure, but they are cumbersome devices. A simpler method is to employ one Cottrell apparatus for pure solvent and another for solution, operating side by side. In this way, changing pressure affects each one equally, though the problem of unequal superheating of solvent and solution may still be present.

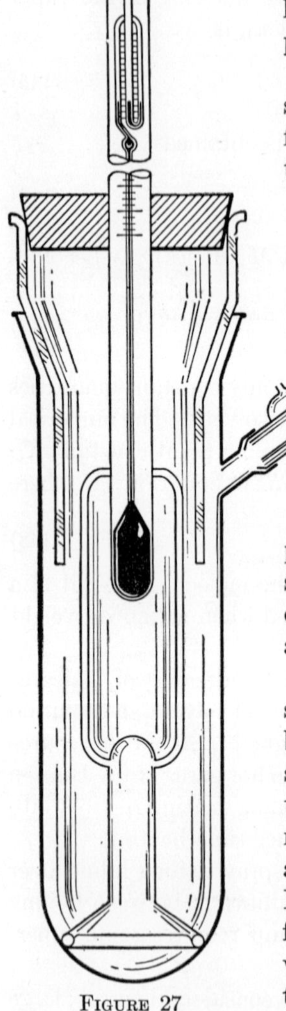

FIGURE 27

The molal boiling point constant of most solvents changes sufficiently with barometric fluctuations to make a correction necessary if the atmospheric pressure is much different from the standard (760 mm.). In this respect the freezing point method is superior since the constant K_f is unaffected by ordinary barometric changes.

Apparatus Any available type of boiling-point apparatus, such as the Beckmann, Davis, Swietoslawski, or McCoy; Beckmann thermometer or special boiling point thermometer; wire gauze; asbestos squares; pellet press (see footnote 3, p. 96); carbon tetrachloride. The directions for setting a Beckmann are given in Expt. 15.

Procedure Accurately pipet 50 ml. or a suitable volume of carbon tetrachloride into the boiling chamber and assemble the apparatus as shown in Fig. 27. Place a small flame under the boiling chamber so that the liquid commences to boil and pump over the thermometer and vapor condenses in the water condenser. It is generally necessary to wait 15–20 minutes for the apparatus to reach thermal equilibrium with the surroundings before readings can be taken. Record the temperature every half minute for five minutes, estimating to the nearest 0.001 degree. Tap the thermometer *gently* before taking a reading as occasionally the mercury sticks in the capillary. Record all readings. Obtain the barometric pressure.

Meanwhile, a weighing bottle (test tube) containing 2–4 g. of solute (naphthalene) is accurately weighed, or a pellet of the sample is prepared and weighed. When the solvent has cooled to room temperature, about one half of the contents of the weighing bottle is transferred into the boiling chamber, or the pellet is dropped in. Determine the amount of solute transferred from the weighing bottle. The boiling point of the solution is obtained using the above procedure. Record the barometric pressure.

A second weighed sample of 1–2 g. (that remaining in the weighing bottle or another weighed pellet) is added to the cooled solution and the boiling point is again determined. Or the apparatus may be emptied of solution, rinsed with pure solvent, dried, and the experiment repeated with a fresh portion of solvent and solute. The apparatus is cleaned after sufficient data have been obtained.

Calculations Calculate the arithmetic mean and the probable error of a single observation for the boiling points of the solvent and the solution.

The boiling point constant K_b for CCl_4 is 5.03 when the barometric pressure is 760 mm. For every millimeter below 760 mm. subtract 0.0013 from the constant K_b, and for every millimeter above 760 mm., add 0.0013. The correction factor is different for each solvent.

The molecular weight is obtained by substituting the results in the following practical formula:

$$\text{Mol. wt.} = \frac{1000 \times \text{wt. of solute} \times K_b\ (\text{corr.})}{\text{wt. of solvent} \times \Delta T} \tag{149}$$

Assuming that the molecular weight of the solute is known, find the value of the constant K_b (eq. 148). Employing this value of K_b and the accepted boiling point of the solvent, calculated the latent heat of vaporization (eq. 147). Obtain the accepted latent heat of vaporization of the solvent and calculate the per cent error.

The estimated error of the molecular weight may be evaluated as in Expt. 15. Since superheating may exist, it would be desirable to have some idea of the extent to which the final result is affected if an error of $\pm 0.01°$ is present. Assume the following probable errors:

Weight of solute, ± 0.002 g.	$\Delta(\Delta T)$, $\pm 0.01°$
Weight of solvent, ± 0.02 g.	ΔK_b, ± 0.03

Calculate the estimated error of the molecular weight from the experimental data. See pages 9 and 10 for further details. If the thermometer reading varied more than 0.01° in the experiment, use a more realistic value for ΔT.

REFERENCES

Cottrell, *J. Am. Chem. Soc.*, **41,** 721 (1919)
Davis, *J. Chem. Ed.*, **10,** 47 (1933)
Smith, *J. Am. Chem. Soc.*, **61,** 497 (1939)
Steinbach and Conery, *J. Chem. Ed.*, **21,** 535 (1944)
Swietoslawski, W., *Ebulliometric Measurements*, Reinhold Publishing Corporation, New York, **1945**
Washburn and Read, *J. Am. Chem. Soc.*, **41,** 729 (1919)

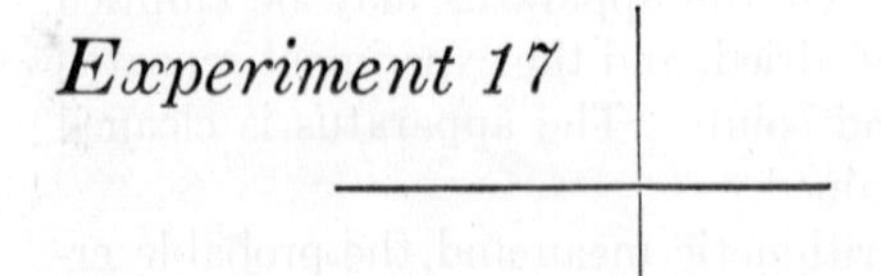

Experiment 17

The Reciprocal Solubility of Phenol and Water

The study of the solubility of two or more substances in each other is a very extensive one. If two substances are mixed, a number of possibilities may occur. For example, they may be completely soluble, partially soluble, or insoluble in each other in either or both the liquid and solid phases. They may react with each other to form a new compound that has distinct properties and solubility of its own.

Applying the phase rule to a two component ($C = 2$) system

$$2 - P + 2 = F. \tag{150}$$

Since the number of degrees of freedom F can never be less than zero, the number of phases P that can be present simultaneously can never be greater than four. If the system is a condensed one wherein the pressure may be regarded as fixed and the vapor phase absent, the phase rule simplifies to

$$C - P + 1 = F \tag{151}$$

and the maximum number of phases that may appear at any one time is three.

A complete investigation of the solubility relationship of two substances requires that the concentration of each component, the temperature and pressure, and the chemical identity of the solid and liquid phases in contact with each other be known.

One of the simplest methods to study solubility is to change the temperature until a new phase appears. When this takes place, the number of degrees of freedom changes and generally the resulting system may be more readily characterized. This method will be used to study the solubility relationship of water and phenol.

Apparatus Thermometer graduated in 0.2° or whole degrees; test tubes 2.5 × 20 cm. and 4.0 × 20 cm.; ring stirrer (chromel wire No. 18); redistilled or C.P. phenol; 1, 2, 10 ml. pipets; large beaker.

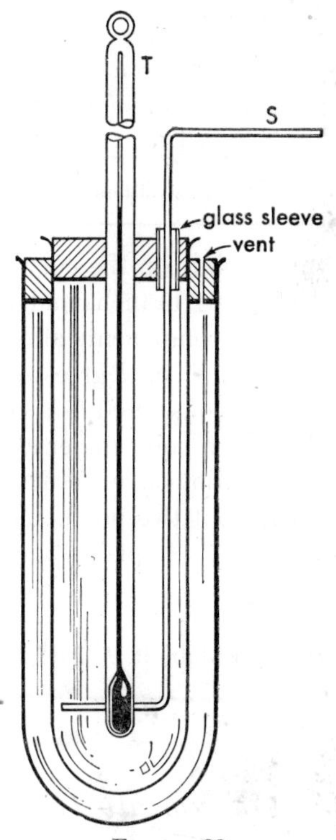

FIGURE 28

Procedure Transfer 10.00 ± 0.01 g. of phenol[1] from a weighing bottle to a smaller test tube and add 10 ml. of water from a pipet. The test tube, with thermometer and stirrer in position, is placed in a beaker of boiling water and the stirrer is operated to hasten solution. When this occurs, remove the tube, wipe dry, and place in a large test tube which serves as an air jacket. This will allow the solution to cool slowly.

The stirrer is then operated vigorously, and when the solution first appears turbid, observe the temperature. The turbidity is due to the sudden appearance of the new liquid phase, the conjugate solution, which has a refractive index different from that of the original solution.

Water is added in the proportions shown in Table 17 and the temperature at which each mixture appears turbid is recorded.

Calculations Calculate the percentage composition by weight of phenol in each mixture. The density of water may be taken as 1.0. Plot the weight per cent of phenol in each mixture (abscissa) against the temperature at which turbidity appeared (ordinate). Draw a smooth curve through the points.

From an inspection of the curve, determine the critical solution temperature of the system and also the composition at this point. Select

[1] Be careful not to spill phenol on the hands; wash with alcohol if any should get on the skin.

TABLE 17 —— g. phenol

ml. H_2O Added	°C.	Weight % Phenol	ml. H_2O Added	°C.	Weight % Phenol
10			2		
1			10		
1			10		
1			4		
1			4		
2			4		
2			4		
Critical temp. = —— °C.			Composition at critical T ——		

three points on the curve, one on the ascending branch, another on the descending branch, and the third at the critical solution temperature. List the components and the nature of each phase present and calculate the number of degrees of freedom at each point. Remember that this may be considered as a condensed system.

Select a point under and another above the curve. What significance or conditions may be attached to these two points?

Pick out two points on the curve that illustrate the term "conjugate solutions." Explain your choice. What is meant by a tie line? Illustrate.

REFERENCE

Hill and Malisoff, *J. Am. Chem. Soc.*, **48**, 918 (1926)

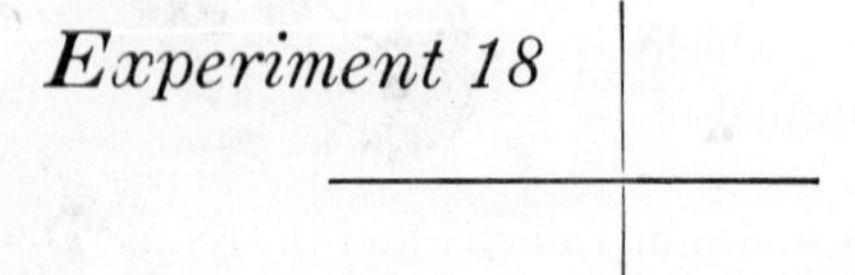

Thermal Analysis of a Binary Alloy

The investigation of phase equilibria may be carried out by a procedure known as thermal analysis. This procedure is resorted to when the mixtures are opaque, as in the case of metallic alloys.

The rate of cooling of a heated object is proportional to the temperature difference between the object and its surroundings and upon its physical dimensions (Newton's law of cooling). Thus, if the temperature of a pure molten substance is measured over a short interval of time in an apparatus such as shown in Fig. 29, the cooling curve will resemble AB in Fig. 30a. However, if a phase transition occurs, such as the transformation of liquid to solid phase, the rate of cooling is altered, due to the appearance of the latent heat for that change. If the system is well

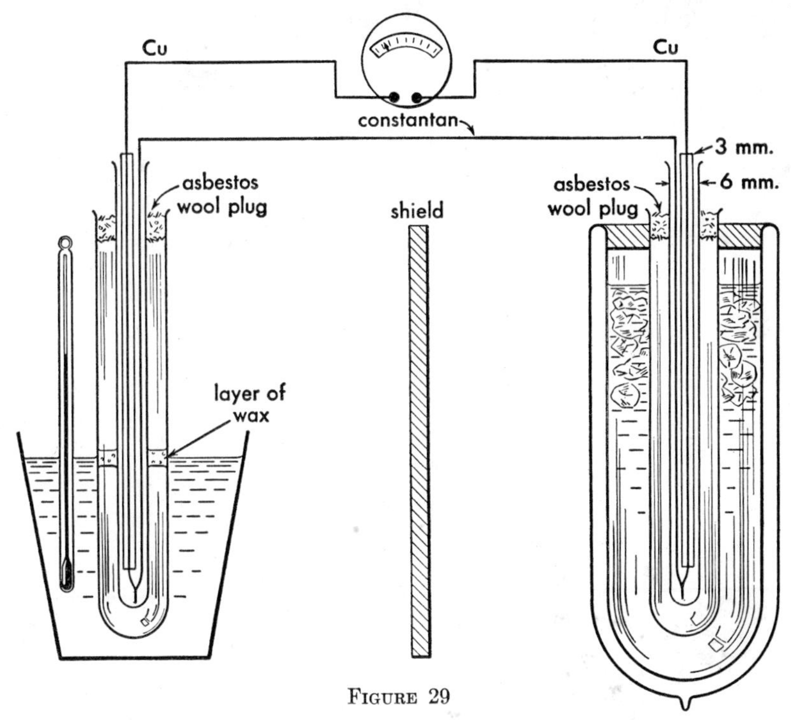

FIGURE 29

insulated, the temperature will remain constant, as shown by BC in Fig. 30a until all liquid has changed to solid. The resulting solid will then cool at a rate proportional to the temperature difference of the object and its surroundings. Over a short interval of temperature, these time-temperature cooling curves are almost straight lines, over longer ranges the curves are logarithmic.

Certain modifications of the cooling curve of Fig. 30a appear in practice. If the substance undercools below its freezing point, the cooling curve appears as shown by the dotted lines in Fig. 30a. The curve at C does not, in general, appear as sharp as drawn, but is rounded instead as it is physically difficult to keep a small quantity of liquid in thermal equilibrium with a large pasty mass of solid.

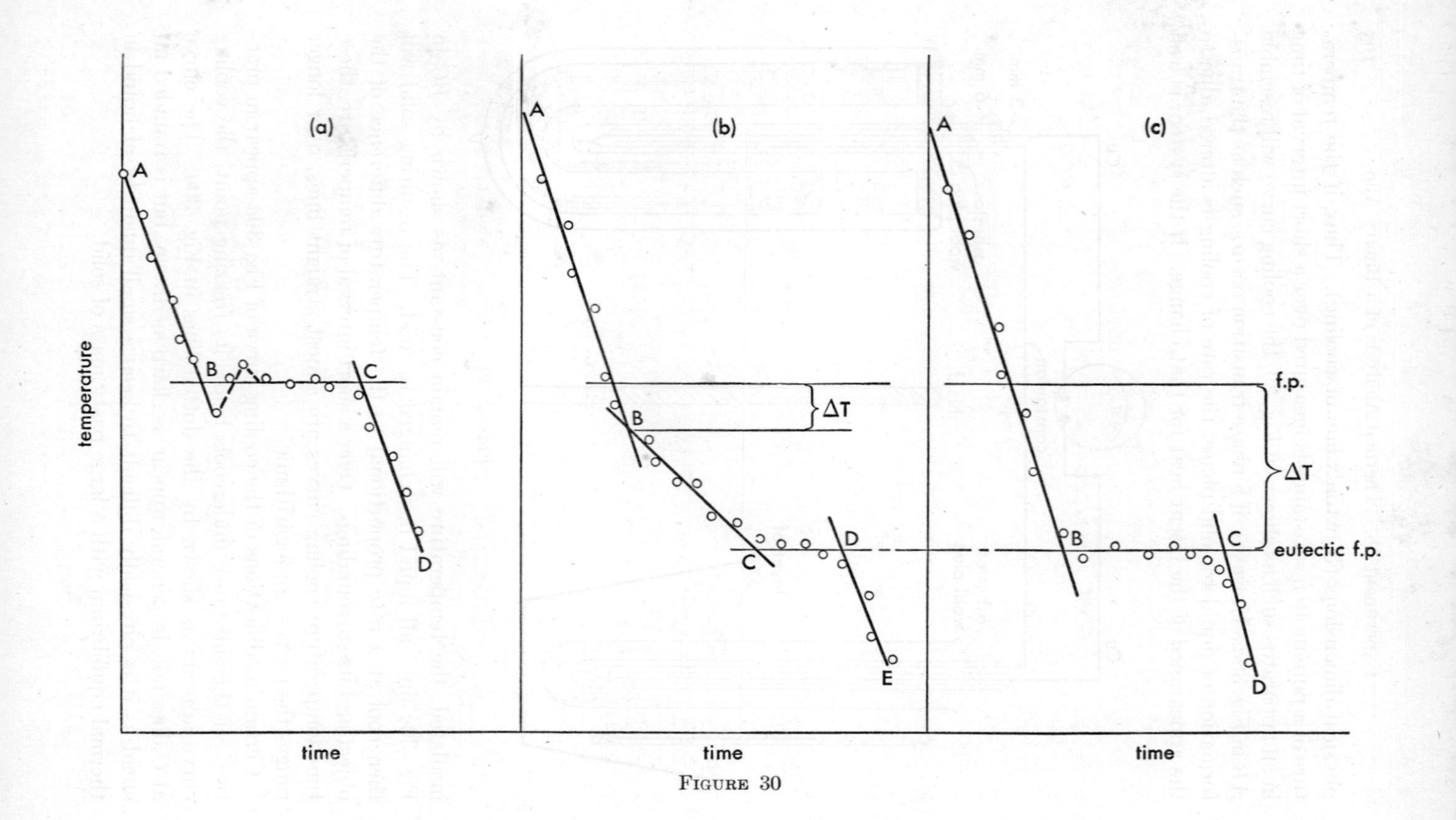
(a)
A
B
C
D
temperature
time
(b)
A
B
C
D
E
ΔT
time
(c)
A
B
C
D
f.p.
ΔT
eutectic f.p.
time

FIGURE 30

A second type of phase transition appears when molten solutions are cooled. In this case, solid "solvent" precipitates due to its reduced solubility at the lower temperatures. This type of transition is shown in Fig. 30*b*. The liquid cooling curve (*AB*) undergoes a distinct change in slope (*BC*) when solid solvent appears. The resulting solution becomes more concentrated and the freezing point is continuously lowered until it ultimately reaches the eutectic temperature (*C*). Curve *BC* represents the freezing point of solutions of varying concentrations. A comparison of the slopes of *BC* in Figs. 39*a* and 39*b* indicates that the phase transitions are different.

A third type of phase transition now appears at *C*, where solid eutectic precipitates from a solution of a definite composition, separate crystals forming of both solute and solvent in this same definite proportion. The temperature at *CD* remains constant as the latent heat of fusion of both solids is released. Finally, when the entire mixture has solidified, the cooling curve follows the course *DE*. The time length of the plateau or eutectic halt depends upon the weight of eutectic mixture present. If the composition of the original solution is considerably removed from that of the eutectic, the temperature halt *CD* may be of very short duration or be missed entirely.

If the original composition of the solution corresponds to that of the eutectic, the cooling curve will appear as in Fig. 30*c*. Obviously, the ratio of the lengths of *CD* in Fig. 30*b* and *BC* in Fig. 30*c* is equal to the ratio of the weights of eutectic present in the solid product.

Since the cooling curve is characteristic of the particular type of phase transition occurring, it furnishes information with respect to the nature of the alloy. There are several other types of phase transition curves possible, besides those described in this experiment.

It was discovered by Seebeck that in a circuit composed of two different metals, if the junctions are kept at different temperatures, an electromotive force is developed which is approximately proportional to the difference in temperature of the two junctions. The actual thermoelectromotive force-temperature curve is a parabola, as the E.M.F. is the difference of two opposing effects, the Peltier and the Thomson effect. The relation between the E.M.F. and the temperature when one junction is kept at 0°C. and the other at t°C. is given by an empirical (interpolation) equation, such as

$$E = At - \tfrac{1}{2}Bt^2 \tag{152}$$

Since the constant B for the Thomson effect is much smaller than the constant A for the Peltier effect, E is practically linear with respect to temperature over a small range. However, over an extended temperature range, it is necessary to construct a calibration curve since the $\frac{1}{2}Bt^2$ term becomes appreciable.

In practice, certain pairs of metals are more suitable than others for the construction of thermocouples, and the following combinations are generally used: copper-constantan, iron-constantan, platinum-platinum rhodium alloy, chromel-alumel. The couples are usually made of fine wire (No. 28) though for heavy duty work, heavier gauge wire is used. The wires are soldered or welded at the junctions to insure good contact. To increase the total thermoelectromotive force, multiple junction thermels are used.

The electromotive force developed by the thermel may be measured by a variety of methods. The most accurate method uses a potentiometer, but a millivoltmeter or a shunted galvanometer may be employed for less precise work.

Apparatus Dewar flask; ceresin wax; several 40-cm. lengths of 5–6 mm. Pyrex tubing; watch or clock; heavy Pyrex ignition test tubes; large iron crucibles filled with sand; millivoltmeter, range 0–20 millivolts for use with copper-constantan thermel or 0–10 millivolt for use with chromel-alumel thermel. The scales should be divided into at least 100 divisions.

A chromel-alumel thermocouple is constructed from two 1-m. lengths of No. 22 chromel wire and a 1-m. length of No. 22 alumel wire. Twist an end of the alumel wire to each chromel wire for a distance of about 0.5 cm. The junctions are heated in an oxygen-gas flame until fused. The free ends of the chromel wires connect directly to the millivoltmeter.

A copper-constantan thermel is made from two 1-m. lengths of No. 28 copper wire and a 1-m. length of No. 28 constantan wire. Twist the ends of the constantan wire to each copper wire for a length of 0.5 cm. Each junction is soldered together by melting borax on the end and placing a small chip of silver solder on the borax. The end is heated in an oxygen-gas flame until the solder melts and wets the wires, and then plunged into cold water to crack off the borax glass. The wires may be electrically welded instead, using rosin or some other noncorrosive flux. The free ends of the copper wires connect directly to the millivoltmeter.

A 40-cm. length of 2–3 mm. glass tubing is slipped over each copper wire leg of the thermel to insulate the two wires. Glass beads or clay pipe stems are a satisfactory substitute. The couples are placed in 40-cm. lengths of 6-mm. Pyrex tubing which have been sealed at one end and act as protective jackets.

Procedure The thermel must first be calibrated so that the readings in volts may be converted to temperature. If both junctions are placed in a mixture of crushed ice and water, the E.M.F. should be zero. The hot junction is placed in a beaker of boiling water while the cold one is immersed in the mixture of crushed ice and water in the Dewar flask (Fig. 29), and the millivoltmeter reading is recorded. The temperature of the hot junction may be obtained from vapor-pressure tables for the observed barometric pressure. Several other points are obtained, such as the melting point of pure tin (231.9°C.), pure cadmium (320.9°C.), pure bismuth (271°C.). Pure lead (327.5°C.) may also be included if an alloy containing this metal is to be investigated. Since thermels made of base metals may undergo permanent changes, frequent calibration must be resorted to, especially when they are employed at high temperatures.

Place approximately 100 g. of one of the above metals in a Pyrex ignition tube. The tube is centered in the iron crucible and sand is packed around it to the level of the metal in the test tube. The crucible is heated with a Meker burner to about 10° above the melting point of the metal, a thermometer placed in the sand bath serving as a rough guide. A small amount of ceresin wax is added to cover the molten metal and prevent oxidation.

The hot junction is placed in the protective jacket, which in turn is placed in the molten metal; the cold junction is placed in the ice-water mixture contained in the Dewar flask. It will be necessary to hold the hot junction with a clamp so that the end is forced into the molten metal. A plug of asbestos wool is then inserted to support the protective jacket (see Fig. 29).

When the millivoltmeter starts to drop back, record the readings at 30-sec. intervals, timing with a watch or clock with a second hand. If the rate of cooling is very slow, a 60-sec. interval may be taken. The observations are continued until the temperature remains constant for several minutes.

Rather than removing the protective jacket from the melt and cleaning it free from adherent metal, it is advisable to employ a new piece of tubing for each of the remaining samples. If the apparatus is kept as a permanent set-up, examine the jackets each time after a sample has been melted preparatory to inserting the thermel, replacing if cracked. The above procedure is repeated with the remaining metals.

Prepare 100 g. mixtures containing 20, 40, 60, and 80 atom per cent of each metal of one of the following pairs: cadmium-tin, cadmium-bismuth, cadmium-lead, bismuth-tin. The samples are weighed on a platform balance to the nearest 0.1 g. and transferred to Pyrex ignition tubes. They are placed in iron crucibles, covered with sand,

and melted as described. The millivoltmeter readings are recorded at 30- or 60-sec. intervals either until the eutectic phase transition appears and the temperature remains constant for several minutes, or until the entire alloy has solidified and the solid is cooling steadily.

If a potentiometer is used to measure the E.M.F., the leads from the thermel take the place of C_x in Fig. 53 page 173. Refer to this experiment for operation of the potentiometer.

Calculations Prepare a graph for each sample of pure metal and alloy used, plotting millivolts as ordinate and time in seconds as abscissa. From the graphs for pure tin, cadmium, bismuth, and water, the millivoltmeter reading corresponding to the freezing points (and boiling point of water) is obtained. The calibration curve for the thermel is then constructed by plotting millivolts as ordinate and temperatures as abscissa. A smooth curve is drawn through the points including the origin (0°C., E.M.F. = 0).

From the millivolt-time curve for each alloy, obtain the readings where the different phase transitions appear. These readings can then be converted to temperature by means of the calibration curve.

Prepare a phase diagram for each series of alloys, plotting temperature (°C.) as ordinate and atom per cent as abscissa, and draw smooth curves through the data (see Fig. 31). Report the eutectic temperature and composition.

REFERENCES

Stull, *Ind. Eng. Chem., Anal. Ed.*, **18**, 234 (1946)
Van Klooster and Stearns, *J. Am. Chem. Soc.*, **55**, 4121 (1933)
The binary system $PbI_2 - KI$.

Experiment 19

The Ideal Solubility Curve and the Phase Diagram

The equilibrium or phase diagram which is obtained when two components are soluble in the liquid state, but insoluble in the solid state, is of the simple type shown in Fig. 31. In this diagram, curve AE represents the lowering of the freezing point of solvent A by solute B; it may also be considered to represent the solubility of A in solution. Similarly, curve BE may be designated either as the freezing point lowering curve of pure B or the solubility curve of B in solution.

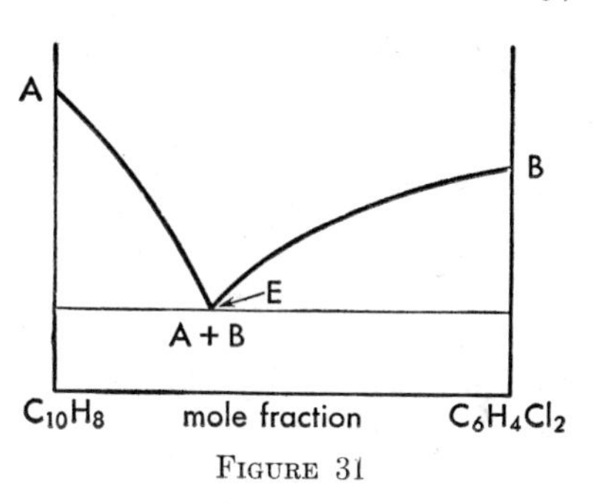

FIGURE 31

The relationship between solubility and freezing point of a component in an ideal binary solution is given by the ideal solubility or freezing point equation (see Expt. 14).

$$R d \ln x = \frac{\Delta H}{T^2} dT \qquad (153)$$

Equation 153 may refer to either component. If ΔH_A is the latent heat fusion of A and the equation is integrated from the melting point of pure A to the temperature in question, $\ln x$ refers to the mole fraction of A. If ΔH_B and T_B are inserted, $\ln x_B$ is obtained. The ideal solubility of each component is independent of the other, or is the same in all ideal solutions at a given temperature. It is to be observed that the distinction between solvent and solute in any mixture is artificial rather than real.

If the latent heat of fusion were constant, equation 153 could readily be integrated. This is often not the case, and the change of ΔH with temperature is best represented by an interpolation equation. For paradichlorobenzene and naphthalene, the following equations are valid over the useful temperature range:

p-$C_6H_4Cl_2$

$$\Delta H = -10{,}250 + 94.07T - 0.1511T^2 \qquad (154)$$

$C_{10}H_8$

$$\Delta H = 4265 - 26.31T + 0.1525T^2 - 0.0002140T^3 \qquad (155)$$

Substituting equations 154 and 155 in 153 and integrating:

p-$C_6H_4Cl_2$

$$R \ln x_B = \frac{10{,}250}{T} + 94.07 \ln T - 0.1511T + C \qquad (156)$$

$C_{10}H_8$

$$R \ln x_A = -\frac{4265}{T} - 26.31 \ln T + 0.1525T - \frac{0.0002140}{2} T^2 + C \qquad (157)$$

When $x = 1$ (pure substance) and hence $\ln x = 0$, T is equal to the absolute melting point; inserting these values, the above equations can be solved for C. This has been done and equations 156 and 157 have been rewritten to include the numerical value of C as follows:

p-$C_6H_4Cl_2$

$$\log x_B = \frac{2239.9}{T} + 47.343 \log T - 0.03302T - 115.0924 \quad (158)$$

$C_{10}H_8$

$$\log x_A = -\frac{932.03}{T} - 13.241 \log T + 0.03332T - 2.3382 \times 10^{-5}T^2 + 27.5264 \quad (159)$$

These equations may be used to calculate the mole fraction of the component which is considered to be the solvent, from the observed freezing point of the solution. It should be emphasized that the calculations cannot be made with a slide rule or even with a four or five place logarithm table. The final answer is a small number which is the sum and difference of several large numbers; consequently it is necessary to use the "longhand" method or a calculating machine.

Apparatus 8 × 1 inch test tubes; chromel wire ring stirrer; thermometer graduated in 0.1° or 0.2°; two thermometers graduated in whole degrees; two large beakers (1–2 liters); large glass stirrer. Pure p-dichlorobenzene and naphthalene may be prepared by distillation. The melting point of pure $C_6H_4Cl_2$ is 53.2°C. and the melting point of pure $C_{10}H_8$ is 80.1°.

Procedure Prepare mixtures of the following approximate proportions of p-$C_6H_4Cl_2$ and $C_{10}H_8$ by weighing the components to ±0.01 g.

TABLE 18

p-$C_6H_4Cl_2$ (B) grams	$C_{10}H_8$ (A) grams	x_A	$t_{obs.}$	$t_{corr.}$	p-$C_6H_4Cl_2$ (B) grams	$C_{10}H_8$ (A) grams	x_A	$t_{obs.}$	$t_{corr.}$
30.00	0.00				20.00	20.00			
25.00	3.00				16.00	20.00			
25.00	5.00				14.00	25.00			
25.00	8.00				12.00	30.00			
25.00	12.00				6.00	30.00			
20.00	15.00				0.00	30.00			

The samples are melted by placing the test tubes in a beaker of water maintained above 80°C. Remove the sample of molten naphthalene from the heating bath and arrange the thermometer and stirrer in place. Immerse in another beaker of hot water (85–90°) and allow to cool slowly, stirring the outer bath at least once every thirty seconds. The sample is also slowly stirred while cooling (once every 2–3 sec.), and the temperature when the first crystals appear is taken as the freezing point.

The temperature difference between the sample and water bath should not differ by more than 2–3°. If necessary a small Bunsen flame should be placed under the water bath to retard the rate of cooling. Obtain the mean stem temperature in order to calculate the corrected temperature (stem correction).

The freezing point is obtained for each sample, using the above procedure. When the freezing point is below 40°, it is advisable to place the sample in an air jacket made from a larger test tube similar to the apparatus used in Expt. 15, as the rate of cooling of the large beaker of water is too slow.

Calculations Calculate the mole fraction of naphthalene present in each sample. The mole fraction of the second component is $1 - x$. Plot the corrected temperature (°C.) of the freezing point against the mole fraction as abscissa. Use a French curve, a spline, or spring brass wire to draw the best curves. Obtain and record the eutectic composition and temperature. It will probably be necessary to extrapolate the curves to the intersection. The eutectic temperature is reported to be 30.2°C. and the mole fraction of naphthalene at the eutectic to be 0.375.[1]

Calculate the ideal solubility of naphthalene (mole fraction) using equation 158 for the experimentally observed temperatures (°A.) between the freezing point of pure solvent and the eutectic temperature. Calculate the ideal solubility of *p*-dichlorobenzene between the freezing point of the pure substance and the eutectic temperature, using experimental temperature values. Plot the results on the above graph, distinguishing between calculated and experimental curves.

From the curves, determine the freezing point lowering constant of each pure substance by drawing a tangent to the curve where it intersects the ordinate.

Using the experimental data of mole fraction and freezing point, prepare a graph using $\log x_A$ and $\log x_B$ as ordinates and the reciprocals of the absolute temperatures as abscissas. Obtain the slope of the curves at the melting points of pure A and B and calculate the average molar latent heat of fusion of each component. Determine the temperature and composition of the eutectic from the intersection of the curves (extrapolate if necessary).

Further suggested experiments Several other binary systems are given by Lee and Warner.[2] The systems are very nearly ideal. These authors also give a ternary system that can be studied.

[1] Morris and Cook, *J. Am. Chem. Soc.*, **57,** 2403 (1935)

[2] Lee and Warner, *J. Am. Chem. Soc.*, **53,** 209, 4474 (1933); **57,** 318 (1935)

REFERENCES

Lee and Warner, *J. Am. Chem. Soc.*, **53**, 209, 4474 (1933); **57**, 318 (1935)
Morris and Cook, *ibid.*, **57**, 2403 (1935)

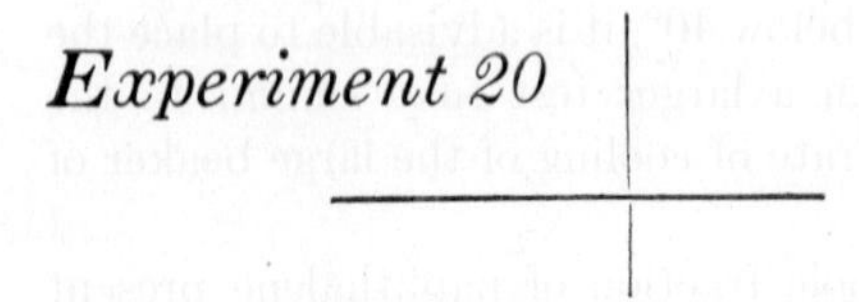

Experiment 20

Principles of Distillation

When two liquids are completely miscible, the distinction between solvent and solute is artificial, and is merely one of convenience. If the simple assumption is made that the vapor pressure of a volatile component (A) in a solution is proportional to its mole fraction, then the laws of Raoult and Henry follow immediately. This statement in differential form is

$$\frac{dp_A}{dx_A} = K \tag{160}$$

Integration of equation 160 gives Henry's law, namely

$$p_A = Kx_A \tag{161}$$

Mathematically it is possible for $K \gtreqless p_A°$. When a solution is ideal over the entire range of compositions, the numerical value of K is found to be equal to $p_A°$, the vapor pressure of pure A. This is shown by the dashed line CED in Fig. 32. If this substitution is made in equation 161

$$p_A = p_A°x_A \tag{162}$$

This equation is known as Raoult's law. It is clear that Raoult's law and Henry's law are identical in the case of the ideal solution.

When K is greater than $p_A°$, the solution exhibits a positive deviation from ideality (curve CFD in Fig. 32), as the escaping tendency (vapor pressure) of component A is greater than in an ideal solution. The line $K_1'D$ has been drawn tangent to the curve CFD in the region ($x_b \approx 1$) where A is nominally the solute. The numerical value of K_1' represents the hypothetical vapor pressure (p_A^*) of a pure A having the same properties as in an infinitely dilute solution of A in B. Since equation

161 is applicable in the region where $x_B \approx 1$, it is generally stated that Henry's law applies to the solute. In the region where $x_A \approx 1$, the tangent to the curve approaches $p_A°$ and compliance with Raoult's law is to be expected; hence it is generally stated that this law applies to the solvent.

When K is less than $p_A°$, the solution exhibits a negative deviation from ideality (curve CGD in Fig. 32), as the escaping tendency (vapor

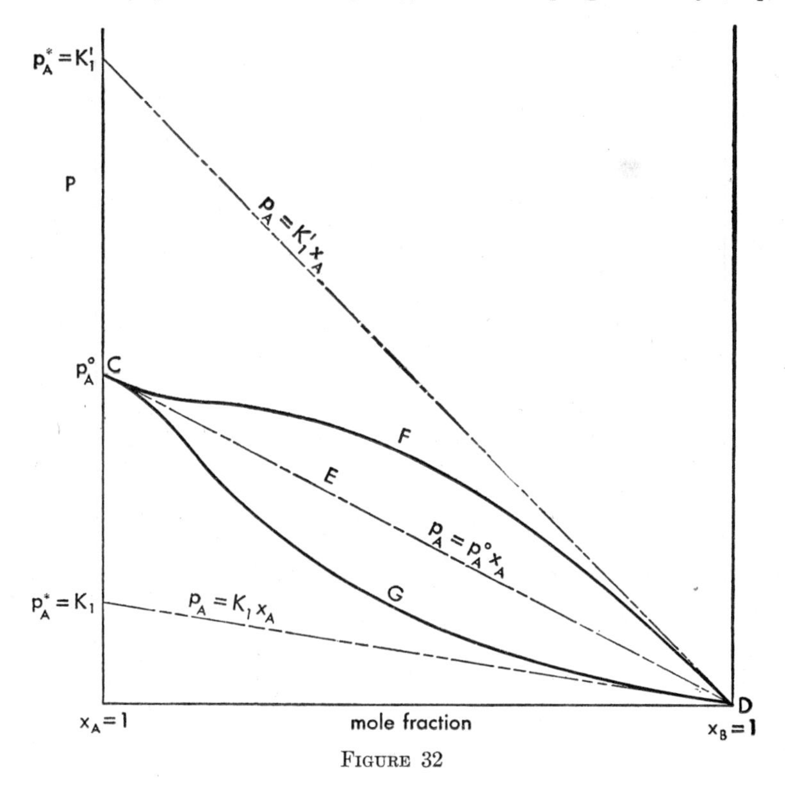

FIGURE 32

pressure) of the component A is less than in an ideal solution. The tangent K_1D has been drawn, and it is to be noted that its extrapolated value in the region where $x_A \approx 1$ is less than $p_A°$ as postulated. The numerical value of K_1 corresponds to the hypothetical vapor pressure p_A^* of a pure A having the same properties as in an infinitely dilute solution of A in B. The above discussion also applies to the component B without any modifications and this is illustrated in Fig. 33.

The total vapor pressure of a mixture is obviously the sum of the partial vapor pressures of each component and may be greater than, equal to, or less than the sum of the partial vapor pressures calculated by the ideal law (eq. 162). If at some composition it is greater than the pressure of the more volatile pure component, the system will have a maximum vapor pressure and a corresponding minimum boiling point. If at some point it is smaller than that of the less volatile pure component, the system will have a minimum vapor pressure and a corresponding maximum boiling point. Finally the actual vapor pressures of all

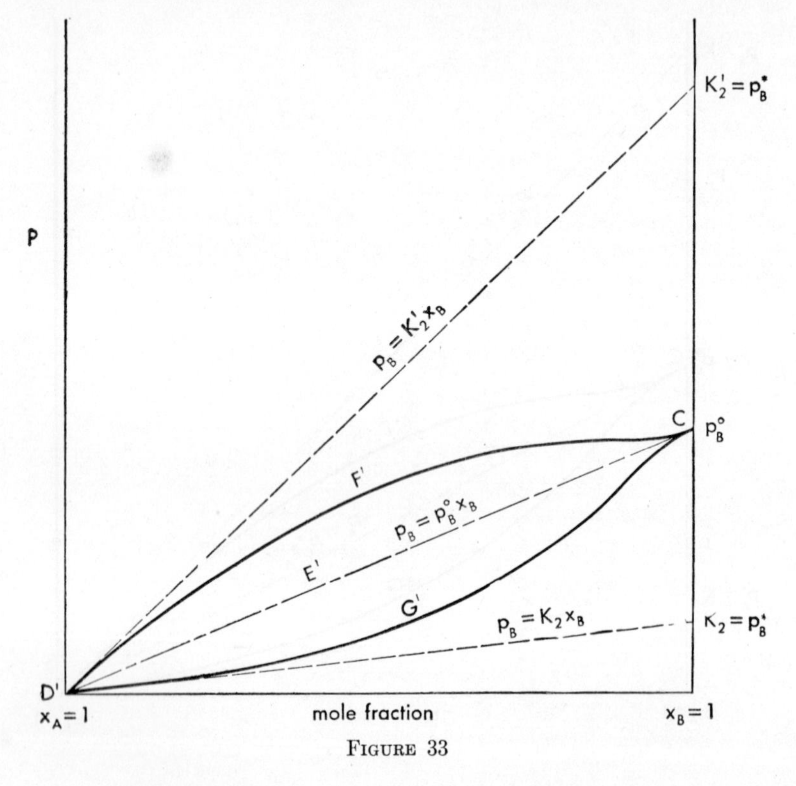

FIGURE 33

mixtures may lie between those of *A* and *B*, in which case the mixture shows neither a maximum nor minimum boiling point.

In conclusion, the equality or inequality expressed by $dp/dx \gtreqless p^\circ$ determines the type of deviation from the ideal solution. The magnitude of the deviations determine whether or not maximum or minimum boiling point solutions will be formed.

Apparatus Two- or three-neck 500-ml. flask; Abbe refractometer preferably provided with temperature control (see Expt. 10); thermometer graduated in 0.1 or 0.2°C., though one graduated in whole degrees will serve if a high degree of accuracy is not required; asbestos squares for shielding; long sample withdrawing tubes prepared from either medicine droppers or 2–3 mm. tubing; a vapor sampler, such as the Brown apparatus or the type described below (Fig. 34).

The vapor sampler is made by drawing out 10–13 mm. glass tubing in a pointed flame as in *A* and trimming at the mark *M*. The end may be lightly fire polished. A similar piece of tubing is sealed at one end and blown out while hot into a thin bubble; it is trimmed when cool as in *B*. When assembled, the throat of the inner tubing should be 2–3 mm. above the point where they are to be joined. The two tubes are joined as shown in *C* by the use of a sharp pointed flame; then they are carefully annealed. The finished sampler is mounted in a 6–10 in. condenser jacket. The throat of the tube should be located at the lowest point in the jacket.

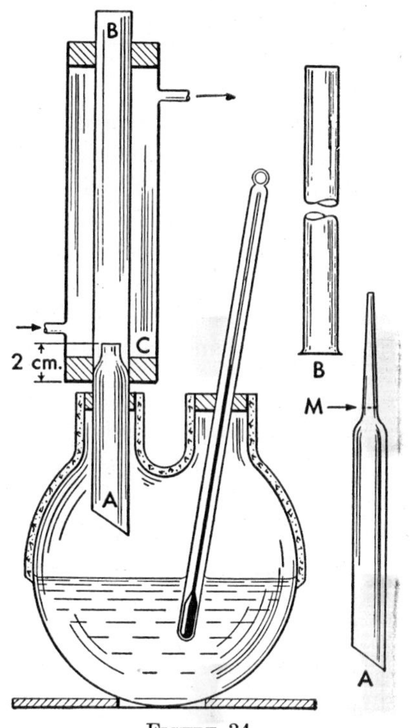

FIGURE 34

The flask should be covered with asbestos paper above the liquid level in order to minimize fractionation of vapor in the flask. The apparatus is not to be considered as a precision type for research problems. The refractive index of vapor from a given mixture will be found to vary approximately ±0.0003 units.[1]

Procedure Place about 100 ml. of *A*[2] (acetone) in the flask of the assembled apparatus. Boiling stones may be added to promote smooth ebullition. Several asbestos squares are placed under the flask so that the flame heats only a small part of it and the hot gases are deflected. A small liquid sample is withdrawn by a long capillary medicine dropper and transferred to the refractometer through the groove provided for

[1] See articles by Othmer, Sameshima, Schultz, and Smyth and Engel in references on page 119.

[2] Previously prepared mixtures of *A* and *B* may be used. They are returned to stock bottles and conserved for future use.

volatile liquids and its refractive index is measured at 25°C. Approximately 10 ml. of *B* (chloroform) is added to the flask and the liquid is then heated to boiling for three to five minutes.

Record the temperature, turn off the burner, and immediately withdraw a sample of the condensed vapor phase from the throat with a long capillary medicine dropper. Transfer at once to the refractometer and obtain the refractive index at 25°C. A 0.5-ml. sample is removed from the liquid phase and stored in a tightly corked test tube. When cool, obtain the refractive index at 25°C.

Repeat the above procedure, using approximately the quantities suggested in Table 19. To study mixtures rich in *B*, empty the flask into the container provided for the waste samples, and place 100 ml. of *B* in the flask. Measure the refractive index of the pure sample and add the quantities of *A* suggested in Table 19, each time measuring the refractive index of liquid and condensed vapor at 25°C. after bringing to a boil, etc.

TABLE 19

100 ml. Acetone (*A*)						100 ml. Chloroform (*B*)					
ml. *B*	*n* Liquid	*n* Vapor	% *B* Liquid	% *B* Vapor	*t*°C.	ml. *A*	*n* Liquid	*n* Vapor	% *B* Liquid	% *B* Vapor	*t*°C.
10						2					
10						5					
10						5					
10						5					
10						10					
10						10					
10						20					
10						20					

The composition of the liquid and vapor phases may be obtained from the data in Table 20. Prepare a graph of the data from this table on large paper (18 × 24 in.) in order to interpolate the results. If the measured values for the refractive index of pure *A* and *B* do not agree with those of the table, add to or subtract from each reading the amount which makes them agree. An alternative procedure is to draw a curve parallel to the one obtained from the data in Table 20, using the observed refractive indices of pure *A* and *B* as the end points of the curve.

Calculations Referring to the composition–refractive index graph, the composition of each of the samples of distillate (vapor) and residue (liquid) is obtained in weight per cent.

TABLE 20

REFRACTIVE INDICES OF ACETONE (*A*) AND CHLOROFORM (*B*) MIXTURES

WEIGHT % *B*	n_D^{25}	WEIGHT % *B*	n_D^{25}
0.0	1.3562	72.276	1.4076
16.664	1.3645	79.884	1.4162
33.039	1.3742	88.409	1.4269
45.832	1.3833	94.292	1.4349
56.298	1.3920	100.0	1.44309
64.507	1.3994		

Plot the temperature (ordinate) against weight per cent composition for each sample of liquid and vapor. Use a different style point and curve for the vapor and liquid phases, and connect points of the vapor and liquid curves of the same sample by light dotted lines. Draw the curve in as smoothly as possible and determine the composition of the azeotrope. Look up the value in a handbook or the *International Critical Tables* or consult the articles by Horsley [1] to obtain the percentage error of your result from the accepted value.

Discuss the graph briefly and describe what would happen upon distilling solutions of various compositions.

Further suggested experiments The following pairs of liquids which form minimum boiling point azeotropes may be studied: benzene–isopropyl alcohol, carbon tetrachloride–methyl alcohol, chloroform–methyl alcohol, benzene–methanol.[2]

If a maximum boiling azeotrope is desired, methyl acetate–chloroform may be used.

If a nonazeotropic mixture is desired, the following pairs may be used: benzene–acetone, benzene–carbon disulfide, toluene–acetone. Consult Horsley [1] for further information.

REFERENCES

Ewell, Harrison, and Berg, *Ind. Eng. Chem.*, **36,** 871 (1944)

Horsley, *Anal. Chem.*, **19,** 508 (1947); **21,** 831 (1949)

Table of azeotropes and nonazeotropes.

Othmer, *Ind. Eng. Chem.*, **35,** 614 (1943); *Anal. Chem.*, **20,** 763 (1948)

Sameshima, *J. Am. Chem. Soc.*, **40,** 1503 (1918)

Schultz, *ibid.*, **61,** 2691 (1939)

Smyth and Engel, *ibid.*, **51,** 2642 (1929)

Williams, *Ind. Eng. Chem.*, **40,** 1273 (1948)

Properties of C_6H_6—CH_3OH mixtures.

[1] *Anal. Chem.*, **19,** 508 (1947); **21,** 831 (1949) [2] Williams, *Ind. Eng. Chem.*, **40,** 1273 (1948)

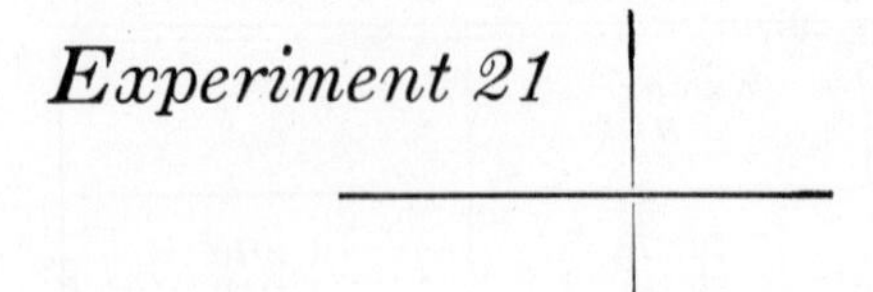

Experiment 21

Steam Distillation

When two liquids are nearly or completely immiscible with each other, the system exhibits a very large positive deviation from ideality, that is $dp/dx \gg p^\circ$ for each component and accordingly a minimum boiling point azeotrope will be obtained.

Due to the large deviation from ideality, neither Raoult's law nor Henry's law can be used to calculate the relationship between vapor pressure and composition. However, a graphical method is well suited

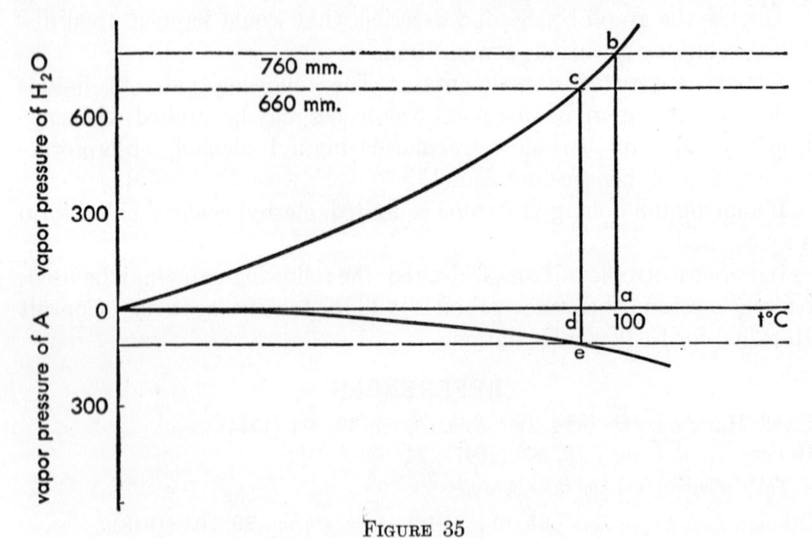

FIGURE 35

for determining the distillation temperature and the composition of the distillate.

The vapor pressures of two immiscible liquids, such as water and A, are plotted as in Fig. 35 and the vertical line *ab* is drawn to indicate the external or barometric pressure (760 mm.). Upon shifting the line *ab* to the left until it just fits between the vapor pressure curves of A and water, the point d where the line crosses the abscissa corresponds to the boiling point of the azeotrope. Obviously at this point the sum of the partial vapor pressures is equal to the external or barometric pressure. Since the length of the lines de and cd represent the partial pressures of the components, the composition of the vapor phase can be obtained. It follows from Fig. 35 that there are 660 molecules or moles of water to every 100 molecules or moles of A in the vapor phase, thus

$$\frac{P_A}{P_{H_2O}} = \frac{n_A}{n_{H_2O}} \tag{163}$$

If W_{H_2O} and W_A denote the weight in grams of water and A in a known weight of vapor, and M_{H_2O} and M_A are the respective molecular weights

$$\frac{P_A\, M_A}{P_{H_2O}\, M_{H_2O}} = \frac{n_A\, M_A}{n_{H_2O}\, M_{H_2O}} = \frac{W_A}{W_{H_2O}} \tag{164}$$

The same result may be obtained in a slightly different way. Plot three curves as shown in Fig. 36: (*a*) $\log P_A$ against $1/T$, (*b*) $\log P_{\text{water}}$ against $1/T$, (*c*) $\log (P_A + P_{\text{water}})$ against $1/T$. Draw a horizontal line

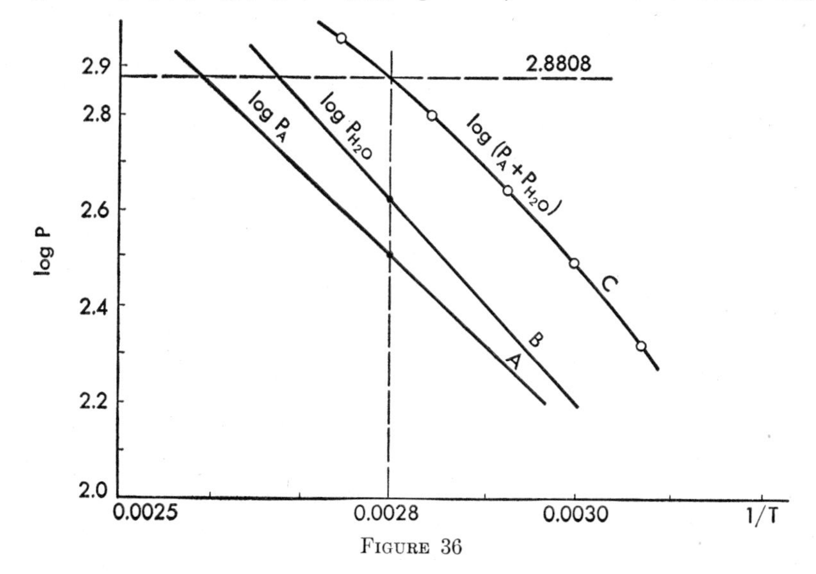

FIGURE 36

corresponding to the log of the barometric pressure (external pressure) and at the intersection of this line with curve C, drop a perpendicular to the abscissa. The intersection on the abscissa gives the temperature of distillation; the intersection of the perpendicular on the curves A and B gives the log of the partial vapor pressures of these substances at this temperature, from which the vapor pressures may be obtained. Obviously the sum of the partial pressures should be equal to the barometric pressure (Dalton's law). The ratio of the partial pressures is equal to the ratio of the number of moles present in the distillate.

Apparatus Steam generator with safety tube (1-liter flask); 500-ml. Claisen flask; steam delivery tube; condenser; 100-ml. graduated

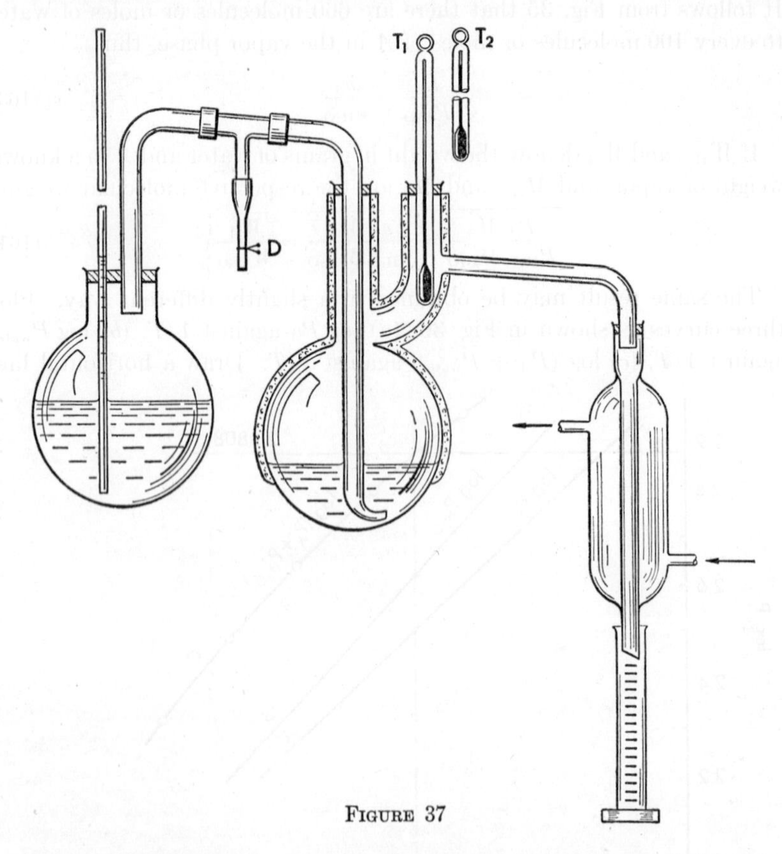

FIGURE 37

cylinder; thermometers, one graduated in whole degrees and the other in 0.2° or 0.1°; toluene; xylene; etc. The Claisen flask should be covered above the liquid level with asbestos paper.

Procedure Place 200–300 ml. of toluene in a Claisen flask and assemble the apparatus (Fig. 37). When the steam starts to issue from *D* vigorously, clamp the rubber tubing at this point. Collect about 20 ml. of distillate in a flask, meanwhile regulating the flame under the steam generator so that two drops per second are obtained. A small flame may be placed under the Claisen flask to keep the condensation of steam at a minimum. Obtain and record the barometric pressure.

Remove the receiving flask, place a dry graduated cylinder in its place, and collect the distillate. Record the temperature T_1 as successive 10-ml. portions are obtained, each time removing the burner from under the Claisen flask before taking the reading. Record the mean stem temperature T_2 whenever the temperature T_1 is observed. When 100 ml. of distillate has been collected, remove and cork the cylinder and set aside until the sample separates. Record the volumes of water and toluene collected. Place all distillates and residues into the bottle reserved for that purpose.

Calculations Prepare a graph similar to Fig. 35 from the data given in Table 21, or more complete data may be obtained from a handbook. Draw a horizontal line equivalent to the barometric pressure on the upper half of the graph. At the intersection of this line with the vapor pressure curve for water, construct a perpendicular to the temperature axis. The intersection on the axis should correspond to the boiling point of water. Obtain the boiling point of water from the vapor pressure tables for the observed barometric pressure. Compare.

TABLE 21

°C/*v.p.* mm.	50	60	70	80	90	100
H_2O	92.5	149.38	233.7	355.1	525.76	760.0
C_7H_8	92.6	139.5	202.5	289.7	404.6	557.2

From the measured length of line *ab*, construct the line *ce* of the same length and obtain the temperature *d*, the boiling point of the azeotrope.

Plot a curve similar to Fig. 36 from the data given (or from a handbook) and determine the temperature of distillation from the graph.

Obtain the mean of the T_1 readings and the stem temperature T_2 readings. Calculate the corrected temperature T_1 and compare with the graphical results. Explain why a difference in the values may be expected.

Employing the corrected temperature T_1, obtain the partial vapor pressure of water and toluene from the graph similar to Fig. 35. Substitute the data in equation 164 and calculate the ratio: weight of toluene to weight of water. From the measured volume and hence mass of water ($d = 1$) collected, calculate the weight of toluene that should theoretically have been distilled. Perform the same calculation employing the graph similar to Fig. 36. Compare.

Assuming the density of toluene to be 0.866 g./ml., calculate the weight of toluene collected in the receiver. Compare this with the theoretically calculated value. What is the percentage efficiency of the apparatus? Obviously if the efficiency were 100 per cent the method could be employed to determine molecular weights of immiscible substances. Note that P_A could be obtained by subtracting P_{H_2O} from the barometric pressure at the temperature T_1.

Calculate the molecular weight of toluene from the experimental data.

Further experimental suggestions Practically any liquid which is immiscible with water and boils above 100°C. may be used in place of toluene. Among such liquids are nitrobenzene, chlorobenzene, bromobenzene, benzaldehyde, acetophenone, diphenyl methane, octyl alcohol, etc.

REFERENCES

Perry, J. H., *Chemical Engineers' Handbook,* McGraw-Hill Book Company, Inc., New York, **1941**

Virtonen and Pulkki, *J. Am. Chem. Soc.,* **50,** 3138 (1928)
Analysis by steam distillation.

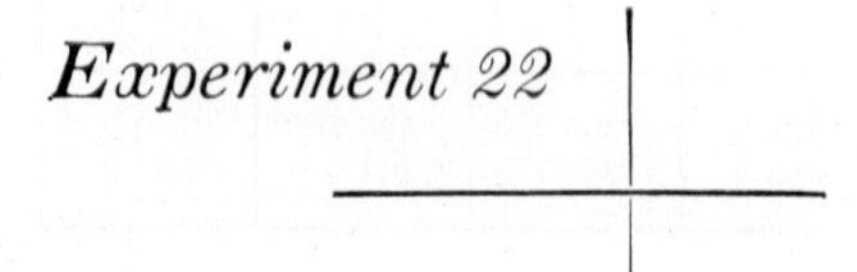

A Three Component Liquid System

In many cases, the addition of a third component to a pair of almost immiscible liquids does not appreciably increase their solubility in each other. However, the addition of a third liquid intermediate in polarity may have a large effect, and such a case is illustrated in this experiment.

The solubility relationships of any three substances can be represented with the aid of an equilateral triangle as shown in Fig. 38. To illustrate how such a diagram is used, points X and Y have been chosen. The coordinates of point Y are $A = 50$, $B = 25$, $C = 25$ per cent, and those of X are $A = 25$, $B = 25$, $C = 50$ per cent. For any lines, such as those joining points 1–5 and B, the ratio of the quantities A and C are constant while the amount of B varies. A similar relation holds for any line drawn from the opposite side to one of the apices.

This principle is applied in constructing the solubility curve. Mixtures of liquids A and C of various proportions are prepared corresponding to the points marked 1, 2, etc. Component B is added until the solubility

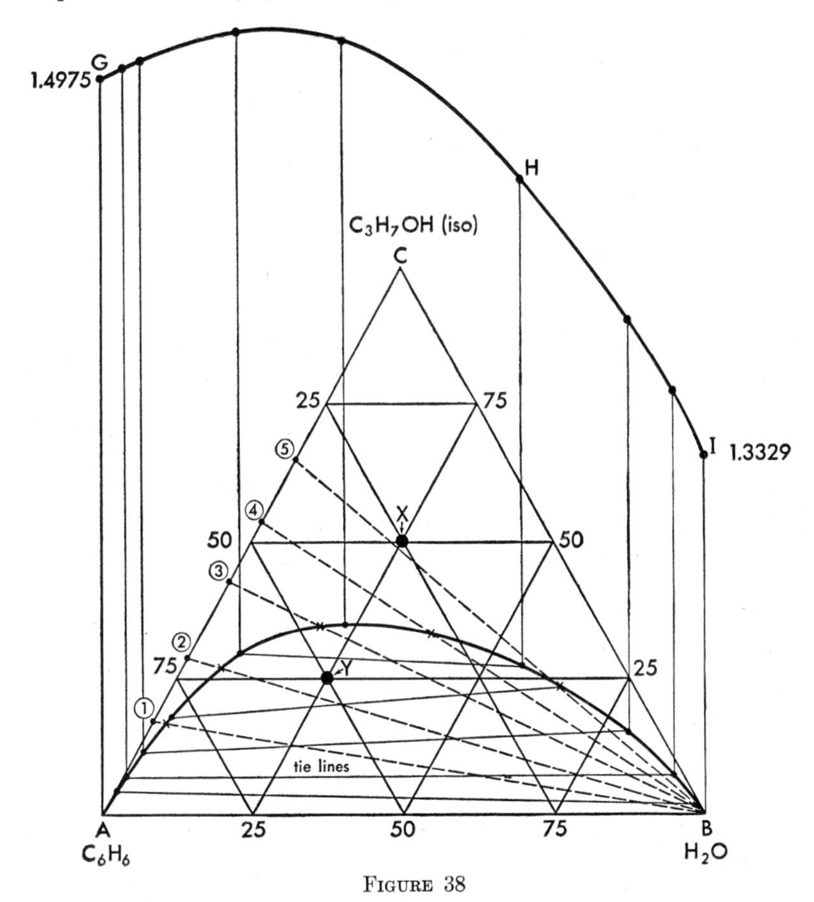

FIGURE 38

curve is intersected, whereupon a second conjugate ternary solution appears, its composition being given by the tie line.

The system studied in this experiment is that of water, benzene, and isopropyl alcohol.[1] In the first part of the experiment, the solubility curve is obtained by using the above procedure. In the second part of the experiment, several ternary conjugate solutions are prepared and

[1] Washburn and Olsen, *J. Am. Chem. Soc.*, **57**, 303 (1935)

analyzed in order to establish the tie lines.[1] While isopropyl alcohol is soluble in all proportions in benzene and water, it is not distributed equally between these two immiscible liquids, and the tie lines joining conjugate solutions are not parallel. That is to say, the distribution coefficient K is not equal to unity or even constant, but changes with concentration of solute.

The triangular diagram may be modified to represent simultaneously a fourth or even more variables such as density, viscosity, refractive index, properties which depend upon composition. Since each conjugate solution has a refractive index or specific property characteristic of the composition, the magnitude of this property may be represented by a line drawn to scale from a *point on the curve*, corresponding to the composition, projected perpendicularly upwards from the base of the triangle. Curve *GHI* represents such a plot.

Apparatus Three burets; micro buret (optional); silicone grease for lubricating stopcocks; small Erlenmeyer flasks; small glass stoppered bottles; anhydrous isopropyl alcohol[2]; benzene.

PART A

Procedure The solubility curve is obtained as follows: Mixtures of benzene and anhydrous isopropyl alcohol are prepared as suggested in Table 22, by measuring the necessary amounts with burets into clean dry Erlenmeyer flasks. The mixtures may be placed in a thermostat at 25°C. although it is not absolutely necessary if the room temperature is reasonably constant. If the experiment is performed at 25 ± 1°C., the data from Part A can be combined with that from Part B.

Each sample is titrated carefully and slowly with water (buret) until the mixture appears cloudy or turbid. The turbidity results because the homogeneous three component solution breaks up into two homogeneous conjugate ternary solutions which have different indices of refraction.

In order to expedite the titrations, withhold about one-third of the alcohol from the initial mixture and titrate rapidly with water until the cloud point is reached. The remaining alcohol is added and the titration is continued to the cloud point. This should be done especially with mixtures that are rich in benzene. A micro buret may be used to advantage in this range.

Calculations From the data, calculate the weight per cent of water, alcohol, and benzene in the mixtures at the cloud point. Water

[1] The slope of the tie lines may be obtained by other methods (see articles by Bancroft and Hubard, and Othmer and Tobias listed on p. 129).

[2] Gilson, *J. Am. Chem. Soc.*, **54**, 1445 (1932).

TABLE 22

ml. C_6H_6	ml. C_3H_7OH iso	ml. H_2O	ml. C_6H_6	ml. C_3H_7OH iso	ml. H_2O
29.4	5.1		9.10	19.4	
27.7	6.6		8.60	18.5	
23.1	10.8		6.00	18.5	
19.7	14.4		1.75	13.9	
15.2	17.4		0.75	11.6	
11.7	18.9				

dissolves to the extent of 0.07 per cent by weight in benzene and the solubility of benzene in water is equal to 0.15 per cent at 25°C. Plot these two points as well as the experimental ones on the triangular graph and draw a smooth curve.

Interpret the meaning of various selected points on the diagram and apply the phase rule to them. The system should be considered as a condensed one as both P and T are fixed. Under these conditions the phase rule reduces to $F = C - P + 0$.

Part B

Procedure In order to locate the tie lines, conjugate solutions are prepared and analyzed as follows:

Pipet 10 ml. each of benzene and water into glass stoppered bottles and add to each mixture the quantities (buret) of isopropyl alcohol indicated in Table 23. Stopper and shake well. The samples are preferably placed in a thermostat maintained at 25° ± 0.1°C. and shaken frequently over a one hour period or longer.

TABLE 23

C_6H_6 (A)	H_2O (B)	Alcohol (C)	n_D^{25} Water Layer	n_D^{25} Benzene Layer
10.0 ml.	10.0 ml.	0.5 ml.		
10.0	10.0	1.0		
10.0	10.0	1.5		
10.0	10.0	2.0		
10.0	10.0	2.5		
10.0	10.0	3.5		
10.0	10.0	5.0		
10.0	10.0	7.5		
10.0	10.0	10.0		
10.0	10.0	12.5		
10.0	10.0	15.0		
10.0	10.0	0.00		

When the solutions have come to equilibrium, remove a sample of the upper liquid with a medicine dropper and obtain the refractive index at 25°C. The lower phase is removed with a medicine dropper which has been drawn out into a capillary. When inserting the dropper through the upper layer, squeeze the bulb gently (air bubbles) to prevent liquid from entering the dropper. Upon withdrawing, likewise squeeze gently so that a small amount of sample is lost into the upper layer. Obtain the refractive index of the sample at 25°C. See Expt. 10 for temperature control of refractometer.

Calculations Construct a triangular diagram on the lower third of a sheet of graph paper at least 17 × 20 in., or paste a sheet of triangular graph paper on the lower edge of the large rectangular graph paper. Construct the solubility curve for the system from the data given in Table 24 or from Part A, in the triangular coordinates. Then construct the refractive index curve from the data given in Table 24.

Obtain and record the composition in weight per cent of the conjugate solutions from the measured refractive indices. Plot these points on the triangular graph paper and draw in the tie lines.

A graph is prepared using per cent alcohol in benzene as ordinate and per cent alcohol in the water layer as abscissa. A line drawn at a 45° angle through the origin represents equal distribution of alcohol in water and the benzene phases. What is your conclusion regarding the distribution coefficient of alcohol in this system?

TABLE 24

WEIGHT PER CENT COMPONENTS

BENZENE	ALCOHOL	WATER	n_D^{25}	BENZENE	ALCOHOL	WATER	n_D^{25}
99.93	0.00	0.07	1.4975	27.17	51.36	21.47	1.4035
87.74	13.20	0.06	1.4759	23.63	50.42	25.95	1.3986
82.06	17.22	0.72	1.4729	17.59	48.16	34.25	1.3902
68.63	28.54	2.83	1.4549	8.71	41.79	49.50	1.3740
57.81	37.95	4.24	1.4403	6.25	39.11	54.64	1.3704
44.55	46.00	9.46	1.4244	2.21	32.51	65.28	1.3619
35.30	50.28	14.42	1.4132	0.80	25.16	74.04	1.3555
29.40	51.00	19.59	1.4062	0.15	0.00	99.85	1.3329

Further experimental suggestions A variety of systems are available for study such as: hydrochloric acid–isoamyl alcohol–water,[1] toluene–isopropyl alcohol–water,[2] benzene–dioxane–water,[3] ethanol–benzene–water,[4] chloroform–acetone–water,[4] chloroform–acetic acid–water.[5]

[1] Reburn and Shearer. [2] Washburn and Beguin. [3] Berndt and Lynch.
[4] Bancroft and Hubard. [5] Findlay and Campbell.

REFERENCES

Bancroft and Hubard, *J. Am. Chem. Soc.*, **64,** 347 (1943)
Berndt and Lynch, *ibid.*, **66,** 282 (1944)
Findlay, A., and Campbell, A. N., *The Phase Rule and Its Applications*, 8th ed., Longmans, Green & Company, New York, **1938**
Gilson, *J. Am. Chem. Soc.*, **54,** 1445 (1932)
Othmer and Tobias, *Ind. Eng. Chem.*, **34,** 690 (1942)
Reburn and Shearer, *J. Am. Chem. Soc.*, **55,** 1774 (1933)
Washburn and Beguin, *ibid.*, **62,** 579 (1940)
Washburn and Olsen, *ibid.*, **57,** 303 (1935)

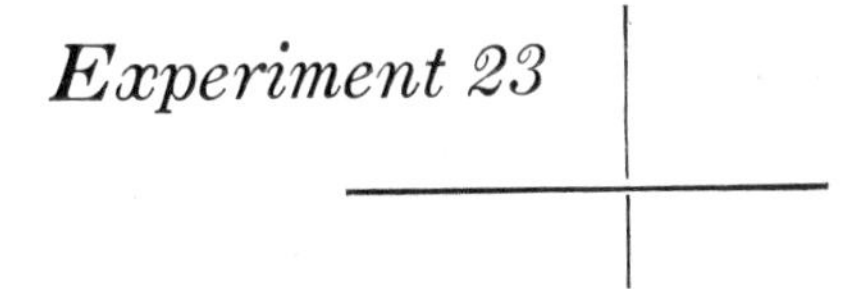

Experiment 23

The Equilibrium Between Aniline and Sulfur Dioxide

When sulfur dioxide gas is passed into aniline, the reaction taking place is

$$C_6H_5NH_2 + SO_2 \longrightarrow C_6H_5NH_2 \cdot SO_2 \qquad (165)$$

The compound of aniline and sulfur dioxide is not very stable and decomposes even at room temperature into the initial reactants when left in an open vessel.

When the above substances are in equilibrium, there are three phases present: liquid aniline, solid compound, and gaseous SO_2. This system contains two components, for upon specifying the quantities of any two of the three substances present, the composition of each phase of the equilibrium mixture is fixed.

The phase rule, namely, $F = C - P + 2$, when applied to the above system becomes $F = 2 - 3 + 2 = 1$. It follows that if the temperature (one of the degrees of freedom) is fixed, the system is completely defined and therefore is invariant. Thus, for every fixed or chosen temperature, there corresponds a definite pressure.

The equilibrium constant in terms of partial pressures for the dissociation

$$C_6H_5NH_2 \cdot SO_2 \longrightarrow C_6H_5NH_2 + SO_2 \qquad (166)$$

is given by the following:

$$K' = \frac{p_{C_6H_5NH_2} \times p_{SO_2}}{p_{C_6H_5NH_2 \cdot SO_2}} \qquad (167)$$

At the temperatures employed in the experiment (25° to 50°), the partial pressure of aniline is small and practically constant, and the partial pressure of the solid compound is also constant. Then

$$K = p_{SO_2} \qquad (168)$$

If K is measured at two or more different temperatures, the heat of the reaction ΔH may be calculated with the use of the van't Hoff equation:

$$2.303 \log \frac{K_2}{K_1} = \frac{\Delta H(T_2 - T_1)}{R(T_2 \times T_1)} \qquad (169)$$

Alternatively, ΔH can be obtained by a graphical method; upon plotting $\log p$ against $1/T$ and determining the slope of the curve

$$\Delta H = 2.303 \times R \times \text{slope of line} \qquad (170)$$

Various other thermochemical calculations may be made from the experimental data.

Apparatus The apparatus shown in Fig. 39, made from 8–10 mm. tubing; three liter beaker; stirrer; thermometer graduated in 0.1° or 0.2°C.; stopcock; manometer; meter stick; mercury; freshly redistilled aniline; SO_2 generator; leveling bulb; gas washing bottle.

Procedure Raise the leveling bulb A until the mercury comes to the mark M and clamp in this position. Introduce 2–5 ml. of freshly redistilled aniline into the bulb B, which is placed in a beaker containing cracked ice. Avoid wetting the upper parts of the apparatus with the aniline. Place a glass delivery tube through the opening F and clamp in position so that the end is just above the surface of the aniline. Connect a SO_2 generator to this tube and pass in a stream of the gas, which is dried by passing it through a gas washing bottle containing concentrated H_2SO_4. The aniline first turns a deep red color as the SO_2 dissolves and as it continues to pass into the bulb, the solid yellow addition compound forms. Continue to pass the gas in for five minutes after the solid has formed, and seal the apparatus at F while still in the freezing bath.

Close the stopcock D and lower the leveling bulb A so that it is at least 76 cm. below the mark M, while the bulb is still kept in the beaker of ice. Connect a piece of rubber pressure tubing from a water aspirator or oil vacuum pump to C, and evacuate the apparatus until the mercury levels remain stationary. Continue to evacuate two to three minutes, after which the stopcock D is closed and the ice bath is removed.

A three-liter beaker containing water which has been heated to 50–52°C. is placed on a ring and raised so that the apparatus is completely immersed. The thermometer and stirrer are arranged and the stirrer is started. The barometer reading B is obtained and recorded. The leveling bulb is adjusted until the mercury is about 0.5 cm. below the mark M. As the bath cools,[1] the pressure decreases; and when the mercury level reaches the mark M, the temperature and the height from the table top to the mark M (h_1) and to the mercury in the leveling bulb (h_2) are recorded.

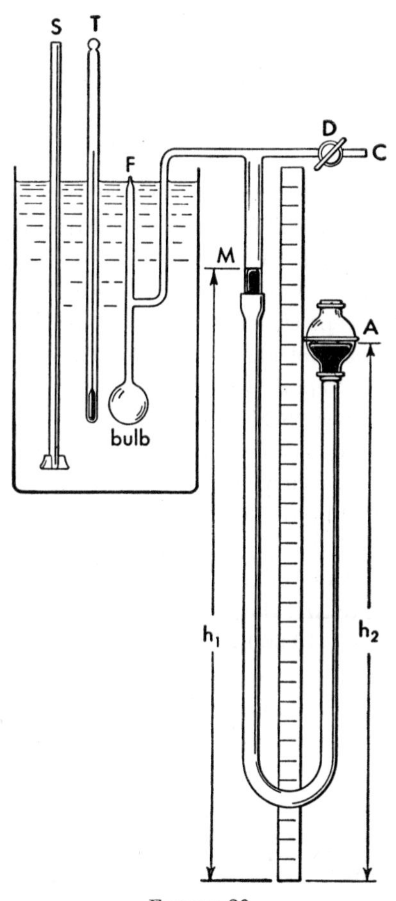

FIGURE 39

Since h_1 is fixed as the apparatus is clamped in position, this observation need only be made once. To obtain successive readings, it is only necessary to adjust the mercury about 1–2 cm. below the mark, and each time as the mercury rises to the mark M, record the temperature and the height h_2 of the mercury in the leveling bulb. The decomposition pressure obviously is $p = B + h_2 - h_1$.

It is sufficient to take readings between 52° and 35°; otherwise the time expended upon the experiment becomes too great. Readings for the above temperature limits take about two hours. Enter the data in Table 25. It may be necessary to employ a stem correction for temperature if the mercury thread is exposed any considerable amount. At the conclusion of the experiment, lower the leveling bulb so that the mercury is about 10 cm. below mark M.

[1] The rate of cooling is satisfactory if the temperature decreases one degree every three to five minutes. A small burner flame placed under the water bath will aid in adjusting the rate.

Time permitting, the experiment may be repeated. It is not necessary to prepare the addition compound anew as it is reasonably stable for 4–6 weeks. All that need be done is to immerse the bulb B in an ice bath and evacuate before starting the experiment, so that any air which may have leaked in is removed.

B____mm.

TABLE 25

t°C.	T°A. Corr.	$\frac{1}{T}$	h_1 (mm.)	h_2 (mm.)	p (mm.)	log p (mm.)	K Atmospheres

Calculations Plot the dissociation pressure in millimeters (ordinate) against the temperature, °C. (abscissa). Since K is equal to the partial pressure of sulfur dioxide (eq. 169), no calculation is needed to obtain K except that it should be expressed in atmospheres. (Divide by 760.0 or subtract log of 760 from log p and obtain the antilog.)

Prepare a plot of log p as ordinate against $1/T$ as abscissa on graph paper (8 × 10 in. size). Construct a straight line so that it passes through the points or so that an equal number of points fall on each side of the curve.[1] As the error is greatest at the lower pressures, these points will be the least reliable in constructing the curve. Extend the curve to include the temperature of 25°C.

Determine the slope of the line, and with the aid of equation 170 calculate ΔH, the heat of the dissociation reaction.[2] ΔH has been reported to be +19,600 cal. What is the percentage error of your result compared to this value?

Extrapolate the curve to find the temperature at which the decomposition pressure is equal to 760 mm. What is the significance of this temperature?

Express the data in the form of an equation: $\log p = A/T + B$. Use the method of average points to obtain the constants A and B. Express the derived equation in the exponential form:

$$p = Ce^{-\frac{\Delta H}{RT}} \tag{171}$$

Obtain the value of $\log p (= \log K)$ at 298.1°A. from the plot of log p and $1/T$, and calculate the standard free energy $\Delta F°$ for the dissociation reaction (eq. 166) by means of the equation $\Delta F° = -2.303RT \log K$. Is the reaction a spontaneous one?

[1] The conditions required are $\Sigma(+\Delta y) = \Sigma(-\Delta y)$ and $\Sigma(+\Delta x) = \Sigma(-\Delta x)$.
[2] Hill, *J. Am. Chem. Soc.*, **53,** 2598 (1931)

The standard free energy of formation of $C_6H_5NH_2$ (l) is +35,400 cal. and of SO_2 (g), −71,735 cal. Calculate the standard free energy of formation of the compound from the elements with the aid of the relation

$$\Delta F^\circ \text{ (reaction)} = \Delta F^\circ \text{ (products)} - \Delta F^\circ \text{ (reactants)}$$

The average experimental value for ΔH may be taken to be equal to the standard heat of the reaction ΔH°. Calculate the change in entropy ΔS° for the reaction using the relation

$$\Delta S^\circ = \frac{\Delta F^\circ - \Delta H^\circ}{T} \tag{172}$$

The entropy of SO_2 (g) is 59.3 entropy units and that for aniline is 45.8 units at 298.1°A.[1] Calculate the entropy of the compound from the relation

$$\Delta S^\circ = S^\circ \text{ (products)} - S^\circ \text{ (reactants)} \tag{173}$$

When the maximum error of the equilibrium constant is calculated by the error function derived from equation 168, it does not have too much significance since the error of duplicating the pressure at any temperature is not considered. For this reason, the maximum error of ΔH is a better criterion than that of K. Assume the following data to be obtained in the course of an experiment:

$T_2 = 321.3 \pm 0.5$°A. $\quad T_1 = 309.9 \pm 0.5$°A. $\quad B = 760.0 \pm 0.2$ mm.
$p_2 = 584 \pm 2.0$ mm. $\quad p_1 = 197 \pm 2.0$ mm.

When a series of results are not very precise, the maximum error can be advantageously calculated (Method 1, p. 9) from the normal and maximum (or minimum) values. Substituting the normal values in equation 169

$$2.303 \cdot 1.987 \cdot \log \frac{\frac{584}{760}}{\frac{197}{760}} = \Delta H \left(\frac{321.3 - 309.5}{321.3 \times 309.5}\right)$$

$$\Delta H_{\text{normal}} = +18{,}190 \text{ cal.}$$

Substituting to obtain the maximum value

$$2.303 \cdot 1.987 \cdot \log \frac{\frac{586}{760}}{\frac{195}{760}} = \Delta H_{\text{max.}} \left(\frac{320.8 - 310.4}{321.8 \times 310.4}\right)$$

$$\Delta H_{\text{max.}} = +21{,}190 \text{ cal.}$$

$$\pm\Delta(\Delta H) = \Delta H_{\text{max.}} - \Delta H_{\text{normal}} = 21{,}190 - 18{,}190 = 3000$$

$$\Delta H = 18{,}190 \pm 3000 \text{ cal.}$$

[1] Parks, Huffman, and Barmore, *J. Am. Chem. Soc.*, **55**, 2783 (1933)

The derived result shows that a maximum error of about ± 16 per cent may be obtained when the temperature is estimated to $\pm 0.5°$. To obtain better results, temperature control should be improved. Calculate the maximum error, assuming a temperature error of $\pm 0.2°$ and employing the experimental data. The above error for the pressure measurements may be used.

The method of error analysis can be extended to include the various other thermochemical results which have been calculated in this experiment.

REFERENCES

Foote and Fleischer, *J. Am. Chem. Soc.*, **56,** 870 (1934)
Hill, *ibid.*, **53,** 2598 (1931)
Hill and Fitzgerald, *ibid.*, **57,** 250 (1935)
Parks, Huffman, and Barmore, *ibid.*, **55,** 2783 (1933)

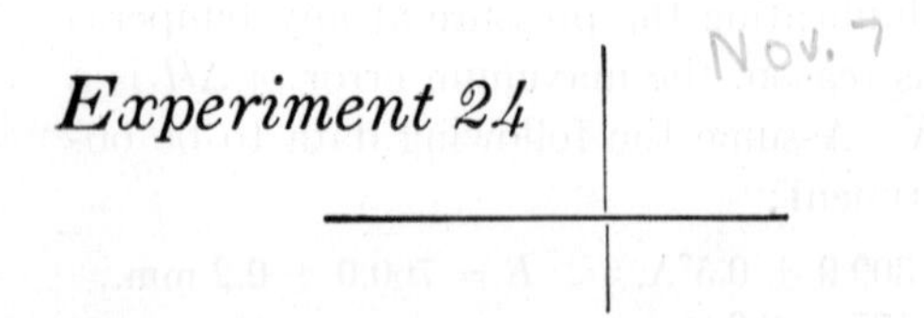

Thermochemistry

Every chemical reaction is accompanied by a change in internal energy E and total energy (heat content or enthalpy) H of the system. The relation between E and H is given by

$$H = E + PV \tag{174}$$

where the pressure-volume product PV is sometimes called the external energy.

E and H are not defined on an absolute scale and only changes in these quantities can be measured. In a chemical or physical process

$$\Delta H = \Delta E + \Delta(PV) \tag{175}$$

At constant pressure, $\Delta(PV) = P\,\Delta V$; if an ideal gas is involved $\Delta(PV) = \Delta nRT$.

The change in heat content or enthalpy is identical with the heat of reaction for a chemical process taking place at constant pressure. The term ΔE may be called the heat of reaction at constant volume; if $\Delta V = 0$, then $\Delta H_V = \Delta E$. For chemical reactions in solution, or between solids, the volume change is in general negligible and $\Delta H \approx \Delta E$.

The change in the heat of a reaction with temperature is given by Kirchhoff's law

$$\frac{d(\Delta H)}{dT} = \Delta C_P \tag{176}$$

where ΔC_P is the difference in heat capacity of products and reactants.

To evaluate ΔH or ΔE, known amounts of reactants are placed in a calorimeter and the change in temperature is measured. When the temperature of the usual isothermal calorimeter differs from that of its surroundings, it loses or gains heat by radiation and conduction. This heat exchange can be reduced with good insulation but cannot be eliminated entirely; however a correction for the heat loss can be made with the aid of Newton's law of cooling. In the adiabatic calorimeter, heat exchange is minimized by constantly maintaining an outer bath at exactly the same temperature as the inner reaction chamber. This may be done automatically and with considerable precision.

In this experiment, the vacuum jacket Dewar flask will be employed as the calorimeter. While this calorimeter suffers from the disadvantage of fragility and from a somewhat uncertain heat capacity, the advantages are small radiation loss and the chemical inertness of glass as compared to metal. Results accurate to about ± 2 per cent can be obtained.

The heat of neutralization per gram equivalent weight of various strong acids and bases is approximately the same, namely 13,700 calories at 20°C. This is to be expected, as the probable reaction of neutralization is $H_3O^+ + OH^- = 2H_2O$ and is independent of the anion and cation. The heat of neutralization does, however, vary slightly with concentration; and the values for weak acids and bases are usually considerably different from that given above.

Apparatus Two 500 ml. Dewar flasks are packed in a large wooden box with asbestos, alpha cellulose, or some other insulating material (Fig. 40). Two thermometers, T_a and T_b, are calibrated against each other by placing them in a large beaker of water, the temperature of which may be varied from 15° to 35°C. Thermometers graduated in tenths of a degree are necessary, and for results requiring greater accuracy, Beckmann thermometers should be used. The stirrers are of the ring type and are made of glass. The whole apparatus should be carefully assembled before any measurements are made. Be certain that the thermometers and stirrers clear the bottom of the Dewar flasks when assembling. Pipets of 200 ml. capacity are needed. If Beckmann thermometers are employed, solutions of exactly 0.5 N NaOH and 0.51 N HCl are required. If tenth degree thermometers are used, the base and acid should be about two to three times more concentrated.

Procedure The first step in the calorimetric determination is to obtain the water equivalent of the calorimeter. This is necessary as the Dewar flask, the thermometer (glass and mercury), and stirrer, as well as the solutions, are heated by the energy evolved during the chemical

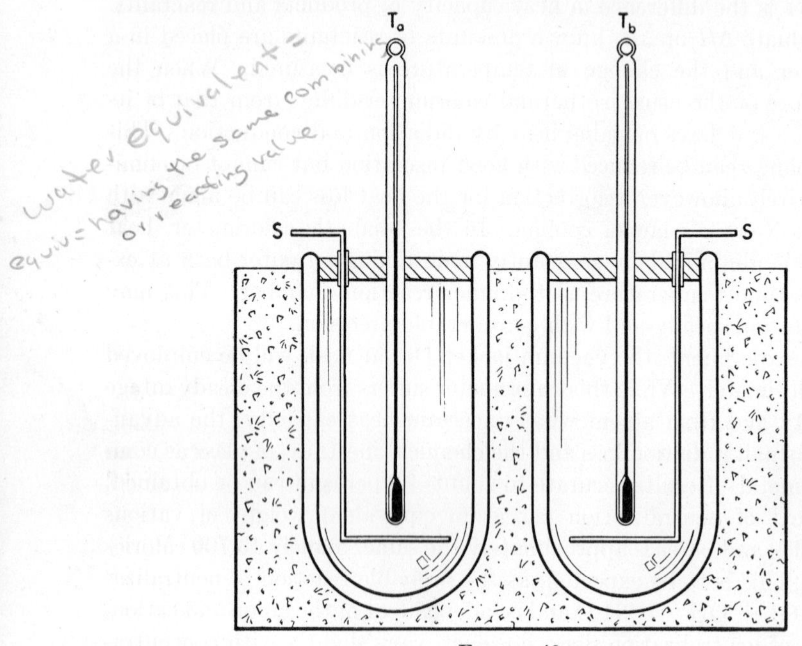

FIGURE 40

change. The method of mixtures is occasionally employed; known masses of warm and cool water are mixed and from the known heat capacity of water and the final temperature, the water equivalent of the calorimeter is determined. A second method is to perform some chemical change whose heat of reaction is accurately known. A third procedure (less satisfactory) is to calculate the water equivalent from the known mass and heat capacity of the materials of construction. The last procedure will be followed in this experiment as lack of time prohibits a more accurate method.

The mass of the glass Dewar flask and glass stirrer are obtained by weighing on an ordinary platform balance. Assuming the specific heat of glass to be equal to 0.2 calorie per gram degree, the total heat capacity of the glass is calculated. Since only about one-third of the glass is in contact with the solution, the actual heat capacity may be taken as one-third of the above value. The heat capacity of the thermometer (either tenth degree or Beckmann) may be assumed equal to two calories per degree and is added to the above.

Approximately 0.5 *N* NaOH, free from carbonate, is prepared from a saturated NaOH solution. The clear solution is pipetted (CAUTION: Use a safety trap) and diluted to the required concentration with freshly boiled, cooled, distilled water. If a larger error can be tolerated, the standard solution is prepared from a good grade of reagent. The base is standardized with potassium acid phthalate or sulfamic acid. The hydrochloric acid is prepared by diluting the concentrated acid so that it is slightly more concentrated than 0.5 *N*; for example, 0.51 *N*. It is standardized against the base.

If Beckmann thermometers are used, they should be set so that at room temperature (20°) the mercury is on the lower part of the scale. The Beckmann scale should also be compared with an ordinary or standard thermometer so as to estimate the initial and final temperatures of the solution.

Pipet 200 ml. of the acid into a Dewar flask which has been previously rinsed with some acid and allowed to drain for two seconds. The temperature of the acid should be about two degrees above room temperature. Transfer 200 ml. of the base into the other Dewar flask with the same pipet, having previously rinsed it with distilled water and base. The temperature of the latter should be about two degrees below that of the room. Assemble the apparatus as in Fig. 40. Record the temperature and time for both solutions every one or two minutes for the next 10–15 minutes, operating the stirrers once every 10–15 seconds.

At a predetermined time (for example, the thirteenth minute), pour the acid into the base, allowing a two second drainage time. Replace the thermometer and stirrer and start to operate the stirrer every 1–2 seconds. Record the time and temperature at one minute intervals until the temperature reaches a maximum, and continue the observations for the next ten minutes. The rate of stirring after passing the maximum is reduced to once every 10–15 seconds. The Beckmann thermometer is gently tapped each time before observing the temperature. The experiment should be repeated at least once.

Test the solution with phenolphthalein. If it is not acid, the experiment will have to be repeated with slightly stronger acid.

Calculations The heat liberated in the reaction is equal to the total heat capacity of the Dewar flask, thermometer, and solution, multiplied by the net temperature change. The temperatures immediately before and after mixing may conveniently be obtained by plotting thermometer readings against time, as illustrated in Fig. 41. Here it is assumed that the solutions were mixed at the tenth minute; the line JF is drawn vertically, since the reaction takes place almost instantaneously. Graphical extrapolation of the lines AC, BH, and DE, which correspond to acid, base, and mixture respectively, to their intersection with JF

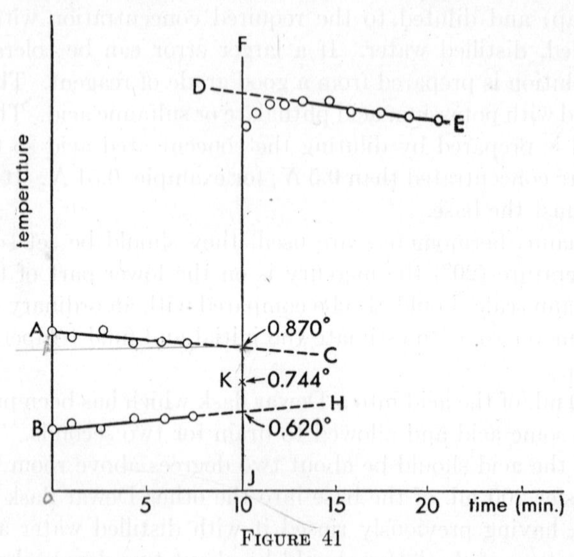

FIGURE 41

gives the three necessary temperatures. Readings immediately after mixing are disregarded in drawing the line DE, since the calorimeter and solution do not reach thermal equilibrium instantly.

In Fig. 41 the temperatures of the acid and base at the time of mixing are shown as 0.870° and 0.620° respectively. Equal volumes of the two solutions are assumed, and the temperature after mixing but before reaction could be taken as the mean of these values, namely 0.745°. With solutions of appreciably different density (d) and specific heat (c_p) or with unequal volumes, a weighted mean temperature must be calculated. Based on the method of mixtures, the following equation can be employed

$$t_m = \frac{c_{\text{base}}\, t_{\text{base}} + c_{\text{Dewar}}\, t_{\text{Dewar}} + c_{\text{acid}}\, t_{\text{acid}}}{c_{\text{base}} + c_{\text{Dewar}} + c_{\text{acid}}} \tag{177}$$

where c refers to total heat capacity = volume × density × c_p. Using values of d and c_p given in Table 26 and 40 cal. per degree for c_{Dewar}, there is obtained in the present case

$$t_m = \frac{200\times1.021\times0.968\times0.620+40\times0.620+200\times1.007\times0.965\times0.870}{200\times1.021\times0.968+40+200\times1.007\times0.965}$$

$$= 0.744°$$

The heat of reaction changes with temperature, and either ΔH_1 for the initial temperature (t_1) or ΔH_2 for the final temperature (t_2) may be calculated.

1. Assuming the heat to be liberated at t_1, the resulting NaCl solution is raised in temperature. The number of calories is given by the total heat capacity of the NaCl solution and calorimeter times the temperature rise. Dividing by n, the number of moles of NaCl, gives the heat of reaction per mole, ΔH_1:

$$\Delta H_1 = \frac{V_{\text{NaCl}} \times d_{\text{NaCl}} \times c_{p(\text{NaCl})} \times (t_2 - t_1) + c_{\text{Dewar}}(t_2 - t_1)}{n} \qquad (178)$$

2. If the total heat capacities of the acid and base solutions are used in equation 178, the heat of reaction at temperature t_2 will be obtained.

The values of ΔH_1 and ΔH_2 are related by the principle of Kirchhoff. Equation 176 may be employed as follows

$$\frac{\Delta H_2 - \Delta H_1}{t_2 - t_1} = c_{\text{NaCl}} - (c_{\text{HCl}} + c_{\text{NaOH}}) \qquad (179)$$

where c refers to the heat capacity of solution containing one mole of solute $= V \times d \times c_p$. Equation 179 may also be used to calculate ΔH at other temperatures than those of the measurement.

The student should calculate both ΔH_1 and ΔH_2 from his experimental results, and from one of these values should calculate ΔH at 20°C, employing equation 179. The best measurements for this neutralization have given the value $\Delta H = -13{,}690$ cal. at 20°C. However, it should be noted that the change is only about 60 cal. per degree, and the experimental inaccuracy may be too great for the above calculation to have much significance.

TABLE 26

Solution		c_p per Gram	Density
0.5 N	NaOH	0.968	1.021
0.5 N	HCl	0.965	1.007
0.5 N	H_2SO_4	0.975	1.009
0.5 N	HAc	0.999	1.003
0.25 N	NaCl	0.981	1.008
0.25 N	Na_2SO_4	0.977	1.030
0.25 N	$NaC_2H_3O_2$	0.963	1.012

If desired, the calculations may be reversed: assuming the heat of reaction to be known, the water equivalent or effective heat capacity of the calorimeter is calculated.

An approximate analysis of the error in the final derived result can be made, employing possible errors for the quantities in equation 178. The original volumes of acid and base may be measured with any desired accuracy, but due to the method of mixing the error in V_{NaCl} should be taken as ± 2 cc. The error of the initial and final temperatures may be assumed to be $\pm 0.005°$ with Beckmann thermometers, ± 0.2 with 0.1° thermometers. The water equivalent of the calorimeter may be in error by ± 10 per cent. The errors of density and specific heat of the solutions may be disregarded.

Calculate the maximum error of the derived result employing the above or other reasonable estimates of the errors involved.

Other experimental suggestions The heat of neutralization of sulfuric acid and acetic acids may be studied. Table 26 contains all data needed for the calculations.

REFERENCES

Kegles, *J. Am. Chem. Soc.*, **62**, 3231 (1940)

The heat of neutralization of NaOH by HCl.

Stow and Elliott, *Anal. Chem.*, **20**, 250 (1948)

White, W. P., *The Modern Calorimeter*, Reinhold Publishing Corporation, New York, **1928**

Experiment 25

Electrical Conductance

The problem of the conductance of electrolytes divides itself into two parts. The first is the measurement of electrical resistance and conductance, the second is the correlation and interpretation of the data in such a way as to be useful to the chemist.

The resistance of any conductor is given by

$$R = \rho \frac{l}{A} \tag{180}$$

where l and A are the length and cross sectional area respectively, and the proportionality constant ρ is the specific resistance, *i.e.* the resistance per cubic centimeter. The specific conductance κ is the reciprocal resistance

$$\kappa = 1/\rho \tag{181}$$

Experimentally it is difficult to measure accurately the length and cross section of a conductance cell. Hence it is customary to measure the resistance of a cell with a solution whose specific conductance κ has been accurately determined. Then the effective ratio l/A, which is known as the cell constant K, can be obtained by combining equations 180 and 181:

$$K = l/A = \kappa R \tag{182}$$

The specific conductance of any other solution can be obtained by measuring its resistance in the cell whose constant K is known.

Direct current is not ordinarily used to determine the conductance of solutions since it produces electrolytic decomposition (electrolysis) and polarization at the electrodes. Alternating current of fairly high frequency (1000 cycles/sec.) is more satisfactory since the above effects are minimized. By using a Wheatstone bridge circuit as illustrated in Fig. 42, very little current actually passes through the conductance cell.

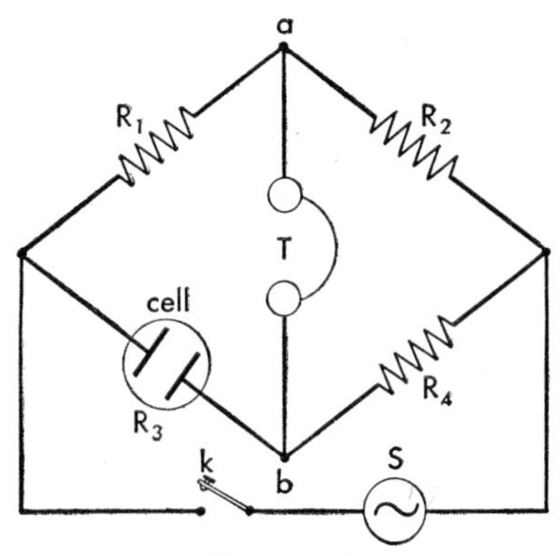

FIGURE 42

In Fig. 42, R_1, R_2, and R_4 are variable known resistances, R_3 represents the resistance of the conductance cell, S is a source of alternating current, and T is a telephone head set which is used to detect the balance of the bridge circuit. When points a and b are at the same potential no current will pass through the telephones, silence will be observed and the bridge is assumed to be balanced. The resistance R_3 may be calculated from

$$R_3 = R_4 \frac{R_1}{R_2} \tag{183}$$

Various sources of alternating current are commonly available. The tuning fork controlled oscillator known as the microphone hummer is satisfactory for many measurements. High frequency motor generators may be used. Sometimes 60 cycle line current is satisfactory. Electronic oscillators are widely used and many circuits are described in the literature.

To increase the ease of detecting the bridge balance, an electronic amplifier is sometimes inserted in place of the telephones in Fig. 43. The telephones are then connected to the amplifier output, or an oscillograph may be used in place of the telephones.

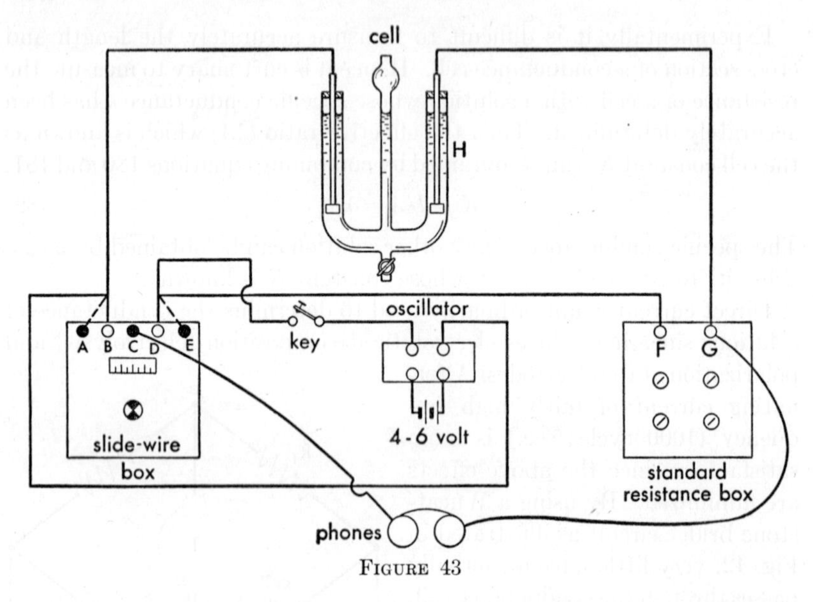

FIGURE 43

Since the cell electrodes introduce capacitance as well as resistance into the circuit, a better bridge balance may be obtained by connecting a variable air condenser with a maximum capacity of 500 micromicrofarads in parallel with the resistance R_4. To eliminate stray capacitance from the proximity of the operator's body, a suitable part of the circuit (points *c* or *g* of Fig. 43) should be grounded (a copper wire firmly attached to a cold water pipe). If a Wagner ground is used, a variable high resistance (100,000 ohms) is connected across the output side of the oscillator and the variable center contact grounded. The resistance is varied until minimum sound is obtained with a balanced bridge.

Various types of Wheatstone bridge are available. The Kohlrausch slide-wire with end coils in conjunction with a standard decade box is quite commonly used; however, three decade boxes, a standard ratio bridge, or post office bridge are often employed. For most measurements, cells made with platinum electrodes electrolytically platinized (coated with platinum black) are satisfactory. The cell resistance should not be less than 500 ohms nor more than 50,000 ohms, and several cells with different constants should be available. Good temperature control is needed, as the conductance may change as much as 2.5 per cent per degree. A thermostat should be available with a control of 0.01–0.05°C.

Water which has a minimum specific resistance of 50,000 ohms may be satisfactorily employed in this experiment. For very accurate work, water should be redistilled from alkaline permanganate solution using a block tin tube condenser, and stored in airtight tin lined cans. During the distillation, the water through the condenser jacket is regulated so that only partial condensation of the steam occurs; discard the first and last fourths and collect the second and third fourths. If the conductance of the ordinary distilled water is due chiefly to carbon dioxide, this can be removed by bubbling CO_2-free air (long soda-lime tube) through it for several hours. The water should have a specific resistance of at least 100,000 ohms when prepared as above.

Apparatus It will be assumed that the apparatus of Fig. 43 is available: a 1000 cycle oscillator; a slide-wire bridge with end coils (A and E) the resistance of each being 4.5 times that of the slide wire BD; a standard decade box with resistances to 10,000 ohms; telephones; a cell with a constant between 1 and 10. A supplementary standard resistance with contacts at 10,000 to 100,000 ohms in series with the decade box is useful for solutions of high resistance. Procedure with other apparatus will be similar.

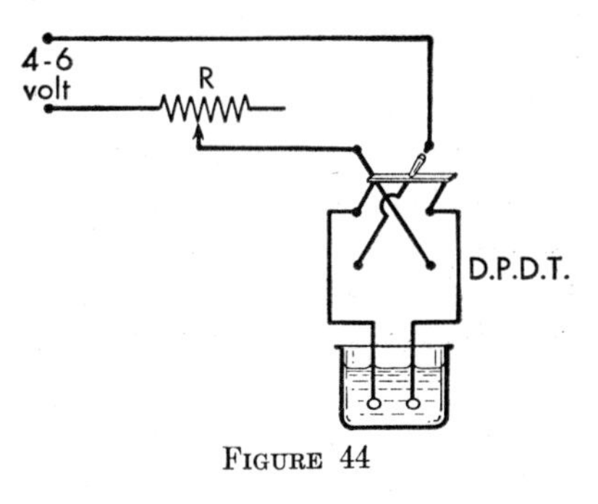

FIGURE 44

Procedure *Plating electrodes.* Bright or new platinum electrodes are cleaned with chromic acid mixture and rinsed. Old or dried out plated electrodes may be carefully treated with aqua regia to remove the platinum black. Electrodes should never be touched with the fingers after cleaning. They are placed in a solution containing 3 g. of platinic chloride and 0.02–0.03 g. of lead acetate in 100 ml. of water, and connected to a storage battery or dry cells through a 50–200 ohm variable resistance and reversing switch as shown in Fig. 44. The current is allowed to flow for 5–10 minutes, and a moderate evolution of gas should occur; the polarity is reversed every half minute. The plating solution may be used many times. The electrodes are rinsed, immersed in 5 per cent sulfuric acid and the electrolysis continued for ten minutes, reversing the current every minute. They are rinsed again, and from this point should always be kept immersed in distilled water when not in use.

The cell constant. The cell is rinsed several times with a 0.1 or 0.02 N KCl solution which has been accurately prepared by weighing oven-dried salt. It is then filled with solution and placed in a thermostat, and its resistance is measured after it has attained temperature equilibrium (allow at least ten minutes).

To accomplish this, set the slide-wire at its midpoint (500) and the standard resistance (decade) box at the approximate resistance of the solution (try 500 ohms). Press the tapping key momentarily and observe the sound in the telephones. Hold tapping keys down for only short periods of time to avoid heating the solution. Adjust the standard resistance until the sound is at a minimum or absent; or after the minimum has been located approximately, the slide-wire may be used to search for it more exactly.

Obtain at least four observations using fresh portions of the standard KCl solution and record the resistance each time. If they differ by more than 1 per cent the determinations should be repeated. The cell resistance and cell constant are calculated, using equations 183 (or 184, p. 145) and 182, respectively. The specific conductance of 0.02 N KCl at 25°C. is 0.002768 reciprocal ohm (mho) and the corresponding value for 0.1 N KCl is 0.01288 mho. Tables should be consulted for other concentrations or temperatures.

The conductance of electrolytes. Solutions of KCl having normalities of 0.1, 0.05, 0.025, 0.0125, 0.00625, 0.003125, and 0.0015625 are prepared by quantitatively diluting 250-ml. samples to 500 ml., employing the necessary volumetric flasks. The resistance of each solution is measured. Alternatively some other strong electrolyte such as HCl may be used; the same range of concentrations is suitable.

TABLE 27

T____°C. Cell constant____cm.$^{-1}$ Acetic acid (or KCl)

Normality (C)	Vol. in liters that contains 1 equiv. weight	$\sqrt{C}$	R_3	κ	Λ	α	K_c

The resistance of a weak electrolyte such as acetic acid is also measured. The following normalities are suggested: 0.2, 0.1, 0.05, 0.025, 0.0125, and 0.00625. The solutions are prepared by dilution of a standard 0.2 N solution. Measurements may be made upon still more dilute solutions if desired.

Calculations Calculate the resistance (R_3) of each solution. If a ratio resistance bridge is used, select equation 183. If a Kohlrausch slide-wire is used (end coils omitted), employ the following equation

$$R_3 = R_4 \frac{A}{1000 - A} \tag{184}$$

where A is the slide-wire reading from 0 to 1000. When the end coils are included, employ the following equation:

$$R_3 = R_4 \frac{4500 + A}{5500 - A} \tag{185}$$

Calculate the specific conductance of each solution with the aid of equation 182.

The equivalent conductance (Λ) is calculated using the following equation:

$$\Lambda_c = \frac{1000\kappa}{\text{normality}} \tag{186}$$

Plot the equivalent conductance (Λ_c) of both HAc and KCl (ordinate) against the normality (abscissa).

Plot the equivalent conductance Λ_c of both HAc and KCl (ordinate) against the volume of solution that contains one gram equivalent weight (abscissa).

Weak electrolytes. For a weak electrolyte the degree of dissociation α may be calculated from the equation:

$$\alpha = \Lambda_c/\Lambda_o \tag{187}$$

Assume the equivalent conductance of the weak electrolyte (acetic acid) at infinite dilution (Λ_o) to be equal to 390.6 mhos at 25°C. and calculate α for each solution.

The dissociation constant of acetic acid is given by the equation

$$K_c = \frac{\alpha^2 C}{1 - \alpha} \tag{188}$$

Calculate K_c for each of the solutions employed.

Neglecting α in the denominator of equation 188 since it is small compared to unity and substituting the value of α from equation 187:

$$\frac{\Lambda_o\sqrt{K_c}}{\Lambda_c} = \sqrt{C} \quad \text{or} \quad \log \Lambda_c = \log(\Lambda_o\sqrt{K_c}) - 0.5 \log C \tag{189}$$

This relation is tested as follows: (*a*) Plot $1/\Lambda_c$ (ordinate) against $\sqrt{C}$ (abscissa). (*b*) Plot $\log \Lambda_c$ (ordinate) against $\log C$ (abscissa). In both graphs, a straight line should be obtained if α is small compared to unity. Obtain the slope of the line in graph (*b*).

Strong electrolytes. For strong electrolytes, Kohlrausch found empirically the following approximate linear relationship:

$$\Lambda_c = \Lambda_o - A\sqrt{C} \tag{190}$$

The form of this equation finds theoretical substantiation in the Debye-Hückel theory. The numerical value of A can be calculated for each strong electrolyte. Plot the equivalent conductance Λ_c (ordinate) against $\sqrt{C}$ (abscissa) for the KCl solutions. Obtain the slope of the curve. Extrapolate the curve to obtain the intercept Λ_o. Record and compare with the known value for KCl.

The estimated error of the equivalent conductance of a solution may be calculated as follows if the following data and probable errors are assumed:

$$K = 10.00 \pm 0.02 \text{ cm.}^{-1} \qquad C = 0.01 \pm 0.00001\ N$$

$$R_4 = 602.4 \pm 1.0 \text{ ohm}$$

$$R_1/R_2 = 1000 \text{ (assume a precise ratio bridge)} = A \text{ (a constant)}$$

The estimated error of R_3 is calculated from equation 183.

Since only one error is involved, equation 28, page 8; reduces to a simple multiplication:

$$R_3 = A \cdot R_4 = 1000(602.4 \pm 1.0)$$
$$= 602.4 \times 10^3 \pm 1.0 \times 10^3$$

The specific conductance and its estimated error are calculated as follows (see eq. 29, p. 8):

$$\kappa = \frac{K}{R_3}$$

$$(d\kappa)^2 = \left(\frac{\partial \kappa}{\partial K}\right)^2 (dK)^2 + \left(\frac{\partial \kappa}{\partial R_3}\right)^2 (dR_3)^2$$

where
$$\frac{\partial \kappa}{\partial K} = \frac{1}{R_3} \quad \text{and} \quad \frac{\partial \kappa}{\partial R} = \frac{-K}{R_3^2} = \frac{-\kappa}{R_3}$$

Then
$$(\Delta\kappa)^2 = \left(\frac{1}{R_3}\right)^2 \cdot (\Delta K)^2 + \left(\frac{-\kappa}{R_3}\right)^2 \cdot (\Delta R_3)^2$$
$$= \left(\frac{1}{602.4 \times 10^3}\right)^2 \cdot (0.02)^2 + \left(\frac{1.66 \times 10^{-5}}{602.4 \times 10^3}\right)^2 \cdot (10^3)^2$$
$$\kappa = 1.66 \times 10^{-5} \pm 4.3 \times 10^{-8}$$

The estimated error of the equivalent conductance Λ_c is obtained from:

$$\Lambda_c = \frac{1000\kappa}{C}$$

$$(\Delta\Lambda_c)^2 = \left(\frac{1000}{C}\right)^2(\Delta\kappa)^2 + \left(\frac{-\Lambda_c}{C}\right)^2(\Delta C)^2$$

$$= \left(\frac{10^3}{1 \times 10^{-2}}\right)^2(4.3 \times 10^{-8})^2 + \left(\frac{-1.66}{10^{-2}}\right)^2(1 \times 10^{-5})^2$$

$$\pm\Delta\Lambda_c = 4.6 \times 10^{-3}$$

$$\Lambda_c = 1.66 \pm 4.6 \times 10^{-3}$$

Calculate the estimated error of the dissociation constant of acetic acid from one of the measurements. The assumed probable errors may be similar in magnitude to those given above.

REFERENCES

Dole, M., *Experimental and Theoretical Electrochemistry*, Chap. 4, McGraw-Hill Book Company, Inc., New York, **1935**

Jones and Joseph, *J. Am. Chem. Soc.*, **50,** 1049 (1928).

Luder, *ibid.*, **62,** 89 (1940)

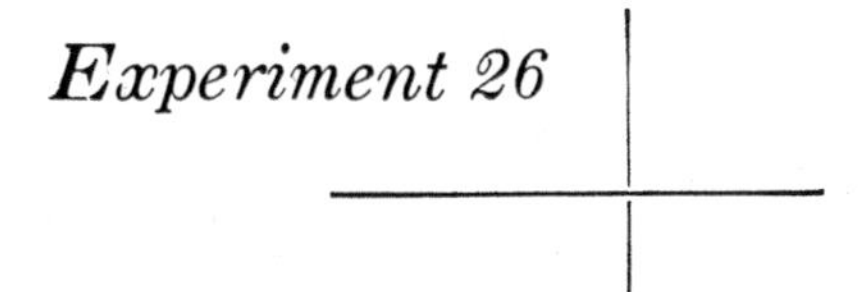

Experiment 26

The Solubility Product Constant

When a saturated aqueous solution of a sparingly soluble salt such as $PbSO_4$ is prepared, the following equilibrium exists:

$$PbSO_4\ (s) = Pb^{++} + SO_4^{=}$$

It is difficult to determine the concentration of the lead ion or sulfate ion in the saturated solution of this salt by the analytical methods commonly employed in quantitative analysis. However, from the measured conductance of such a solution, the ion concentrations can be calculated and the solubility and solubility product can be evaluated. Since the solvent water has a specific conductance of a similar order of magnitude to that of the dissolved salt, it is necessary to measure the specific conductance of the water and subtract it from that of the solution in order to obtain the specific conductance due to the ions of the salt. Thus

$$\kappa_{\text{ions}} = \kappa_{\text{solution}} - \kappa_{\text{water}} \tag{191}$$

The relation between equivalent conductance Λ_c, the specific conductance κ_{ions}, and the normality C is given by

$$C = \frac{1000\kappa_{\text{ions}}}{\Lambda_c} \tag{192}$$

Hence in order to determine the concentration or normality of dissolved salt, the equivalent conductance Λ_c of the salt must also be known for the same salt concentration as is present in the saturated solution. It is usually assumed, since the solubility is small, that the equivalent conductance Λ_c for the saturated salt solution is the same as that for infinite dilution Λ_o. Then

$$C = \frac{1000\kappa_{\text{ions}}}{\Lambda_o} \tag{193}$$

The value of Λ_o for lead sulfate may be obtained with the aid of Kohlrausch's law of the additivity of ionic conductances, applied to the salts $Pb(NO_3)_2$, K_2SO_4, KNO_3; or it may be taken from the literature.

Apparatus Conductivity apparatus as in Expt. 25; several standard 10,000-ohm resistances or conductivity cell designed for high resistance measurements; conductivity water of approximately 100,000-ohm specific resistance; C.P. $PbSO_4$.

Procedure A saturated solution of $PbSO_4$ is prepared by adding 0.025 mole of the salt to 0.5 liter of conductivity water and boiling for several minutes. Shake the solution occasionally while it is cooling. When it is sufficiently cool, place it in a thermostat at 25°C. for two hours and shake at fifteen-minute intervals.

The salt may also be prepared by adding a slight excess of 0.1 *M* sulfuric acid to 0.1 *M* lead nitrate solution, digesting, and washing. The saturated solution is then prepared as above.

While it is advisable to use a conductance cell with electrodes of large area placed rather close together, the cell used in the previous experiment may be employed. Otherwise it will be necessary to determine the cell constant of the new cell, using a KCl solution of known specific conductance.

While waiting for the solution to come to equilibrium, determine the resistance and hence the specific conductance at 25° of the conductivity water used for preparing the saturated solution of $PbSO_4$.

In order to balance the bridge, it may be necessary to insert one or more standard 10,000-ohm resistances in series with the resistance box and conductivity cell (between connection *G* and *H* in Fig. 43, page 142, making the connection of the phones to the side of the resistance leading to *H*). The resistance of the cell (end coils are used) is determined at 25°C. The conductivity water must have a minimum specific resistance of 100,000 ohms, otherwise the results will be worthless and the experiment will have to be repeated with water of the required resistance. Empty the conductivity water from the cell and rinse it several times with the clear saturated lead sulfate solution. Avoid introducing any solid salt particles into the cell. Finally place some of the sample in the cell and obtain the resistance. Repeat with fresh samples until constant values are obtained.

Calculations Calculate the resistance and specific conductance of the conductivity water.

Calculate the resistance and specific conductance of the solution.

Obtain the specific conductance of the ions alone using equation 191.

Assuming the equivalent conductance Λ_o of $PbSO_4$ to be 151.8 at 25°C., calculate the normality of the solution using equation 193.

Finally, calculate the solubility product.

The estimated error of the specific conductance of the salt and water, and of the concentration and ion product, might be calculated by a procedure similar to that illustrated in Expt. 25. However, it should not be assumed that the actual error in the conductance of the water corresponds to the precision of measurement of its resistance. Unless extremely pure water is prepared and kept out of contact with glass, air, and other sources of contamination, the water in the saturated salt solution, and water alone, may differ in conductance by 100 per cent or more.

By comparison all other errors may be neglected. The solubility product may have finally a numerical value such as $(1.9 \pm 0.9) \times 10^{-8}$, and it might seem at first glance that such a large error makes the measurement worthless. However, this is not the case since it is often useful merely to know the order of magnitude, and other methods of determining solubility may have equally large errors. Further, the conductance measurements may be greatly refined by workers who have time and the necessary equipment.

Further experimental suggestions The following salts may be employed in this experiment: silver sulfate, silver acetate, lead iodide, calcium sulfate, strontium sulfate. (See the reference to Johnson and Hulett below.)

REFERENCES

Johnson and Hulett, *J. Am. Chem. Soc.*, **57**, 256 (1935)

Kolthoff and Rosenblum, *ibid.*, **55**, 2656 (1933)
Solubility of $PbSO_4$ by an analytical method.

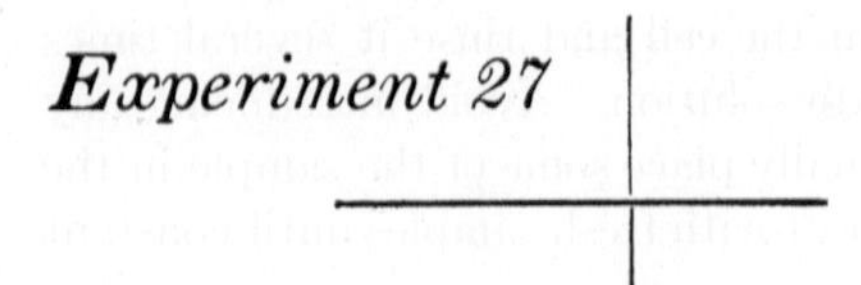

Experiment 27

An Acid-Base Equilibrium Constant

Hydrolysis is defined in the older literature as the reaction of a salt with water to produce an acid and a base. In the Brönsted treatment of acids and bases, the term has no special significance, as in general an acid and a base react to form another conjugate acid and base. Nevertheless, it is advantageous to retain the term "hydrolysis" to denote this type of acid-base reaction. The acid-base equilibrium constant, which is also known by the older name "hydrolysis constant," may be determined by conductimetric methods.

The salt, aniline hydrochloride, when dissolved in water, reacts as follows

$$\underset{\substack{a_1 \\ C(1-x)}}{C_6H_5NH_3^+} + Cl^- + \underset{b_2}{H_2O} \rightleftharpoons \underset{\substack{b_1 \\ Cx}}{C_6H_5NH_2} + \underset{\substack{a_2 \\ Cx}}{H_3O^+} + Cl^- \qquad (194)$$

where a_1 and b_1, a_2 and b_2 are the conjugate acids and bases of the anilinium ion–water system. Observe that since Cl^- ion appears on both sides of the equation, it may be canceled out. According to the Brönsted view, anilinium ion is an acid and the acid dissociation or strength constant K_a is

$$K_a = \frac{[C_6H_5NH_2] \times [H_3O^+]}{[C_6H_5NH_3^+]} \qquad (195)$$

the quantities within the brackets representing activities or concentrations. The term for the concentration of water has been omitted in the denominator since it is practically constant.

The aniline also reacts with water:

$$\underset{b_1}{C_6H_5NH_2} + \underset{a_2}{H_2O} = \underset{a_1}{C_6H_5NH_3^+} + \underset{b_2}{OH^-} \tag{196}$$

The basic dissociation constant of aniline is then

$$K_b = \frac{[C_6H_5NH_3^+] \cdot [OH^-]}{[C_6H_5NH_2]} \tag{197}$$

Upon multiplying equation 195 by equation 197 there is obtained

$$K_a \cdot K_b = [H_3O^+] \cdot [OH^-] = K_w \tag{198}$$

If both K_a and K_b can be measured independently, the degree of ionization and ionization constant K_w of water can be calculated. Since K_w is known more accurately from other methods one would more commonly calculate either K_a or K_b from measurements of the other.

The relation between the degree[1] of dissociation (x) or hydrolysis of anilinium ion and the dissociation or hydrolysis constant K_a may be obtained by applying the law of mass action to equation 194:

$$K_a = \frac{Cx^2}{(1 - x)} \tag{199}$$

If anilinium chloride underwent complete hydrolysis with water, the total equivalent conductance would be equal to that of hydrochloric acid Λ_2 since molecular aniline is a nonelectrolyte. If the degree of dissociation were zero, the equivalent conductance Λ_1 of the solution would be equal to that of anilinium chloride only. If Λ_3 is the actual conductance of the solution, then

$$x = \frac{\Lambda_3 - \Lambda_1}{\Lambda_2 - \Lambda_1} \tag{200}$$

where all conductances are measured at the same concentration and temperature.

Apparatus Conductivity outfit as used in Expt. 25; conductivity water of 50,000–100,000 ohm specific resistance; aniline (redistilled); aniline hydrochloride. The crystals of the latter salt should be white. If they are discolored, the salt should be recrystallized from water with the aid of activated charcoal.

Procedure (*a*) Prepare 500 ml. each of exactly 0.03 N, 0.015 N, and 0.0075 N solutions of aniline hydrochloride by accurately weighing the pure dry salt.

(*b*) Prepare 2 liters of 0.03 N solution of aniline, the amine being weighed out on a platform balance. Shake until the aniline dissolves.

[1] The degree of dissociation is defined as the fraction of total salt hydrolized, *i.e.* $x = [C_6H_5NH_2]/C$ in equation 194.

(*c*) Weigh out the same quantities of aniline hydrochloride as in (*a*) above to prepare 0.03 *N*, 0.015 *N*, and 0.0075 *N* solutions and transfer each to 500-ml. volumetric flasks with the aid of a salt funnel. Wash the aniline hydrochloride into the flasks with the 0.03 *N* aniline solution prepared in (*b*) and make up to the mark with this solution.

In this way, six solutions corresponding to those in Table 28 will have been prepared.

$t = 25°C.$ TABLE 28 K(cell constant) = ____ cm.$^{-1}$

Solution	R	κ	Λ	x	K_a	K_b	$K_w \times 10^{14}$
0.03 *N* $C_6H_5NH_3Cl$							1.37
0.015 *N* $C_6H_5NH_3Cl$							1.25
0.0075 *N* $C_6H_5NH_3Cl$							1.15
0.03 *N* $C_6H_5NH_3Cl$ 0.03 *N* $C_6H_5NH_2$							1.37
0.015 *N* $C_6H_5NH_3Cl$ 0.03 *N* $C_6H_5NH_2$							1.25
0.0075 *N* $C_6H_5NH_3Cl$ 0.03 *N* $C_6H_5NH_2$							1.15

The conductivity cell employed in the previous experiments may be used; if a different one is used, the cell constant must be determined. It is not necessary to use the end coils in the following procedure. Rinse the cell with the 0.03 *N* solution of $C_6H_5NH_3Cl$ several times, finally filling it and placing it in a thermostat (25° ± 0.05°). When the solution has attained temperature equilibrium, obtain its resistance, making four independent readings. Repeat the above procedure for each of the remaining solutions and enter the data in Table 28. Upon completing the measurements, rinse the cell several times with dilute hydrochloric acid and then with distilled water, finally filling with distilled water.

Calculations Calculate the resistance, the specific conductance κ, and the equivalent conductance Λ of each solution using equations 184, 182, and 186, respectively, of Expt. 25.

The degree of dissociation or hydrolysis x is calculated, using equation 200. The equivalent conductance Λ_1, of anilinium hydrochloride, when the degree of dissociation of the anilinium ion is zero, corresponds to the measured conductance of the salt in the presence of excess free amine or base. The equivalent conductance Λ_2 of 0.03 *N*, 0.015 *N*, and 0.0075 *N* solutions of hydrochloric acid is 393, 399, and 401 mhos respectively at 25°C. If solutions of different concentrations and temperatures were chosen, the equivalent conductance of the acid at these concentrations should be obtained by reference to standard tables

The acid dissociation constant K_a of the anilinium ion is calculated, using equation 199. The basic dissociation constant K_b of aniline is calculated, using equation 198.

The dissociation constant of water depends upon the total salt concentration, and in Table 28 the values of K_w correspond to the ionic strength of the solutions. It is assumed that aniline is a nonelectrolyte and makes no contribution to the ionic strength.

The experimental data may be used to calculate either the maximum or estimated error of K_a. The magnitude of the errors may be taken from previous experiments.

REFERENCE

Harned and Mannweiler, *J. Am. Chem. Soc.*, **57**, 1873 (1935)
The ionization of water in salt solutions.

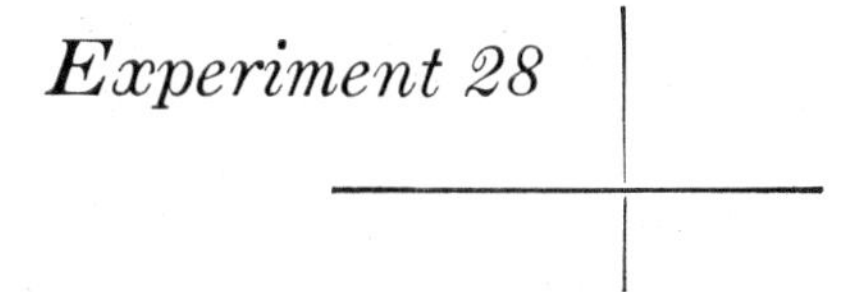

Conductometric Titrations

One of the very practical uses of conductance measurements is the determination of titration endpoints in reactions involving neutralization, precipitation, complex formation, etc. Consider the titration of hydrochloric acid with a standard sodium hydroxide solution; the chemical reaction is

$$H_3O^+ + Cl^- + Na^+ + OH^- \longrightarrow 2H_2O + Na^+ + Cl^-$$

As the base is gradually added, the highly conducting hydrogen (H_3O^+) ions are replaced by less conductive Na^+ ions, and the specific conductance of the solution decreases (or the resistance increases). Upon passing the endpoint, the specific conductance increases again, since excess Na^+ and highly conducting OH^- ions are now being added.

Fig. 45 shows the progress of such a titration. The curve *AC* shows the specific conductance of mixtures of acid and salt plotted against milliliters of NaOH added, while curve *BD* corresponds to mixtures of salt and excess base after the endpoint has been passed. The intersection at *E* represents the conductance of salt and water. The curves *AC* and *BD* are nearly linear, and the intersection is most accurately located, if the volume of the solution is not increased much during the titration. Accordingly, the titrating reagent should be more concentrated (10–100 times) than the solution to which it is being added.

With reagents other than strong acid and base, the position of the curves representing conductance before and after the endpoint will be different, but proper choice of the titrating reagent will usually allow a sharp endpoint to be obtained. For instance if acetic acid (HAc) is titrated into sodium hydroxide the reaction is

$$HAc + Na^+ + OH^- \longrightarrow H_2O + Na^+ + Ac^-$$

As neutralization proceeds, the highly conducting OH^- ion is replaced by the less conductive Ac^- ion, and the specific conductance falls. After the endpoint, addition of excess acetic acid leaves the conductance practically unchanged, since the ionization of the weak acid is repressed by the Ac^- ions present. The curves obtained are indicated in Fig. 46. If sodium hydroxide were titrated into acetic acid (Fig. 47), the conductance would start at a low value and increase regularly; after the endpoint the increase would be more rapid as excess of highly conducting OH^- ions was added. Due to hydrolysis of the salt at the endpoint the curves are not straight lines, and these conductance values (shown by x's) are not employed to establish the endpoint.

Excellent conductance-titration curves are obtained in titrating sulfuric acid with barium hydroxide, since practically all ions are removed from solution at the endpoint. Silver salts can be titrated accurately with chlorides; some metal salts with strong bases. It is obvious that conductance titrations can sometimes be employed in cases where indicators are useless. However, if the precipitated salt product adsorbs the reagent or initial reactant, erroneous results are obtained. For example, the titration of $BaCl_2$ with H_2SO_4 is not very accurate.

In practice it is unnecessary to know the cell constant of the conductance cell or to calculate the specific conductance of the solutions. The reciprocal of the measured resistance is proportional to the latter and may be plotted as ordinate against milliliters of reagent to give curves like those of Figs. 45 and 46. To locate the endpoint it is often sufficient to plot the measured resistance against milliliters of reagent, although

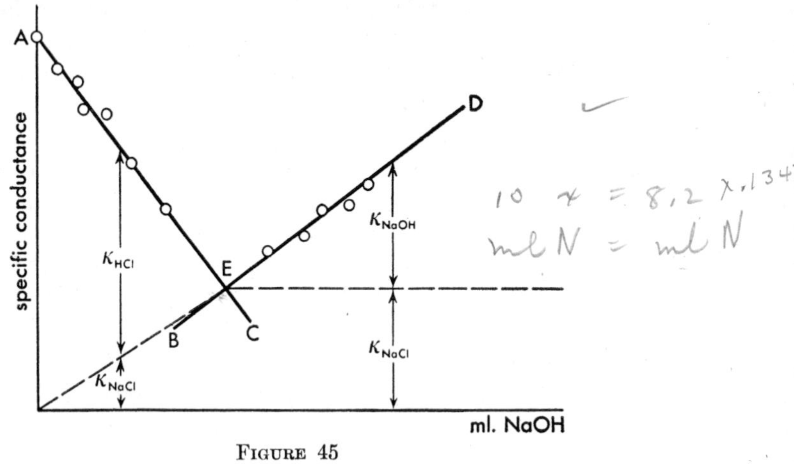

FIGURE 45

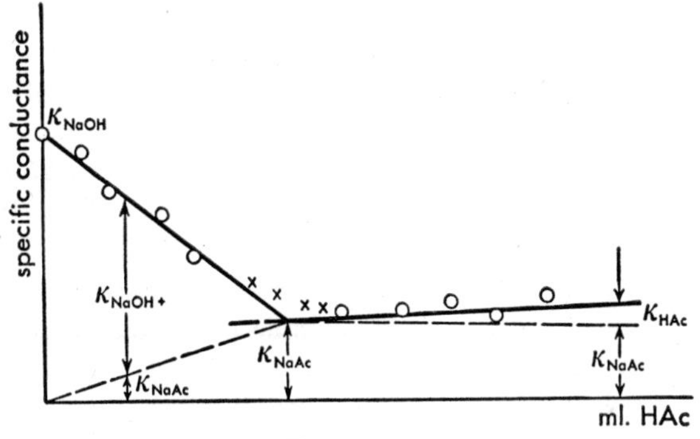

FIGURE 46

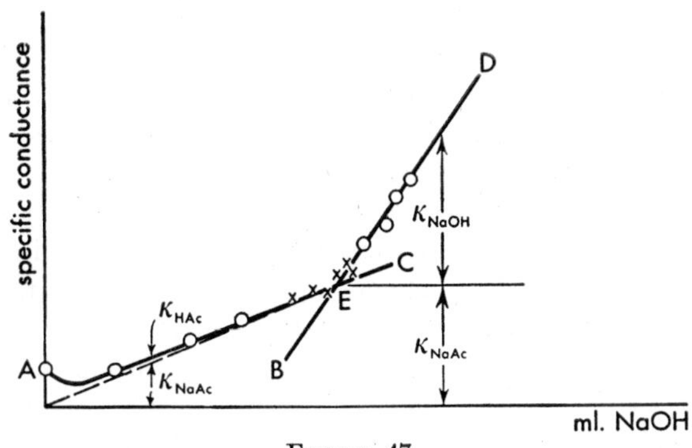

FIGURE 47

straight lines are not obtained and extrapolation to the point of intersection is not quite as accurate. A third procedure, easy and rapid, is to adjust only the slide-wire as the titration is made; the slide-wire readings are plotted against milliliters of reagent and the endpoint found from the curves obtained.

Apparatus The conductivity apparatus of Expt. 25 is used. A "dipping" type conductance cell may be mounted in a 400-ml. or 600-ml. beaker and the solution stirred mechanically; or the cell illustrated in Fig. 48 may be employed. The electrodes are prepared by sealing short pieces of platinum wire into soft glass tubes, which are braced with soft glass rods. The electrodes may be platinized as described in Expt. 25.

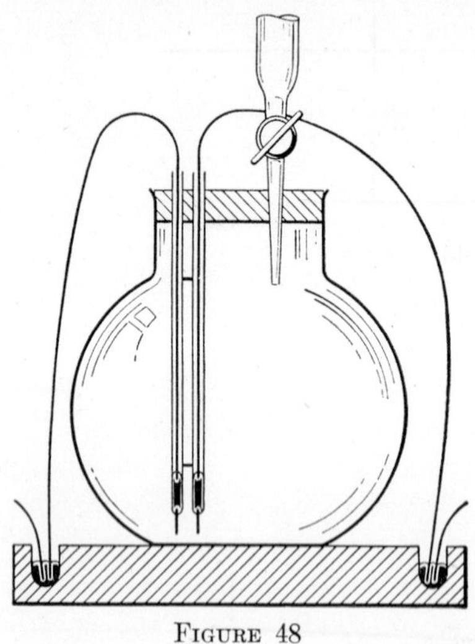

FIGURE 48

A simplified conductance apparatus which gives accurate results has been described by Buras and Reid.[1] Standard 0.1 *M* NaOH; approximately 0.1 *M* HCl and 0.1 *M* HAc; 50-ml. burets; 10- or 25-ml. pipet.

Procedure Place 100 ml. distilled water in the titration vessel (or enough to cover the electrodes completely) and add 10 ml. or 25 ml. of approximately 0.1 *M* HCl carefully, from a pipet. Mount the dipping cell or prepared electrodes, clamp the buret in place (filled with standard 0.1 *M* NaOH), and arrange for thorough stirring (mechanical stirrer, compressed air, or be sure the cell can be swirled by hand). Connect the cell to the conductance bridge (Fig. 43, Expt. 25) through the mercury cups or by means of clean, sharp clips.

The titration may be performed without temperature control when dilute solutions are used. In cases where the heat of reaction raises the temperature appreciably, the cell should be thermostated.

Adjust the bridge slide-wire to read approximately 500 (the end coils are not needed). Adjust the standard resistance box until a minimum sound is obtained in the ear phones upon depressing the tapping key. Adjust the slide-wire slightly if necessary, and record its reading. Do not change the setting of the standard resistance during the determination.

[1] *Ind. Eng. Chem., Anal. Ed.*, **16**, 591 (1944)

Add 2 ml. or 5 ml. of standard NaOH (depending on the HCl sample), stir thoroughly, and determine the new resistance by adjusting the slide-wire. Add similar increments of base, obtaining and recording the slide-wire readings after each addition, until as many readings have been taken after the endpoint as before. Be sure to record each buret reading.

The titration of sodium hydroxide with acetic acid is carried out in a similar manner. Place a suitable amount of distilled water in the cell and add a sample of the standard NaOH by accurate pipetting. Titrate with similar increments of approximately 0.1 *M* HAc, recording buret and slide-wire readings as before.

If the above titrations are repeated, take several readings in the immediate neighborhood of the endpoint.

Determine the molarity of the HCl and HAc by the ordinary volumetric procedure, using phenolphthalein as the indicator.

Calculations Plot the slide-wire readings (ordinate) against the milliliters of reagent added (abscissa). Draw smooth curves through the points and establish the point of intersection.

Calculate the resistance R from each reading and plot in the same manner. Draw smooth curves and extrapolate to the intersection.

Finally calculate the reciprocal of the resistance ($1/R$) and plot as ordinate against milliliters of reagent; draw smooth curves or straight lines and establish the point of intersection.

On each graph, note whether any readings near the endpoint should be disregarded in drawing the best lines. If so, how do you explain this fact?

Calculate the molarity of the HCl and HAc from each graphical endpoint and compare with each other and with the molarity obtained by the titration with phenolphthalein.

Further experimental suggestions Other pairs of solutions which may be used have already been mentioned. Unknowns may be prepared by adding a pink dye which does not change color with *p*H, to HCl or other acids.

REFERENCE

Buras and Reid, *Ind. Eng. Chem., Anal. Ed.*, **16,** 591 (1944)

Experiment 29

Faraday's Law

When one faraday (96,500 coulombs) of electricity is passed through a solution, one gram equivalent weight of material is either formed or decomposed at the cathode and at the anode.

Faraday's law is one of the exact laws of science. However, if any electrolytic decomposition is to be used to measure the quantity of electricity passing through a solution, the process measured at either the cathode or anode must be 100 per cent efficient; secondary or side reactions should not take place. Thus the deposition of copper from a nitric acid solution is not 100 per cent efficient, for even if an equivalent of copper is deposited per faraday, some of it will simultaneously dissolve in the acid.

Several kinds of coulometers are available, such as weight, titration, and volume types. The silver (weight) coulometer is undoubtedly the most accurate of all. The silver titration coulometer [1] is a very useful and accurate one for smaller amounts of electricity. The iodine coulometer [2] may also be considered as a precision instrument. The copper (weight) coulometer employs a solution of copper sulfate, sulfuric acid, and alcohol between copper anodes and cathodes; the deposited copper is weighed. Results that are accurate to within 1 per cent can be obtained.

The two most common volume coulometers are the hydrogen-oxygen [3] and the mercury [4] types. In the former the electrolyte consists of 0.5 *M* K_2SO_4 or KOH, and the volume of hydrogen and oxygen produced by electrolysis between platinum electrodes is measured. Results that are accurate to 0.12 per cent can be obtained. It can also be used for the measurements of comparatively large quantities of electricity. The mercury coulometer employs a solution of K_2HgI_4, and the volume

[1] Kistiakowsky, *Z. Electrochem.*, **12**, 713 (1906)
[2] Washburn and Bates, *J. Am. Chem. Soc.*, **34**, 1341 (1912)
[3] Lingane, *J. Am. Chem. Soc.*, **67**, 1916 (1945)
[4] Ambers and Newton, *J. Phys. & Colloid Chem.*, **52**, 955 (1948)

(or weight) of mercury collected indicates the quantity of electricity passing through the circuit. This coulometer is most satisfactory for the measurement of very large quantities of electricity.

Apparatus Silver coulometer; copper coulometer; hydrogen-oxygen gas coulometer; 0–500 milliammeter; stopwatch; rheostat; source of direct current. The gas coulometer may be constructed from a Jones reductor tube and a Mohr buret.

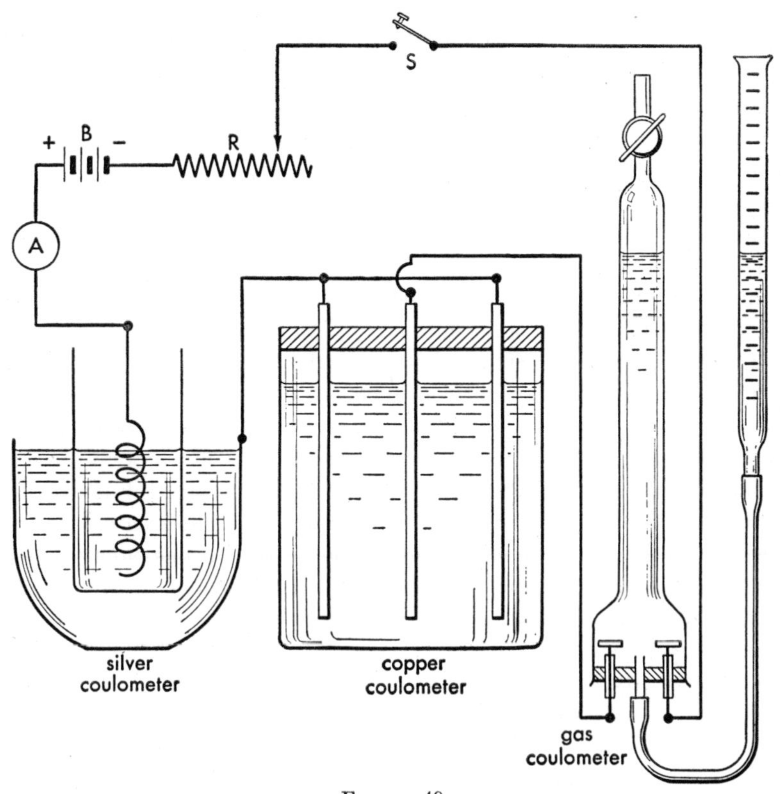

FIGURE 49

Procedure The three coulometers are placed in series with each other, proper care being taken in connecting the positive and negative leads to their positions as shown in Fig. 49. Use moistened starch iodide paper to establish the polarity of the leads.

The electrolyte used in a silver coulometer is prepared by dissolving 15 g. of pure $AgNO_3$ in 85 ml. of water. The silver anode is made from a spiral of pure electrolytic silver wire and is suspended in either a small porous cup or less preferably in an extraction thimble. The purpose of the latter is to prevent silver particles which may be dislodged from the spiral from falling into the crucible. When 3 g. of silver per 100 ml. of solution has been deposited, the electrolyte must be renewed. The platinum crucible (cathode) is of course clean and accurately weighed before the passage of current. The current density should not be greater than 0.02 ampere/$cm.^2$ of cathode surface.

When silver is deposited from the above electrolyte, it consists of rather large loosely adherent crystals, and considerable care must be employed in removing the silver nitrate solution from the deposit. Distilled water is poured into the crucible and swirled gently; most of the water is removed with the aid of a pipet. This must be repeated until a test portion no longer gives any indication of Ag^+ when tested with dilute hydrochloric acid. The crucible is finally washed several times with warm distilled water (70–90°), dried in an oven at 150°, cooled in a desiccator, and weighed.

The copper coulometer consists of two copper anodes and one copper cathode plate; or a cylindrical anode may surround the cathode plate. The electrolyte consists of a solution containing 150 g. of $CuSO_4 \cdot 5H_2O$, 50 g. of concentrated H_2SO_4, and 50 g. of ethanol in one liter of solution. The current density may be from 0.002 to 0.02 amp./$cm.^2$ of cathode surface. The electrolyte should be stirred during electrolysis with a mechanical stirrer or by bubbling a slow current of CO_2 through the cell.

The cathode and anode plates are prepared from electrolytically deposited sheet metal. They should be free of oxide and grease. Do not handle with fingers. The electrodes are polished with fine emery paper, thoroughly rinsed with distilled water and with alcohol (fat free), and dried in air. The initial weight of the cathode is obtained and recorded. After electrolysis has taken place, the cathode is removed and washed several times by dipping in a beaker of distilled water. Repeat with several fresh portions of distilled water. Finally dip the cathode in a beaker of ethanol, remove, and allow to dry in the air. It is then accurately weighed, the increase in weight representing the amount of copper which has been deposited. The electrolyte is returned to the stock bottle and may be used over many times. Do not allow electrodes to remain in the electrolyte when not in use.

The gas coulometer consists of a Jones reductor tube and a Mohr buret. The electrodes are made of bright platinum foil and should have an area of 1–2 $cm.^2$ The electrolyte employed is a 0.5 M K_2SO_4 solution. It is recommended that the current be allowed to pass through the gas coulometer before making measurements in order to saturate the solution (stopcock open) with gas. The accuracy can be improved if it is surrounded by a water jacket so that the final temperature of gas is accurately known. The volume of water displaced by the gas is measured with a Mohr buret.

The electrolyte is adjusted to the uppermost part of the reductor tube by means of the Mohr leveling buret and the stopcock is closed. The reading of the buret, which should be about 40 ml., is recorded. During the electrolysis, keep the liquid levels within 1 cm. of each other at all times. When the current is turned off, approximately equalize the levels; the final adjustment is made after the gas has cooled to the temperature of the surroundings. Record the volume of displaced liquid, the temperature of the surroundings, and the barometric pressure.

The reaction corresponding to the passage of one faraday of electricity is

$$\tfrac{1}{2}H_2O + 1F = \tfrac{1}{2}H_2 + \tfrac{1}{4}O_2$$

That is, one faraday liberates 1.008 g. of H_2 (11.2 liters) and 8 g. of O_2 (5.6 liters), a total of 16.8 liters of dry gas at S.T.P.

The general procedure to be followed with all coulometers is to adjust the current by means of the resistance within a few seconds after closing the switch, to the previously calculated values (about 0.1 to a maximum of 0.2 ampere) based upon the allowable current density. A stopwatch (or a watch with a second hand) is started when the current is started and stopped at the end when the circuit is opened.

The milliammeter will give a reasonable approximation of the amount of current passing. Record its reading. If the ammeter is to be calibrated, it will be necessary to readjust the resistance in order to maintain constant current strength. It is unnecessary to do this if the ammeter is not being calibrated.

The current should be allowed to pass through the coulometers about an hour or until approximately 40 ml. of gas has been produced in the gas coulometer. The experiment can be performed with one or any combination of coulometers.

Calculations From the weight of Ag deposited and the electrochemical equivalent of Ag, namely 0.0011180 g. per coulomb, the number of coulombs Q which have passed through the circuit is calculated.

From the value of Q and the total time in seconds, the number of coulombs per second is calculated. One coulomb per second is the unit of current, the ampere. Compare this value with that recorded by the ammeter. What is the percentage error of the ammeter?

From the known weight of Cu deposited in the Cu coulometer, and the electrochemical equivalent of the cupric ion, namely 0.0003294 g. per coulomb, calculate the number of coulombs which have passed through the circuit. Compare this value with that obtained from the Ag coulometer and calculate the percentage error of the copper coulometer.

The volume of H_2 and O_2 collected in the gas coulometer must first be corrected to S.T.P. and the correction for the vapor pressure of water should be used. Table 29 gives the vapor pressure of water over 0.5 *M* solutions of K_2SO_4.[1]

TABLE 29

t °C.	*p* (mm.)	*t* °C.	*p* (mm.)
20	17.2	26	24.7
21	18.4	27	26.2
22	19.4	28	27.8
23	20.6	29	29.4
24	22.2	30	31.2
25	23.3		

From the corrected volume of gas and from the volume electrochemical equivalent of water, namely 16.80 liters per faraday or 0.1741 ml./coulomb of dry mixed gases at S.T.P., calculate the number of coulombs that passed through the circuit. What is the percentage error of the gas coulometer as compared to the silver coulometer?

Calculate the value of the faraday from the accepted electrochemical equivalent and the experimental results and determine the percentage error between the calculated and accepted values.

REFERENCES

Abers and Newton, *J. Phys. & Colloid Chem.*, **52,** 955 (1948)
Kistiakowsky, *Z. Electrochem.*, **12,** 713 (1906)
Lingane, *J. Am. Chem. Soc.*, **67,** 1916 (1945)
Stewart, *ibid.*, **53,** 3366 (1931)
Washburn and Bates, *ibid.*, **34,** 1341 (1912)

[1] Lingane, *loc. cit.*

Experiment 30

Transference Number

When a source of direct current is connected to two electrodes dipping into a solution of an electrolyte, the ions migrate toward the electrodes of opposite sign. Since anions and cations do not, in general, travel with the same velocity, unequal changes in concentration appear in the regions near the cathode and anode. In other words, oppositely charged ions do not necessarily participate equally in the transfer of electricity.

According to Faraday's law, one gram equivalent weight of anion and one gram equivalent weight of cation are discharged at their respective electrodes for every 96,500 coulombs (one faraday) of electricity supplied. Thus while equal equivalents of anion and cation disappear from the anode and cathode compartments by electrolysis, unequal migration of ions leads to unequal concentrations in these compartments.

TABLE 30

−	Cathode	Middle	Anode	+
a	40+ 40−	40+ 40−	40+ 40−	
b	45+ 40−	40+ 40−	35+ 40−	
c	45+ 39−	40+ 40−	35+ 41−	
d	39+ 39−	40+ 40−	35+ 35−	

This may be illustrated as in Table 30. Originally equal numbers of cations (+) and anions (−) are present in each compartment at the right of *a*. Suppose that five cations migrate to the left producing condition *b*. One anion migrates to the right and condition *c* is obtained. During this time six anions and six cations are discharged at the electrodes and condition d arises. It is obvious that the final concentrations in the two compartments are unequal. Furthermore the ratio of the concentration changes in the compartments should be proportional to the relative ionic velocities. In the example cited $\frac{40 - 39}{40 - 35} = \frac{1}{5}$, which is the ratio of the anion to cation velocities.

The ratio of the velocity of one ion to the combined velocity of both anion and cation is defined as the transference number, n. In the above example $n_c = \frac{5}{1 + 5} = \frac{5}{6}$ and $n_a = \frac{1}{1 + 5} = \frac{1}{6}$, and $n_c + n_a = 1$. The transference number may also be defined as

$$n_c = \frac{u}{u + v} \tag{201}$$

$$n_a = \frac{v}{u + v} \tag{202}$$

in terms of the velocity u of the cation and v for the anion.

Since the number of equivalents of cation and the number of equivalents of anion transferred are proportional to the actual speed of these ions, the transference number may be defined as

$$n = \frac{\text{equivalents of ion transferred}}{\text{equivalents of electricity passed through the cell}} \tag{203}$$

Transference numbers defined as above are called Hittorf transference numbers. They are calculated on the assumption that the solvent (water) remains stationary during the electrolysis. "True transference numbers" are the result of correcting the Hittorf numbers for the extent of water migration. In dilute solution the two are very nearly the same, but in concentrated solutions they may differ.

Transference numbers change with concentration, the greatest change being observed with electrolytes that form unstable complex ions. Smaller variations result from interionic attraction since the mobility of anions and cations decreases unequally as the ionic strength is increased.

One important application of transference is the calculation of the equivalent conductance of the individual ions λ. The following equations give this relation:

$$n_c\Lambda_c = \lambda_c \tag{204}$$

$$n_a\Lambda_c = \lambda_a \tag{205}$$

In the present experiment, the transference number of silver ion is measured in the apparatus illustrated in Fig. 50, employing a solution of silver nitrate and a silver anode and a silver cathode. As electricity passes through the circuit, silver ions migrate into the cathode region and are deposited on the electrode, while nitrate ions migrate out of the cathode compartment. At the anode compartment, nitrate ions enter while silver ions leave and simultaneously metallic silver leaves the anode

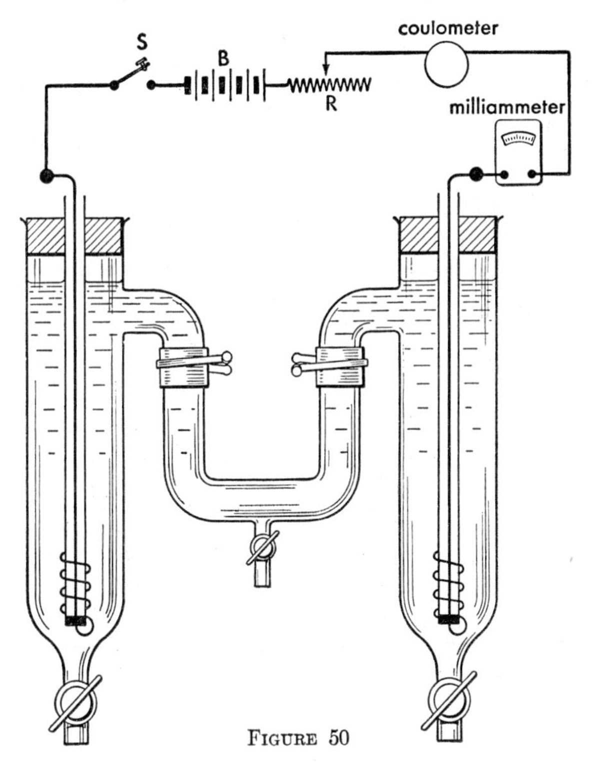

FIGURE 50

to become silver ions. The anode compartment loses silver ion by migration but gains some by solution of the electrode. That is, the final concentration in equivalents e for either anode or cathode compartment is

$$e_{\text{final}} = e_{\text{initial}} \mp e_{\text{electrodes}} \mp e_{\text{migration}} \tag{206}$$

Experimentally the number of equivalents of electricity that are supplied to the electrodes is measured by a coulometer. The number of equivalents of silver ion present in the compartments initially and the number present finally are determined analytically. The number of equivalents that migrate can then be calculated from equation 206. The transference number is then calculated from the following:

$$n = \frac{e_{\text{migration}}}{e_{\text{electrode}}} \tag{207}$$

Apparatus The apparatus illustrated in Fig. 50 is required. The electrolyte is approximately 0.05 N $AgNO_3$ and the electrodes are of heavy silver wire. The wire is cemented into 6-mm. glass tubing with sealing wax or other cement. Five to ten turns of the wire are wound around the glass tubing as shown so as to increase the electrode area. Coat the wire with cement from the point where it leaves the tube to the first turn. A source of direct current of 30–45 volts is necessary so that a current of 10–20 milliamperes is obtained. If a 110-volt d.c. source is available, a variable resistance R (1000 ohm) is included in the circuit, otherwise a smaller one may be used for the 45-volt current source. To measure the current approximately a milliammeter (0–100) is included. This need not be an accurate meter.

To measure the quantity of electricity, any one of the three coulometers described in Expt. 29 may be employed. Sufficiently accurate results are obtained with either the gas or copper coulometer. For very accurate work, the silver coulometer must be used and the transference apparatus must be kept at constant temperature.

In addition there is required standard 0.05 N KCNS (500 ml.), 40 per cent solution of ferric alum indicator, starch iodide paper.

Procedure Determine the polarity of the leads by touching them to moist starch iodide paper. Be sure that your hands are dry and are insulated from bare wire if the source is 110 volts, direct current.

The cell is filled with approximately 0.05 N silver nitrate until it is above the side tubes, and the electrodes are put in place. Reserve a portion of the original electrolyte (75 ml.) for analysis. Make all necessary electrical connections. If a copper coulometer is employed, be certain that the center plate is the negative electrode. Obtain the weight of the clean dry copper cathode (see Expt. 29). The apparatus should be set up so that it is not subjected to vibration or sunlight or drafts. This is done to prevent mixing between compartments.

Adjust the rheostat so that its entire resistance is included in the circuit. Close the switch S and adjust the resistance so that a current of 10–20 milliamperes is obtained. The current is allowed to flow for 100–150 minutes or until 0.001–0.003 faraday has passed through the circuit. Calculate the time necessary from the milliammeter reading.

At the conclusion of the experiment, open the knife switch and close the clips leading to the middle compartment. If a copper coulometer is used, remove the cathode, rinse with water and alcohol, dry, and weigh. If the gas coulometer is used, adjust the levels, record the room temperature, and obtain the barometric pressure.

The solution from the middle compartment is drawn off into a clean, dry, previously weighed, 250-ml. Erlenmeyer flask and weighed to the nearest 0.01 g. The solutions in the anode and cathode compartments are also drawn off into clean, dry, previously weighed flasks and weighed to the nearest 0.01 g. Depending upon the size of the compartments, it may be necessary after weighing to remove aliquot portions of the three solutions with a 25-ml. pipet. Transfer to clean dry flasks and weigh. Pipet 25 ml. of the original solution into another clean, dry, weighed flask and weigh to the nearest 0.01 g.

The analysis of the solutions is carried out by the Volhard method. Add 1 ml. of ferric alum indicator solution, acidify with 5 ml. of 6 *N* HNO_3, and titrate with standard 0.05 *N* thiocyanate solution. The first color change to orange-red takes place before the equivalence point; continue titrating until a permanent brownish tinge is obtained upon vigorous shaking.[1]

Calculations From the increase in weight of the copper cathode or from the volume of mixed gas in the coulometer, calculate the number of coulombs that passed through the circuit. This corresponds to $\pm e$ (electrodes), after dividing by the value of the faraday (96,500 coulombs).

Calculate the weight of silver nitrate present in all four samples from the known equivalence of the standard thiocyanate. Obtain the weight of water present in each sample by subtracting the weight of silver nitrate from the weight of solution taken for analysis.

Divide the weight of silver nitrate found in each compartment and in the original sample by the equivalent weight to obtain the number of equivalents present.

Calculate the number of equivalents of silver nitrate in the original sample which would be found in the weight of water present in the middle compartment. The number of equivalents of silver nitrate present initially and at the end, in this compartment, should agree within an experimental error of not more than ± 1 per cent. If agreement is not obtained within this limit, the experiment will have to be repeated, as mixing has taken place. Reduce the current or time in the succeeding experiment.

From the number of equivalents of silver nitrate found in the middle compartment, calculate the number of equivalents that would be present initially in the weight of water found in the anode compartment. Repeat the calculation to obtain the number of equivalents that would be found initially in the weight of water found in the cathode compartment.

Calculate the transference number of silver ion from the above data using equations 206 and 207.

[1] Kolthoff and Sandell, *Textbook of Qualitative Inorganic Analysis*

Calculate the transference number of the nitrate ion.

Calculate the equivalent conductance of silver and nitrate ions (eqs. 204 and 205). The value of Λ_c for $AgNO_3$ may be found in a handbook. Compare the results with those published which are nearest in concentration to your solution.

Further experimental suggestions The transference number of hydrogen ion may be determined with a suitable apparatus.[1] Transference numbers may also be determined by the moving boundary method.[2] Cells especially designed to prevent mixing by convection may be used.[3]

REFERENCES

Brady, *J. Am. Chem. Soc.*, **70,** 911 (1948)

Analytical boundary method for transference numbers.

Collins, *J. Chem. Ed.*, **11,** 52 (1934)

Kolthoff, I. M., and Sandell, E. B., *Textbook of Quantitative Inorganic Analysis*, p. 563, The Macmillan Company, New York, **1937**

Longsworth, *J. Chem. Ed.*, **11,** 420 (1934)

MacInnes, D. A., *The Principles of Electrochemistry*, Chap. 4, The Reinhold Publishing Corporation, New York, **1939**

MacInnes and Dole, *J. Am. Chem. Soc.*, **53,** 1357 (1931)

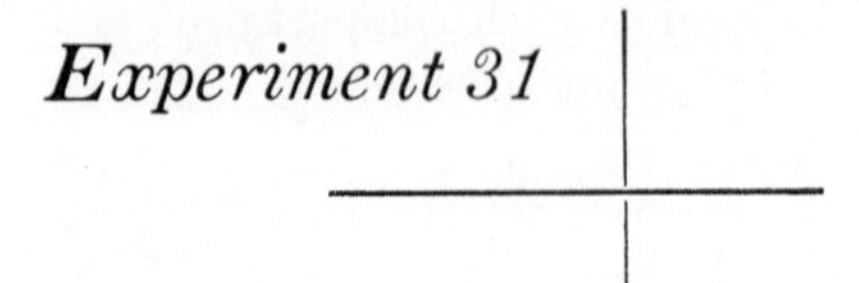

The Measurement of Electromotive Force: Standard Cells

If two primary cells such as

$$-Zn \mid Zn^{++} \mid H_3O^+ \mid H_2, Pt+ \quad \text{and} \quad -Cd \mid Cd^{++} \mid H_3O^+ \mid H_2, Pt+$$

are constructed, it will be found that the same quantity of electricity (96,500 coulombs) will be obtained when one gram equivalent weight of Cd or Zn dissolves. However, the electromotive force of the two cells

[1] Collins [2] Brady; MacInnes and Dole [3] D. A. MacInnes

is not the same and this indicates that the amount of electrical energy or equivalent chemical energy from each cell is different. This is to be expected since two different chemical reactions are occurring. The energy of an electrical current is given by

$$W \text{ (in calories)} = 0.239\boldsymbol{E} \cdot \boldsymbol{I} \cdot t \tag{208}$$

where $\boldsymbol{E}$ is the electromotive force (E.M.F.) in volts, t is the time in seconds, $\boldsymbol{I}$ is the current in amperes, and $\boldsymbol{I} \cdot t$ is the number of coulombs.

The potential is a measure of the driving force of a chemical reaction (intensity factor), while $\boldsymbol{I} \cdot t$ is the capacity factor. From the measurement of the electromotive force ($\boldsymbol{E}$) the free energy change (ΔF) of a chemical reaction may be calculated:

$$\Delta F = -n\boldsymbol{F}\boldsymbol{E} = -96{,}500n\boldsymbol{E} \text{ (joules)} = -23{,}070n\boldsymbol{E} \text{ (calories)} \tag{209}$$

Here n is the number of equivalents undergoing chemical change and $\boldsymbol{F}$ equals one faraday (96,500 coulombs).

It is also possible to calculate the equilibrium constant. The following equations indicate the relation between the equilibrium constant (K), the standard free energy (ΔF°), and the standard electrode potential $\boldsymbol{E}^\circ$

$$\Delta F^\circ = -RT \ln K \tag{210}$$

$$n\boldsymbol{F}\boldsymbol{E}^\circ = RT \ln K \tag{211}$$

where R is the gas constant, T is the absolute temperature, and K is the equilibrium constant. If the change of electromotive force with temperature ($d\boldsymbol{E}/dT$, temperature coefficient) is also known, the heat of reaction (ΔH) may be calculated by the Gibbs-Helmholtz equation:

$$\Delta H = -n\boldsymbol{F}\boldsymbol{E} + n\boldsymbol{F}T\left(\frac{dE}{dT}\right) \tag{212}$$

The potential $\boldsymbol{E}$ measured at arbitrarily chosen concentrations is related to the standard electrode potential $\boldsymbol{E}^\circ$ by the following important equation:

$$\boldsymbol{E} = \boldsymbol{E}^\circ - \frac{0.05914}{n} \log \frac{\text{conc. of products}}{\text{conc. of reactants}} \text{ at } 25°\text{C.} \tag{213}$$

In the case of nonideal solutions, it is necessary to substitute activities for concentrations.

The potential developed by a chemical cell can be measured accurately by the method suggested by Poggendorff. The schematic wiring of a potentiometer is shown in Fig. 51, where $W.C.$ is the working cell with an E.M.F. greater than that of either the standard cell ($S.C.$) or the cell X whose potential is to be determined, G is a sensitive galvanometer, AB is a wire of uniform resistance, and R is a variable rheostat. When the points C and C' are chosen so that no current passes through the auxiliary circuit ABG, the galvanometer is not deflected and

$$\frac{E_X}{E_{S.C.}} = \frac{L_X}{L_{S.C.}}$$

where L_X and $L_{S.C.}$ are the lengths of bridge wire in Fig. 51 needed to meet the above requirements.

The standard cell serves as a fixed reference of potential and is used to calibrate the working cell. The cell most often used is the Weston saturated cell, although other equally satisfactory ones are available.

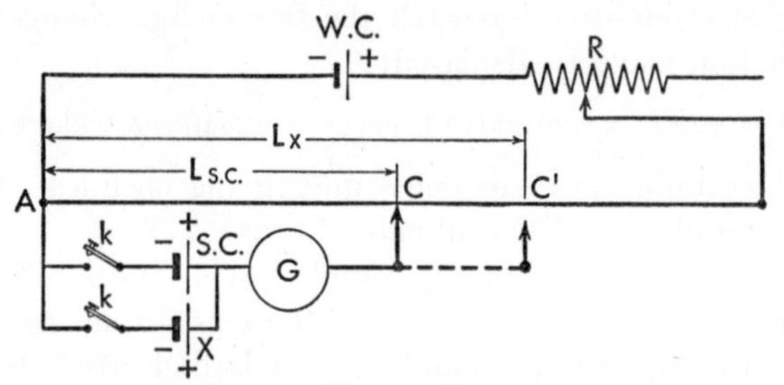

FIGURE 51

Since very little current flows when such a cell is used properly, its E.M.F. will remain constant over a long period of time.

Apparatus **H** tube as in Fig. 52 or two side arm test tubes which may be joined by rubber tubing; student-type potentiometer and accessories; sealing wax; two platinum-point electrodes; Hg; Hg_2SO_4; $CdSO_4 \cdot \frac{8}{3}H_2O$; Cd.

Procedure The actual E.M.F. obtained when a Weston standard cell is prepared is governed by the purity of the reagents employed. In order to prepare a cell with an E.M.F. equal to those purchased through commercial sources, reagents of the highest purity are required.[1] The choice of purity is left to the instructor.

The glass **H** cell is thoroughly cleaned with warm cleaning mixture, rinsed, and dried. A cadmium amalgam is prepared in the left arm (*a*) of the cell (Fig. 52) by weighing 21.0 ± 0.1 g. of mercury and 3.0 ± 0.1 g. of clean cadmium metal and placing the cell in a beaker of boiling water for ten minutes, the cell being loosely stoppered. Remove the stopper occasionally and stir with a warm glass rod. The **H** cell is removed and supported vertically in a clamp until cool. Introduce 21 g. of mercury into the right arm (*b*).

A saturated solution of the hydrate $CdSO_4 \cdot \frac{8}{3}H_2O$ is prepared by dis-

[1] Mack and France, *Laboratory Manual of Elementary Physical Chemistry*

solving 100 g. of the salt in 75 ml. of water at a temperature not over 40°C. This solution should be prepared in advance, or a motor-driven stirrer may be used to speed up the process.

The amalgam (*a*) is covered with a 3-mm. layer of finely powdered cadmium sulfate crystals (*c*), after which a few large crystals (*e*) are placed on top. Thoroughly grind 1 ml. of Hg, 5 g. of Hg_2SO_4 and 5 g. of

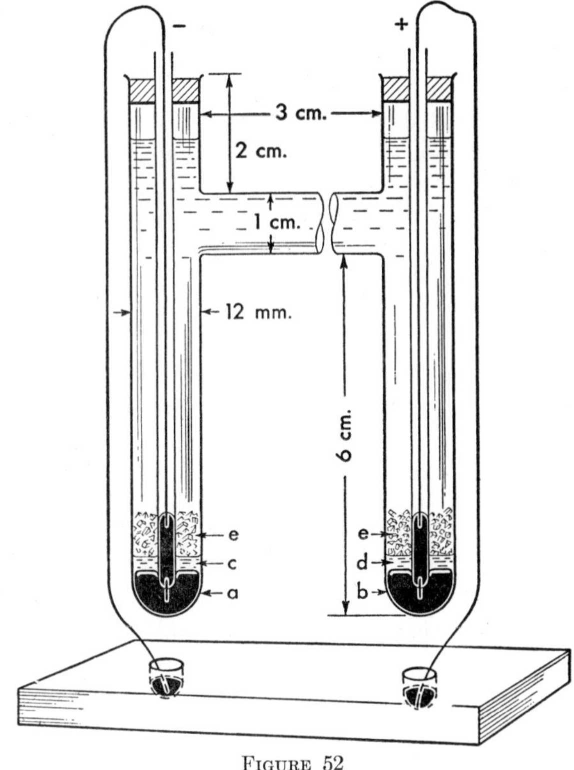

FIGURE 52

the hydrated $CdSO_4$ in a mortar with a few drops of the saturated solution of $CdSO_4$ until a gray paste is obtained. Transfer sufficient paste to cover the mercury in the right arm with a 3-mm. layer (*d*) and then place a few large crystals of the hydrate on top (*e*). The saturated cadmium sulfate solution is poured to within 1 cm. of the top of the cell.

Two platinum point electrodes are prepared by sealing short pieces of No. 22 B. & S. gauge wire into suitable lengths of 3-mm. soft glass tubing. The electrodes are mounted in stoppers which are fitted to the **H** cell as shown so that the exposed platinum metal points are completely immersed in the amalgam (*a*) and the mercury (*b*). If the cell is to be kept for any length of time, warm sealing wax or paraffin is poured over the stoppers to seal the cell.

Electrical contact with the electrode is obtained by adding a small amount of ordinary mercury so that the platinum wire inside each 3-mm. glass tube is completely covered. Previously amalgamated No. 18 copper wire leads are inserted below the surface of the mercury, the free ends leading to binding posts or mercury cups. The **H** cell may be fastened to a wooden support.

The chemical reaction in the cell is a simple displacement; cadmium, the more active metal, displaces mercurous ion from the salt Hg_2SO_4 when the cell is delivering current. The cadmium electrode, which is the source of electrons, is by convention called the negative pole.

When the cell has been properly prepared, the E.M.F. at 20°C. is 1.0183 volts. The following equation gives the E.M.F. at temperatures (t) between 15° and 40°C.:

$$E_t = 1.0183 - 4.06 \times 10^{-5}(t - 20) \tag{214}$$

After the cell has been prepared, it is best to allow it to age for a week before making measurements. Only by continuously determining the E.M.F. over a period of months can it be decided whether or not a cell is defective.

The unsaturated Weston cell is similarly prepared; the cadmium sulfate solution is unsaturated at room temperature.

While a simple meter stick potentiometer can be used to measure E.M.F.'s, the accuracy is only about ± 1 per cent. For this reason, it is assumed that a "student potentiometer" will be used in most of the following experiments.

The discussion of the potentiometer circuit (Fig. 53) may be simplified if it is assumed that the resistance R_1 is made up of 15 equal resistances connected in series with a slide-wire R_2 whose resistance is equal to one of the coils making up R_1. The readings of R_1 are numbered from 0 to 1.5 volts in increments of 0.1 while R_2 is divided from 0 to 0.100 volt; hence any value between 0 and 1.6 may be obtained. A secondary connection is provided to obtain readings from 0 to 0.016 volt more accurately. The limit of error may be 0.5 millivolt on the large scale and 0.005 millivolt on the small one.

To prevent polarization of the standard cell and injury to the galvanometer, a high resistance R_3 (10,000 ohms) is included in the circuit. This resistance is introduced by means of the tapping key k_1 at the beginning of each measurement until a close approximation has been made and the galvanometer does not deflect. The final adjustment is made by the tapping key k_2 which by-passes the high resistance and allows R_2 to be adjusted until the galvanometer no longer deflects. Never hold tapping keys down.

The resistance R_4 may be a four-dial box (1000 ohms) which can be adjusted to tenths of an ohm. A wire-wound rheostat of this resistance with an attached micro adjustment may be substituted.

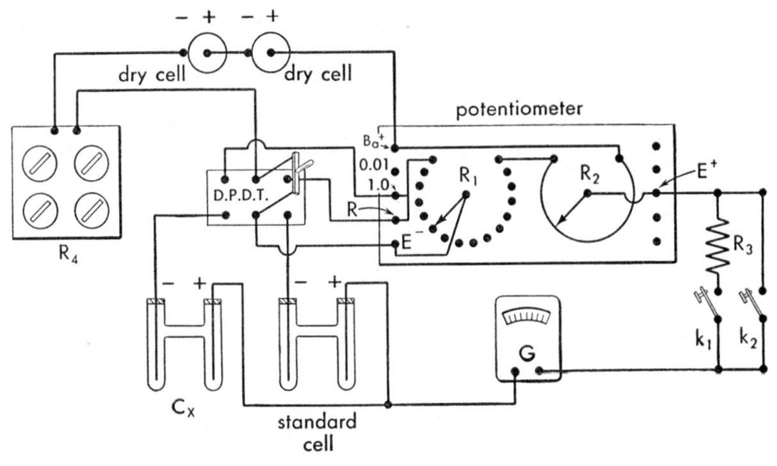

FIGURE 53

The resistance R_4 must first be adjusted so the potentiometer readings will give the measured potentials in volts. This is accomplished by setting resistance R_1 to correspond to 1 volt and R_2 to 0.0183, a total of 1.0183, the voltage of the standard cell. If another value is stated by the manufacturer, R_2 is set accordingly. If results of greater accuracy are required, the corrected voltage obtained from equation 214 should be employed.

The resistance R_4 is set at about 140 ohms (2 dry cells supplying the current of the working battery). The key k_1 is tapped while adjusting R_4 until the galvanometer no longer deflects, whereupon key k_2 is tapped and the final adjustment, with 1-ohm and 0.1-ohm resistances, is made until the galvanometer no longer deflects.

The double pole double throw (D.P.D.T.) switch is changed to the reverse position to place the cell C_x into the circuit. The resistances R_1 and R_2 are adjusted until the galvanometer no longer deflects upon tapping key k_1. Continue to adjust the slide-wire resistance R_2 while tapping key k_2 until the galvanometer no longer deflects. The sum of

R_1 and R_2 is the reading of the unknown E.M.F. Do not change R_4 once it has been fixed except to recheck with the standard cell.

Certain difficulties encountered in using a potentiometer are as follows. If the resistance R_4 must be set at 100 ohms or less, the dry cells should be replaced. If it is impossible to obtain a balance with the unknown cell, reverse the connections as the polarity may be opposite to that assumed. It is also possible that the E.M.F. of the cell is larger than 1.6 volts. If it is impossible to obtain a galvanometer deflection at any setting of the resistances R_1 and R_2, look for a loose connection or a broken wire.

The working cell should be checked against the standard cell about every half hour in order to correct for any change in its voltage. For most work, a galvanometer with a sensitivity of 0.5 microampere (0.5 μa.) is sufficient. When small potentials are measured on the 0.016-volt scale, a more sensitive galvanometer (0.014 μa.) is desirable.

Read the directions for the operation of the potentiometer. Make all connections but do not insert the batteries or cells until the instructor has approved the hookup. Measure the E.M.F. of the prepared cell several times, comparing it with a commercial standard cell, and report the average.

Further experimental suggestions The unsaturated Weston cell or a Clark cell, or other types of cells similar to standard cells may be prepared.[1]

REFERENCES

Mack, E., and France, W. G., *Laboratory Manual of Elementary Physical Chemistry*, 2d ed., D. Van Nostrand Company, Inc., New York, **1934**

Vosburgh, *J. Am. Chem. Soc.*, **47,** 1255 (1925); **47,** 2531 (1925); **49,** 78 (1927); **53,** 2819 (1931)

[1] Vosburgh

Experiment 32

The Normal Calomel Reference Electrode

The calomel half cell is frequently used as a standard reference electrode for potentiometric measurements. This electrode has the following characteristics:

$$Hg \mid Hg_2Cl_2(s), \quad KCl\ (N = x)$$

The potential of the mercury-mercurous ion electrode or half cell depends upon the concentration of the potassium chloride, since the concentration (activity) of mercurous ion present in a saturated solution of calomel is regulated by the chloride ion concentration (common ion effect) and the ionic strength of the potassium chloride solution (salt effect).

In practical measurements, three types of calomel half cell are in common use, differing only in the concentration of the potassium chloride solution employed. Generally used are the tenth normal, normal, and saturated calomel half cells. The potential of the half cells also depends upon temperature, and the following empirical equations give this relationship:

$$0.1\ N\ \text{KCl} \quad E_t = 0.336 - 7 \times 10^{-5}(t - 25)$$
$$1.0\ N\ \text{KCl} \quad E_t = 0.2805 - 2.4 \times 10^{-4}(t - 25)$$
$$\text{sat. KCl} \quad E_t = 0.246 - 7.6 \times 10^{-4}(t - 25)$$

The potential of the calomel electrode cannot be very precisely duplicated (impurities in materials being one of the contributing factors). For this reason, the electrode is used for potentiometric measurements where a high degree of accuracy is not required. The silver chloride electrode should be employed for more exact work.

Apparatus Calomel half cell vessels or apparatus shown in Fig. 54, which employs bottles of 40–60 ml. capacity; Hg; Hg_2Cl_2; agar; KCl; platinum-point electrode. In order to obtain results comparable to those recorded above highly purified reagents should be used. For student work or even for precise practical potentiometric titrations where only changes in the E.M.F. are to be recorded, ordinary mercury and C.P. salts may be used with reasonable success.

Procedure Thoroughly clean the apparatus with cleaning solution, rinse with water, and dry. The calomel half cell is prepared as follows: Place sufficient mercury (double distilled) to form a layer 0.5–1.0 cm. deep in the cell *D* (Fig. 54). A 1 *N* solution of KCl is prepared

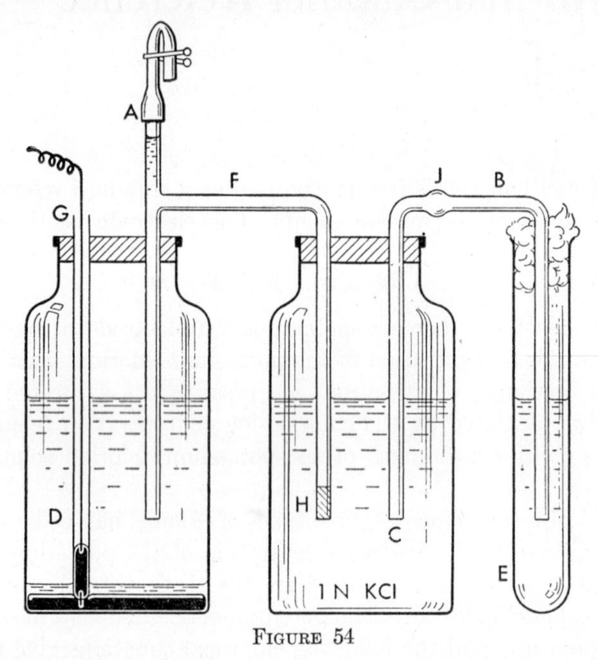

FIGURE 54

by accurately weighing sufficient oven-dried salt (recrystallized) to make 250 ml. To a 100-ml. portion, add about 2 g. of calomel and shake vigorously so as to obtain a saturated solution. It is probably best to prepare this solution at least a day before the cell is to be assembled.

Place a few drops of mercury in a mortar and add approximately 7 g. of calomel (Hg_2Cl_2), moisten with a few drops of the above calomel-saturated KCl solution, and grind together until the mixture has a decided black or grayish black appearance. Wash the mixture several times by decantation with the clear supernatant liquid from the calomel-saturated KCl solution. After the last decantation, transfer a sufficient amount of the mixture to the cell (glass or porcelain spatula) to form a 0.5-cm. layer on top of the mercury. The remaining portion of the calomel-saturated KCl solution is added to cell *D* so that it is about two-thirds full.

A short piece of No. 22 platinum wire is sealed into the end of 2–3 mm. soft glass tubing, care being taken that the seal does not leak. This is inserted in a rubber stopper and adjusted so that the platinum wire is completely submerged below the surface of the mercury.

The bottle *C* is filled to a slightly higher level than *D* with 1 *N* KCl (without calomel). The tube *F* is put in place; apply suction at *A* and fill the siphon tube completely with liquid, fold the rubber tubing over on itself and clamp. The salt bridge (*B*) is made from 6–8 mm. tubing, and preferably has a small enlargement at *J* to prevent the gel from slipping out. The latter is prepared by heating 3 g. of agar in 100 ml. of water on a steam bath with stirring until the solution is clear; 30 g. of KCl is then dissolved with continued stirring and heating.

The warm liquid is poured into tube *B* while inverted. If shrinkage of the gel occurs on setting, the glass siphon legs are cut back with a file to expose it. Slip one end of the tube through the rubber stopper of the bottle *C*. The other end is placed under a one normal solution of KCl, contained in test tube *E*, when not in use. If the solution being analyzed reacts with the chloride ion of the salt bridge, a gel can be made by substituting KNO_3 or NH_4NO_3 for the KCl (see Expt. 38).

The purpose of the container *C* is to prevent impurities from entering the calomel cell. An optional construction is to place a plug of tightly rolled filter paper at *H* and connect *A* to a short-stem dropping funnel. The funnel is filled with 1 *N* KCl solution and is used to flush out the side arm between measurements.

In order to make electrical connection to the cell, a small amount of ordinary mercury is placed in the tube *G* and a No. 18 copper wire which has been previously amalgamated is inserted below the surface of the mercury.

The tenth normal and saturated calomel half cells may be prepared by a procedure similar to that described for the normal electrode.

REFERENCES

Clark, W. M., *The Determination of Hydrogen Ions,* 3d ed., The Williams and Wilkins Company, Baltimore, **1928**

Mudge and Fales, *J. Am. Chem. Soc.*, **42,** 2434 (1920)

Randall and Young, *ibid.*, **50,** 989 (1928)

Scatchard, *ibid.*, **47,** 696 (1925)

Experiment 33

The Standard Potential of a Metal Electrode

The potential of a metal when placed in a solution of its salt depends upon the activity of the ions. If the metal is dissolved in mercury, then the potential is further governed by the activity of the dissolved metal.

The potential of a metal electrode, such as zinc immersed in a solution of a zinc salt, can be measured by combining it with a reference electrode, such as a calomel half cell. In this way the following cell is obtained:

$$-\mathrm{Zn} \mid \mathrm{Zn^{++}} \mid \mathrm{KCl},\ \mathrm{Hg_2Cl_2} \mid \mathrm{Hg}+$$

The E.M.F. of a cell may be regarded as being equal to the difference of the single potentials at the positive and negative poles:

$$E_{\text{cell}} = E_{+} - E_{-} \tag{215}$$

The potential E_{-} of a zinc electrode, with any arbitrarily chosen activity (a), or concentration, is related to that in the standard state $E°$ by:

$$E_{-} = E° - \frac{2.303RT}{nF} \log \frac{a_{\mathrm{Zn}}}{a_{\mathrm{Zn^{++}}}} \tag{216}$$

The potential of the normal calomel half cell at 25°C. is 0.2805 volt referred to the normal hydrogen electrode, and equation 215 may be written:

$$E_{\text{cell}} = 0.2805 - E_{-} \quad \text{at } 25°\text{C.} \tag{217}$$

Combining equations 216 and 217, inserting numerical values for R, T, n, and F, and considering the activity of pure zinc to be unity ($a_{\mathrm{Zn}} = 1$)

$$E_{\text{cell}} = 0.2805 - E°_{\mathrm{Zn}} - \frac{0.0591}{2} \log a_{\mathrm{Zn^{++}}} \quad \text{at } 25°\text{C.} \tag{218}$$

The standard potential $E°$ of a metal electrode is defined as the potential when both the activity of the metal and its ions are equal to unity, compared to the standard hydrogen electrode at 25°C. It is not necessary to prepare a solution of metal ions of unit activity since the standard potential E° can be calculated if the activity in any chosen solution is known.

The sign of the electrode potential in this discussion is that of the electrode when combined with a standard hydrogen half cell.

Apparatus Normal calomel electrode[1]; standard cell; potentiometer and accessories; electrode vessels; $ZnSO_4$; four zinc rods (3 mm. in diameter); mercury; emery cloth; cotton swab.

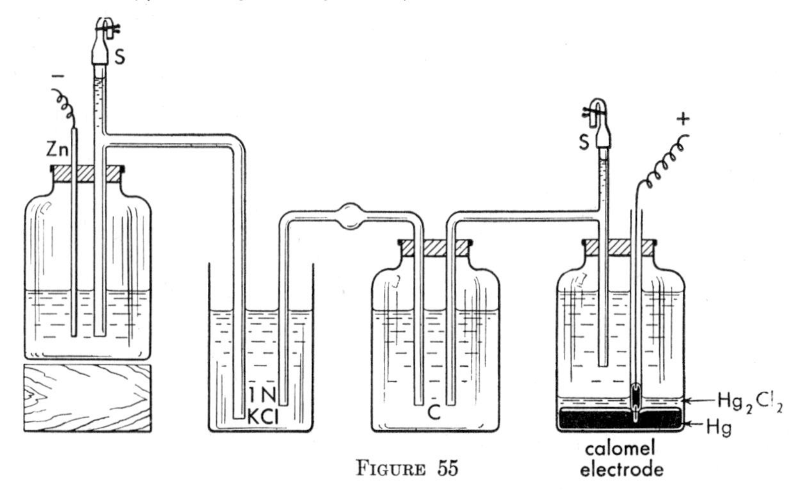

FIGURE 55

Procedure Four zinc electrodes, mounted in rubber stoppers to fit the glass cells, are polished with emery cloth and then immersed for a short time in 5 per cent H_2SO_4. The rods are amalgamated by rubbing with a cotton swab while holding them in a dish containing a few drops of mercury. The amalgam[2] should be spread on evenly (no drops of mercury in local spots). The rods are washed thoroughly with water and placed in a zinc sulfate solution when not in use.

Prepare 250 ml. of a 1.0 *M* solution of zinc sulfate by dissolving the requisite amount in recently boiled distilled water and prepare, by quantitative dilution, solutions which are 0.5, 0.1, 0.05, and 0.01 molar. Add one of the above solutions to each electrode vessel until it is about one-half full. Insert a tightly rolled plug of filter paper into the tip of each siphon arm to minimize convection, and fill each siphon arm by apply-

[1] Commercial calomel electrodes intended for use in glass electrode *p*H meters are very convenient. It is unnecessary to use salt bridges with them unless silver salts are present.

[2] The potential of the saturated zinc amalgam has been found equal to that of pure zinc.

ing suction at S, the tip being immersed in the same solution in a beaker. Fold the rubber tubing over on itself and clamp.

The siphon arms from each cell and the calomel electrode are dipped into a beaker containing 1 N KCl or 2 N NH_4NO_3 (see Fig. 55). The liquid level in the zinc half cells must be slightly higher than that in the beaker to prevent entrance of KCl into the electrode cell.

The leads are placed in mercury cups to make connection with the potentiometer. This may also be made with binding posts or clean tight alligator clips. The E.M.F. of each cell is measured at least twice to be sure that equilibrium has been established (see Expt. 31). Record all observations.

Calculations Average the values for each zinc electrode. Calculate the standard potential $E°$ with the aid of equation 218; use concentration units for the time being. The percentage error from the accepted $E°$ is calculated for each electrode.

The activity of zinc ion can be calculated from the equation $a = \gamma C$, where γ is the activity coefficient. The mean activity coefficients in various solutions of $ZnSO_4$ are:

C	γ	C	γ
1.0 M	0.045	0.05 M	0.20
0.5 M	0.065	0.01 M	0.39
0.1 M	0.16		

Employing activities, calculate the standard potential $E°$, the standard free energy change $\Delta F°$, and the equilibrium constant K for each zinc cell. The percentage error of $E°$ from the accepted value is obtained.

It is tacitly assumed that the salt bridge has eliminated the liquid junction potential between the zinc half cells and the reference electrode. Due to this limitation, the standard potential as obtained above cannot be considered to be very accurate.

The maximum error of the standard electrode potential may be calculated from the following assumed data, employing the method of normal and maximum (minimum) values:

$$Zn^{++} = 1.00 \pm 0.01\ M \qquad E_{\text{cell}} = 1.0825 \pm 0.0005 \text{ volt}$$
$$\gamma = 0.045 \qquad E_{\text{c.e.}} = 0.2805 \text{ volt}$$

Substituting the above data in equation 218

$$1.0825 = 0.2805 - E°_{Zn} - \frac{0.0591}{2} \log (0.045) \qquad \text{normal value}$$
$$E° = -0.7622 \text{ volt}$$
$$1.0830 = 0.2805 - E°_{Zn} - \frac{0.0591}{2} \log (0.04545) \qquad \text{maximum value}$$
$$E° = -0.7628 \text{ volt} \qquad \pm \Delta E° = 0.0006 \text{ volt}$$

The magnitude of the maximum error indicates that good precision can be expected. If greater deviations occur, it may be due to lack of equilibrium at the electrode caused by oxidation (clean and amalgamate). The necessity of employing activities instead of concentrations is obvious.

Calculate the maximum error of the standard potential from several of the results.

Further experimental suggestions Various other metal electrodes, such as silver, copper, or cadmium, may be employed. The above procedures and concentration ranges may be used. It is not necessary to amalgamate the silver and copper electrodes. The student should consult Latimer, *Oxidation Potentials*, to obtain the activity coefficients.

REFERENCES

Gerke, *J. Am. Chem. Soc.*, **44,** 1684 (1922)
La Mer and Parks, *ibid.*, **56,** 90 (1934)
Latimer, W. M., *Oxidation Potentials,* Prentice-Hall, Inc., New York, **1938**

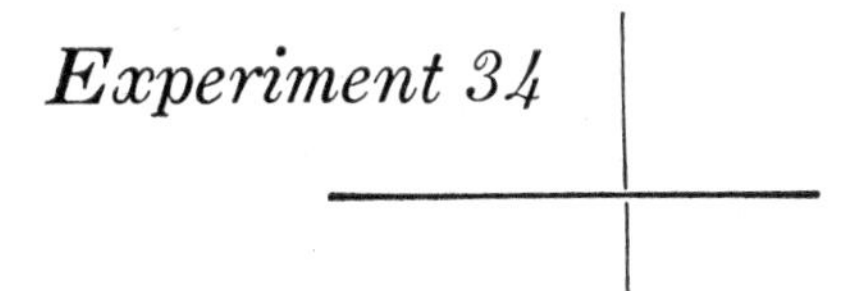

Amalgam Concentration Cells

The potential of a half cell composed of a metal in equilibrium with its ions is given by

$$\boldsymbol{E} = \boldsymbol{E}^\circ - \frac{0.0591}{n} \log [M]/[M^+] \qquad \text{at } 25°\text{C}. \tag{219}$$

where $\boldsymbol{E}^\circ$ is the standard potential when the metal and its ions are at unit activity. It may be seen from the above equation that the potential in any other state depends upon the activity of the metal and its ions.

Thus it should be possible to construct cells wherein both the metal and its ions are at different activities as illustrated by the following arrangement:

$$\text{Zn}(a_1) \mid \text{Zn}^{++}(a_2) \mid \text{Zn}^{++}(a_3) \mid \text{Zn}(a_4)$$

The direction of electron flow in the external leads will depend upon the respective driving force or potential of each half cell.

The problem can be simplified by first studying the cell when the activity of the zinc ions in each half cell is the same and the activity of the metal in each half cell is different. Secondly the activity of the metal in each half cell may be the same while the activity of the ions may be different.

A cell of the first type can be obtained by preparing amalgams containing different amounts (activities) of dissolved metal. The concentration cell thus formed may be written as

$$-\mathrm{Zn}(a_1) \mid \mathrm{Zn}^{++}(a) \mid \mathrm{Zn}(a_2) +$$

The cell reaction when $a_1 > a_2$ is:

$Zn^{++}(a) = Zn(a_2)$	positive pole	E_+
$Zn^{++}(a) = Zn(a_1)$	negative pole	E_-
$Zn(a_1) = Zn(a_2)$		$E_{cell} = E_+ - E_-$

The E.M.F. of this cell in volts E may be calculated from

$$E_{cell} = -\frac{0.0591}{s \cdot n} \log \frac{a_2}{a_1} \quad \text{at } 25°\text{C.} \tag{220}$$

where s is equal to the number of atoms in a molecule of the metal and n is the valence of the metal ions in solution.

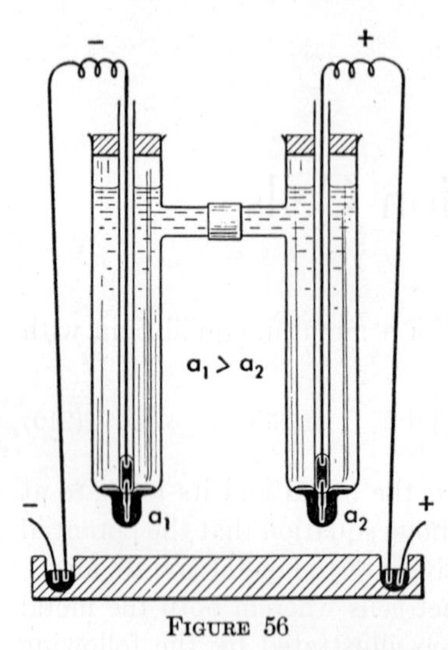

Figure 56

The necessary condition that $a_1 > a_2$ readily follows. As the E.M.F. of the cell will be positive, the free energy change is negative and the reaction will be spontaneous.

Apparatus Zinc sulfate; mercury; C.P. zinc; two platinum-point electrodes; potentiometer and accessories. The glass **H** cell may be made by joining two side neck test tubes with a piece of rubber tubing. The small E.M.F. given by these cells requires the use of a sensitive galvanometer (such as 0.014 μa.).

Procedure Prepare two zinc amalgams by adding clean zinc to mercury in the following proportions:

a_1 100.0 g. Hg to 2.000 g. Zn (left half cell)
a_2 100.0 g. Hg to 0.2000 g. Zn (right half cell)

The mercury and zinc are weighed accurately. Add the zinc to the mercury which has been placed in the **H** cell and stir with a clean glass rod. Since the amalgams oxidize quite readily in air, prepare them shortly before use or else keep them in tightly stoppered bottles.

An approximately 0.25 M solution of zinc sulfate is added to the **H** cell until the liquid level is above the connecting arm. The platinum-point electrodes, mounted in grooved rubber stoppers, are inserted in each half cell, with the platinum completely submerged in the amalgam. A small amount of ordinary mercury is placed in each electrode tube and a previously amalgamated No. 18 copper wire is inserted to establish connection to the potentiometer. The arm containing the more concentrated amalgam is connected to the negative lead of the potentiometer. The E.M.F. is measured, following the procedures described in Expt. 31. At least five independent readings are obtained over a period of fifteen minutes and should agree to within ± 0.001 volt. Enter the data in Table 31. The amalgams are disposed of into special containers.

TABLE 31

m_1	m_2	m_2/m_1	E.M.F. (OBSERVED)	E.M.F. (CALC.) $s = 1$	E.M.F. (CALC.) $s = 2$	a_2/a_1	γ_2/γ_1

Calculations Since $a_1 = \gamma_1 m_1$ and $a_2 = \gamma_2 m_2$, if it is assumed that $\gamma_1 = \gamma_2$ then $a_2/a_1 = m_2/m_1$. This assumption may be made since the amalgams are dilute. Calculate the molality of each amalgam and their ratio.

When calculating the E.M.F. from equation 220, some estimate must be made of s, the integer which multiplies the faraday in order that the electrical energy correspond to the number of gram atoms of metal per mole in the amalgam. Two assumptions are made; the first that $s = 1$ corresponds to the possible existence of dissolved zinc as monatomic molecules, the second that $s = 2$ considers the possibility that zinc atoms may exist as diatomic molecules in the amalgam. The following equations illustrate these possibilities:

$$Zn^{++} + 2F = Zn \qquad 2Zn^{++} + 4F = (Zn)_2$$

Calculate the E.M.F. of the cell employing these two assumptions in order to decide which is correct.

Calculate the free energy of the cell reaction.

The original assumption that the activity coefficients of the dissolved zinc in each amalgam are equal may be tested by calculating the ratio a_2/a_1 from the observed E.M.F. Obtain this ratio.

Since $a_2 = \gamma_2 m_2$ and $a_1 = \gamma_1 m_1$, then

$$\frac{m_1 a_2}{m_2 a_1} = \frac{\gamma_2}{\gamma_1}$$

Calculate the ratio of the activity coefficients.

Further experimental suggestions Cadmium amalgams of the same percentage composition may be substituted for the zinc amalgams. The amalgam half cells may be combined with calomel half cells and the E.M.F. determined.

REFERENCES

Clayton and Vosburgh, *J. Am. Chem. Soc.*, **58**, 2093 (1936)

Lewis, G. N., and Randall, M., *Thermodynamics and the Free Energy of Chemical Substances*, McGraw-Hill Book Company, Inc., New York, **1923**

Liebhafsky, *J. Am. Chem. Soc.*, **57**, 2657 (1935)

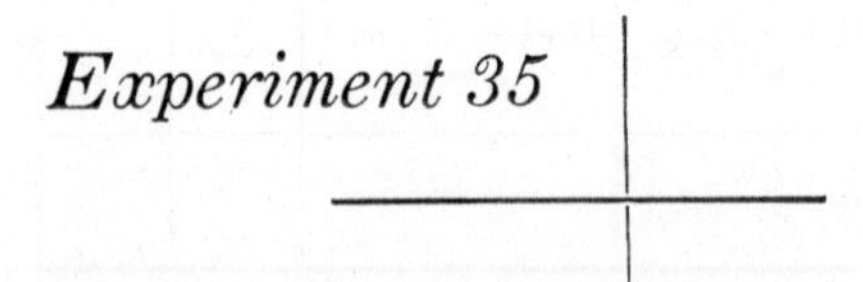

Experiment 35

Concentration Cells

The study of concentration cells has furnished very useful information in electrochemistry. Three types of concentration cells are met with and may be illustrated as follows:

$$-Zn(a) \mid ZnSO_4(a_1), Hg_2SO_4 \mid Hg \mid Hg_2SO_4, ZnSO_4(a_2) \mid Zn(a)+ \qquad \text{I}$$

$$-Zn(a) \mid ZnSO_4(a_1) \mid ZnSO_4(a_2) \mid Zn(a)+ \qquad \text{II}$$

$$-Zn(a) \mid ZnSO_4(a_1) \mid KCl \mid ZnSO_4(a_2) \mid Zn(a)+ \qquad \text{III}$$

Cell I is the so-called double concentration type; it does not contain a liquid junction. It furnishes accurate information regarding relative activities of ions. It is also known as a cell without transference. Cell II contains a liquid junction which gives rise to its own potential. Cells of this type give information regarding transference numbers but cannot be relied upon to give accurate values for ion activities. Cell III contains a salt bridge of KCl, the purpose of which is to minimize or eliminate the liquid junction potential. It does not furnish information about transference numbers or give accurate values for the activity coefficient. However, in practical analytical potentiometric analysis it is invaluable since absolute values of the E.M.F. are not required, and the change in E.M.F. per milliliter of reagent furnishes sufficient information.

The processes taking place in these cells are somewhat different. Thus, in cell I the following reactions occur:

LEFT CELL

$$\begin{aligned} Zn &= Zn^{++}(a_1) + 2\epsilon \\ Hg_2^{++} + 2\epsilon &= 2Hg(l) \\ Hg_2SO_4(s) &= Hg_2^{++} + SO_4^{=}(a_1) \\ \hline Zn + Hg_2SO_4(s) &= Zn^{++}(a_1) + SO_4^{=}(a_1) + 2Hg(l) \end{aligned}$$

RIGHT CELL

$$\begin{aligned} Zn^{++}(a_2) + 2\epsilon &= Zn \\ 2Hg(l) &= Hg_2^{++} + 2\epsilon \\ Hg_2^{++} + SO_4^{=}(a_2) &= Hg_2SO_4(s) \\ \hline Zn^{++}(a_2) + SO_4^{=}(a_2) + 2Hg(l) &= Zn + Hg_2SO_4(s) \end{aligned}$$

Adding the two equations, the net result for the entire cell is

$$Zn^{++}(a_2) + SO_4^{=}(a_2) \longrightarrow Zn^{++}(a_1) + SO_4^{=}(a_1) \quad \text{where } a_2 > a_1$$

The E.M.F. of the above cell is given by the following equation

$$\boldsymbol{E}_1 = -\frac{2RT}{nF}\ln\frac{(\gamma m)_1}{(\gamma m)_2} \qquad a_2 > a_1 \tag{221}$$

where γ is the mean activity coefficient and m is the concentration.

The process in the second cell is as follows:

1. One mole of Zn dissolves from the negative electrode and goes into solution as zinc ions of activity a_1.
2. n_c (cation transference number) moles of zinc ion travel from left to right across the liquid junction, while n_a (anion transference number) moles of sulfate ion cross the junction from right to left.
3. One mole of zinc ions in a solution of activity a_2 deposits as zinc on the anode.

The net process is the transfer of n_a moles of zinc and sulfate ions from a solution where the activity is a_2 to one where the activity is a_1. That is

$$n_aZn^{++}(a_2) + n_aSO_4^{=}(a_2) \longrightarrow n_aZn^{++}(a_1) + n_aSO_4^{=}(a_1)$$

The E.M.F. of the cell is given by

$$E_2 = -2n_a\frac{RT}{nF}\ln\frac{(\gamma m)_1}{(\gamma m)_2} \qquad a_2 > a_1 \tag{222}$$

The process which is chiefly responsible for the E.M.F. of cell three is as follows:

$$Zn^{++}(a_2) \longrightarrow Zn^{++}(a_1)$$

While zinc and sulfate ions move into the salt bridge, this does not contribute to the potential if the bridge is completely effective. The equation relating activity and E.M.F. is

$$E_3 = -\frac{RT}{nF} \ln \frac{[Zn^{++}]_1}{[Zn^{++}]_2} \tag{223}$$

It is impossible to measure or calculate the single ion activities $[Zn^{++}]_1$ and $[Zn^{++}]_2$, and accordingly it is assumed that these are practically equal to the mean ion activities $(\gamma m)_1$ and $(\gamma m)_2$. Equation 223 is simplified to

$$E_3 \approx -\frac{RT}{nF} \ln \frac{(\gamma m)_1}{(\gamma m)_2} \qquad a_2 > a_1 \tag{224}$$

The E.M.F. (E_4) arising at the liquid junction in cell two is equal to the difference in potential of cells two and three:

$$E_4 = E_2 - E_3 \tag{225}$$

This may be expressed by the two following approximate equations:

$$E_4 \approx (1 - 2n_a) \frac{RT}{nF} \ln \frac{(\gamma m)_1}{(\gamma m)_2} \tag{226}$$

$$E_4 \approx (n_c - n_a) \frac{RT}{nF} \ln \frac{(\gamma m)_1}{(\gamma m)_2} \tag{227}$$

Apparatus Student potentiometer and accessories; bottles to make half cells; potassium chloride agar salt bridge. The apparatus shown in Fig. 59 is made by sealing a male and female ground glass joint to side arm test tubes. The male joint is drawn out at the lower end into a heavy wall narrow constriction (1 mm.). U tube with side arms; Hg; Hg_2SO_4(s); Zn rods; platinum-point electrodes; 1 *M* $ZnSO_4$ solution prepared by dissolving the salt $ZnSO_4 \cdot 7\,H_2O$ in water. The small E.M.F. of the cells in Part *C* requires a sensitive galvanometer (0.014 μa.).

Procedure *Part A*. Prepare 500 ml. of 0.5, 0.25, 0.10, 0.05, 0.025, and 0.01 *M* solutions of zinc sulfate by quantitative dilution of the 1 *M* solution. Prepare zinc rod electrodes as described in Expt. 33. Each half cell is filled with a zinc sulfate solution and a zinc electrode is fitted to each (see Fig. 57). The siphon arm is dipped into some of the same concentration of zinc salt and filled by applying suction at the mouthpiece; fold the rubber tubing over and clamp.

Mercury is added to each of the four U tubes so that it is about 1 cm. above the bend. Sufficient solid mercurous sulfate is placed on top of the mercury to form a 0.5-cm. layer, and zinc sulfate solution is added until it comes up to the side arm of the U tube. The siphon arms are placed in beakers and filled by applying suction.

For precise work the cells should be placed in a thermostat, though the measurements may also be made at room temperature. Arrange the half cells so that the following combinations are obtained:[1]

$-Zn \mid ZnSO_4(0.01\ M), Hg_2SO_4(s) \mid Hg \mid Hg_2SO_4(s), ZnSO_4(0.1\ M) \mid Zn+$
$-Zn \mid ZnSO_4(0.025\ M), Hg_2SO_4(s) \mid Hg \mid Hg_2SO_4(s), ZnSO_4(0.25\ M) \mid Zn+$
$-Zn \mid ZnSO_4(0.05\ M), Hg_2SO_4(s) \mid Hg \mid Hg_2SO_4(s), ZnSO_4(0.50\ M) \mid Zn+$
$-Zn \mid ZnSO_4(0.10\ M), Hg_2SO_4(s) \mid Hg \mid Hg_2SO_4(s), ZnSO_4(1.0\ M) \mid Zn+$

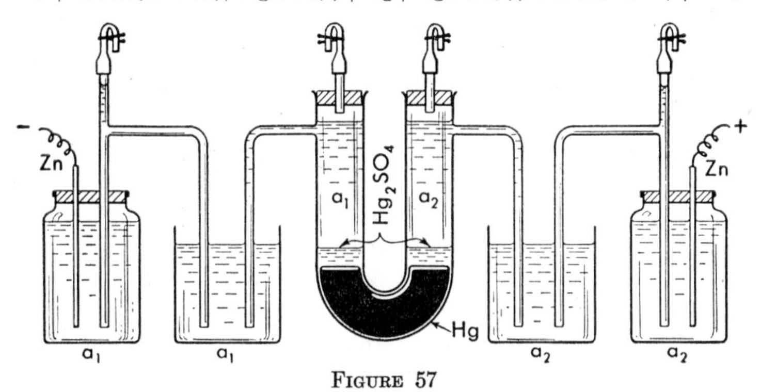

FIGURE 57

Connect the zinc terminals to No. 18 copper wire, using sharp clean alligator clips. Measure the E.M.F. developed by each cell. Review Expt. 31 for operation of the potentiometer. See Part *B* before discontinuing the experiment.

Part B. The E.M.F. of cells of type three may be obtained as soon as the above measurements have been made. The **U** tube is removed and a potassium chloride agar salt bridge is inserted in its place. The resulting cell is illustrated in Fig. 58. Obtain the E.M.F. of the above cells when

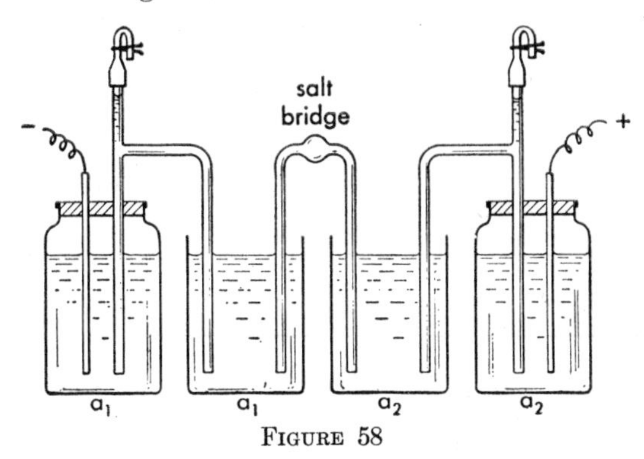

FIGURE 58

[1] See "Further experimental suggestions" for an optional arrangement of cell combinations.

the salt bridges have been inserted. The E.M.F. of various other combinations of the half cells may be obtained if desired.

Part C. To obtain the E.M.F. of the cells when a liquid junction potential exists, the apparatus shown in Fig. 59 is used.[1] Prepare a 5 per cent zinc amalgam by heating at 100° the required amount of zinc and mercury. Wash the cooled amalgam with dilute H_2SO_4, then with water, and dry with filter paper. The amalgam is placed in a stoppered bottle and kept in the oven at 100°C. in order to keep it liquid. Slip a short piece of rubber tubing, one end of which is closed by glass rod, over the tip *C* of cell *A* and add the more dilute solution of zinc sulfate, being careful to fill the siphon arm completely so that no air bubbles remain. Add 3–5 ml. of the warm amalgam and adjust the platinum-point electrode so that the platinum is completely submerged in it. The cell *B* is filled with the more concentrated zinc sulfate solution, the amalgam is added, and the electrode is put in place. The rubber tubing is removed and the two parts are fitted together as shown. The equilibrium E.M.F. is obtained in about one hour. A sensitive galvanometer is required for these measurements.

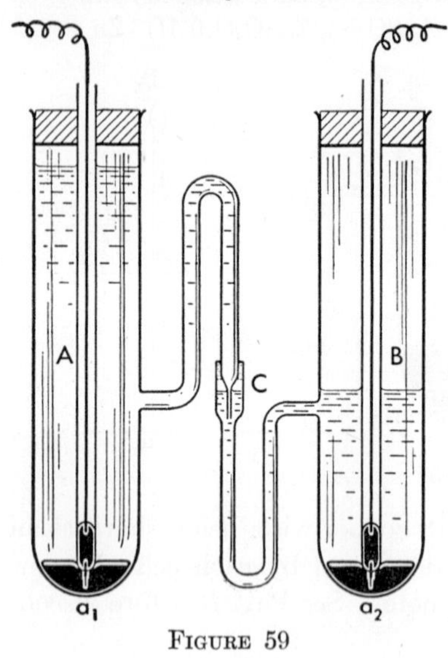

FIGURE 59

The same combination of concentrations employed in Parts *A* and *B* should be used in the present half cells. If desired, other concentrations may be employed and should preferably match the combination of half cells employed in Part *B*.

TABLE 32

m_1	m_2	CELL TYPE	E

Calculations Concentration cells of Class I are useful for calculating the relative activities of an electrolyte. Assuming that the activity

[1] See articles by Stokes and Levien, and by McLeod and Gordon in references at end of experiment.

coefficient of $ZnSO_4$ is equal to 0.045 in a 1 *M* solution, 0.065 for a 0.5 *M*, and 0.15 for a 0.25 *M* solution, calculate the activity coefficient for each of the remaining solutions, using equation 221.

Theoretically, according to equations 221 and 224 the ratio of E_1/E_3 should be 2. Test this relation.

According to equations 221 and 222, the ratio of E_2/E_1 should equal n_a. Calculate n_a and n_c from the ratio of the E.M.F. for the two types of cells. This transference number is an average value over the concentration range used in obtaining E_2 and E_1.

Employing the previously calculated values of γ, calculate the transference numbers n_a and n_c, using equation 222.

Calculate the activity coefficients from the measured values of E_3 for the cells containing the salt bridge, employing equation 224. Use the values for γ given above. How do the results compare with those obtained from the cells without transference?

Providing the salt bridge completely eliminates the junction potential, the latter can be estimated by equation 225. Employing either equation 226 or 227 and the previously calculated activity coefficients, calculate E_4 and compare it with the results obtained from equation 225.

Further experimental suggestions The experimental arrangement of Part *A* may be modified by employing cells of the following type:

$$Zn(a) \mid ZnSO_4(a_1) \mid Hg_2SO_4 \mid Hg$$

H type cells are used for their construction. The combined E.M.F.'s of cells containing different concentrations of $ZnSO_4$ are equivalent to those in Part *A*. This is the usual procedure employed since all concentrations can then be compared with fewer measurements.

The experiment may also be studied with Cd | $CdSO_4$ half cells, the range of concentrations selected being similar to that used in the present procedure.

REFERENCES

Guggenheim, *J. Am. Chem. Soc.*, **52,** 1315 (1930)
Lucasse, *ibid.*, **51,** 2605 (1929)
McBain and Van Rysselberge, *ibid.*, **50,** 3009 (1928); **52,** 2336 (1930)
MacInnes and Dole, *ibid.*, **53,** 1357 (1931)
McLeod and Gordon, *ibid.*, **68,** 58 (1946)
Stokes and Levien, *ibid.*, **68,** 333 (1946)
Wolten and King, *ibid.*, **71,** 576 (1949)

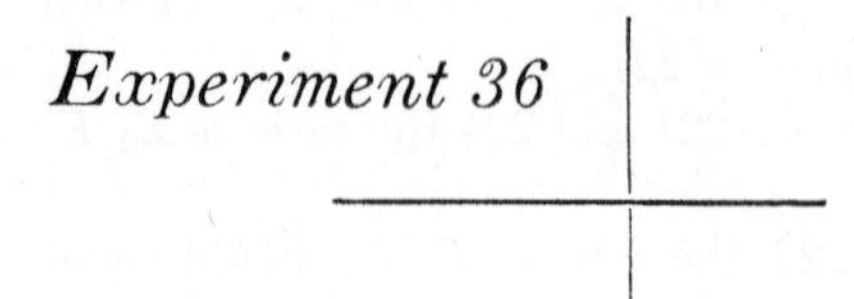

Experiment 36

The Determination of Hydrogen Ions

The use of electromotive force measurements in analytical chemistry is based upon the fact that the potential of a given system depends upon its concentration. Consider the change $A^+ + \epsilon \rightleftharpoons A$ and suppose an electrode which indicates the activity of A^+ ion is present. The E.M.F. of a cell composed of the indicator electrode and a reference electrode is given by

$$E = \pm \left(E^\circ_A - \frac{0.0591}{n} \log \frac{A}{A^+} \right) \pm (E \text{ reference}) \qquad \text{at } 25°\text{C}. \qquad (228)$$

The problem of measuring the hydrogen ion activity resolves itself into finding a suitable indicator electrode. A number of such electrodes are known; among the more important ones in use are the hydrogen gas electrode, the quinhydrone electrode, the glass electrode, and the antimony oxide electrode.

The hydrogen gas electrode consists of a platinum wire or foil upon which finely divided platinum has been electrolytically deposited. The equilibrium between hydrogen ions and hydrogen gas

$$2H_3O^+ + 2\epsilon \rightleftharpoons 2H_2O + H_2$$

is established rather slowly in the presence of finely divided platinum. With a normal calomel reference electrode the following cell is obtained:

$$-\text{Pt}, H_2(1 \text{ atm.}) \mid H_3O^+(a) \mid \text{KCl(sat.)} \mid \text{KCl}(1\ N), Hg_2Cl_2 \mid Hg+$$

The electromotive force of this cell is given by

$$E = E_{c.e.} - E^\circ_{H_2} + \frac{0.0591}{2} \log \frac{a_{H_2}}{a^2_{H_3O^+}} \qquad (229)$$

$E^\circ_{H_2}$ is assigned a value of zero volts when the pressure of the hydrogen gas is one atmosphere ($a_{H2} = 1$), and the activity of hydrogen ions is unity. Then

$$E = 0.2805 - 0.0591 \log a_{H_3O^+} \qquad \text{at } 25°\text{C}. \qquad (230)$$

The hydrogen ion activity may be expressed directly in pH units; since $p\mathrm{H} = -\log a_{\mathrm{H_3O^+}}$:

$$p\mathrm{H} = \frac{E - 0.2805}{0.0591} \quad \text{at } 25°\mathrm{C}. \tag{231}$$

For very precise work it is necessary to employ the exact partial pressure of hydrogen gas calculated from the barometric pressure and hydrostatic pressure, corrected for the vapor pressure of water over the solution. For dilute solutions, the latter may be assumed equal to that for pure water.

The quinhydrone electrode is also used as an indicator electrode for hydrogen ions. The substance quinhydrone dissociates in aqueous solution to form an equimolecular mixture of quinone (Q) and hydroquinone (H_2Q):

$$\text{quinhydrone} \rightleftharpoons \text{hydroquinone} + \text{quinone}$$

The electrode reaction is a redox reaction wherein quinone is reduced to hydroquinone, the reaction being governed by the usual laws of chemical equilibrium:

$$2\mathrm{H_3O^+} + \mathrm{Q} + 2\epsilon \rightleftharpoons 2\mathrm{H_2O} + \mathrm{H_2Q} \tag{232}$$

Again selecting the normal calomel electrode for reference, the following cell is obtained:

$$-\mathrm{Hg} \mid \mathrm{Hg_2Cl_2},\ 1\,N\ \mathrm{KCl} \mid \mathrm{KCl(sat.)} \mid \mathrm{H_3O^+}(a)\ \text{quinhydrone},\ \mathbf{Pt}+$$

The E.M.F. of this cell in volts $\boldsymbol{E}$ is given by

$$E = 0.6994 + 0.0591 \log a_{\mathrm{H_3O^+}} - 0.2805 \quad \text{at } 25°\mathrm{C}. \tag{233}$$

The quantity, 0.6994, corresponds to the standard potential $E°$ of the quinhydrone half cell. Expressing the above equation in pH units

$$p\mathrm{H} = \frac{0.4189 - E}{0.0591} \quad \text{at } 25°\mathrm{C}. \tag{234}$$

The glass electrode is very useful in the routine measurement of pH. While the glass membrane is fragile and has a resistance of several million ohms, it can be built into a rugged instrument which employs a "vacuum tube voltmeter" or electron tube potentiometer to measure E.M.F. The electrode system may be arranged as follows:

saturated	saturated	H_3O^+	glass	0.1 N	silver chloride	
− calomel	KCl salt	sample	membrane	HCl	or	+
cell	bridge				calomel electrode	

The glass electrode cannot be used in strongly alkaline solution.

Apparatus Calomel electrode; quinhydrone electrode; hydrogen electrode; glass electrode (optional); potentiometer and accessories;

sodium-monohydrogen phosphate; citric acid; 50- and 100-ml. burets; glass-stoppered bottles.

The preparation of a hydrogen electrode Prepare a platinum electrode by sealing a short piece of No. 22 B. & S. gauge wire or foil with attached wire into a length of 3 mm. soft glass tubing. Clean and roughen the wire with fine emery paper and then allow to stand in warm cleaning mixture for fifteen minutes. Remove and rinse with distilled water. Coat with platinum black as described in Expt. 25. The electrode should be the cathode in the final step of electrolysis in dilute sulfuric acid as in this way it is not contaminated with oxygen or chlorine.

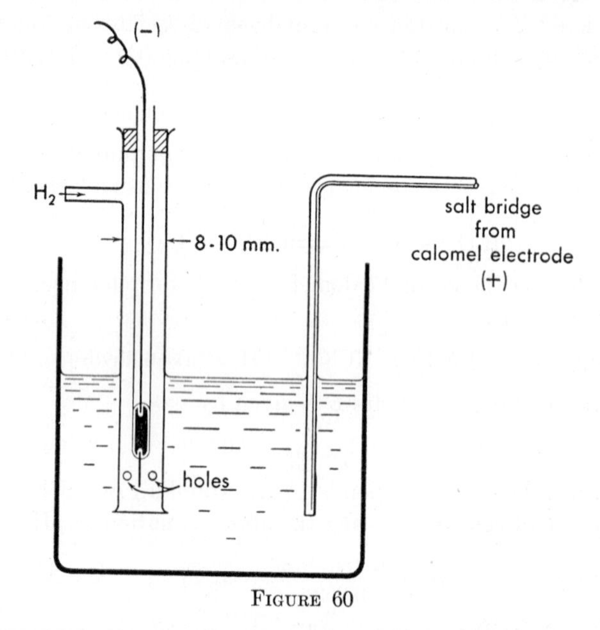

FIGURE 60

It is mounted in a rubber stopper, fitted to the gas tube as illustrated in Fig. 60, and immersed in distilled water until needed.

The quinhydrone electrode This indicator electrode is made of either a bright platinum or gold wire. The platinum wire electrode is prepared as described above with the exception that it is not electroplated. It is cleaned with fine emery paper, immersed in warm cleaning mixture, washed with distilled water, and then heated to redness in the oxidizing flame of a Bunsen burner.

The gold wire electrode is made by soldering a short piece of gold wire to braided copper wire. The wire is cemented into a glass tube with an acid-resistant cement so that only the gold part of the wire extends from the tube. It is cleaned with fine emery paper and warm cleaning mixture and rinsed with distilled water. Gold wire electrodes are generally preferred to platinum as there is less tendency for them to produce catalytic decomposition.

The quinhydrone electrode should not be used in solutions when the *p*H is greater than 8, as hydroquinone is rapidly oxidized by the atmosphere in alkaline solution. In addition, hydroquinone is a weak acid and would be partly neutralized.

The glass electrode Since there are a number of different commercial *p*H meters employing glass electrodes, it is not possible herein to describe how each one operates. Generally it is necessary to standardize the electrode system with a buffer of known *p*H before it can be used to measure that of a given sample. This must be done frequently during the course of a day's work. The directions for operating the instrument should be carefully read before attempting to use it.

Procedure Prepare 1 liter each of 0.2 *M* Na_2HPO_4 and 0.1 *M* citric acid solutions. Buffer solutions of the *p*H values listed in Table 33 are prepared, using ten times the quantities suggested in Table 14, page 82. Store in clean glass-stoppered bottles.

TABLE 33

Accepted *p*H	H_2 Electrode			Quinhydrone Electrode			Glass Electrode *p*H
	E	*p*H	$a_{H_3O^+}$	E	*p*H	$a_{H_3O^+}$	
2.4							
3.0							
3.4							
4.0							
4.4							
5.0							
5.4							
6.0							
6.4							
7.0							
7.4							
8.0							

The *p*H of the sample is measured with a glass electrode, following the procedure described by the instrument manufacturer; obtain at least two independent readings for each sample. The results should agree to within 0.1 *p*H unit; otherwise the instrument is not working properly (possibly the batteries are dead or an electrode needs replacing).

To measure the *p*H of the samples with the hydrogen electrode, arrange the apparatus as shown in Fig. 60. The hydrogen electrode is supplied with electrolytic tank gas and the rate of flow is adjusted so that 2–3 bubbles of gas per second are obtained. If a Kipp generator is used as a source for hydrogen, the gas must be purified by passing it through a series of wash bottles containing alkaline pyrogallate, potassium permanganate, and water in the order given.

The potentiometer is first calibrated with the standard cell according to the directions of Expt. 31. The above cell is put in place of C_x (Fig. 53, p. 173) and the E.M.F. is measured. The electrode should be in contact with the solution about three minutes before measuring the voltage; readings are taken at three-minute intervals until agreement to within ± 0.001 volt is obtained. If a constant value is not obtained within nine minutes, it is probable that the electrode has been poisoned and should be replaced or replated. After a measurement has been completed, the electrode is washed with distilled water and rinsed with small portions of the new sample. Do not discard the samples as they may be used for the measurements with the quinhydrone electrode.

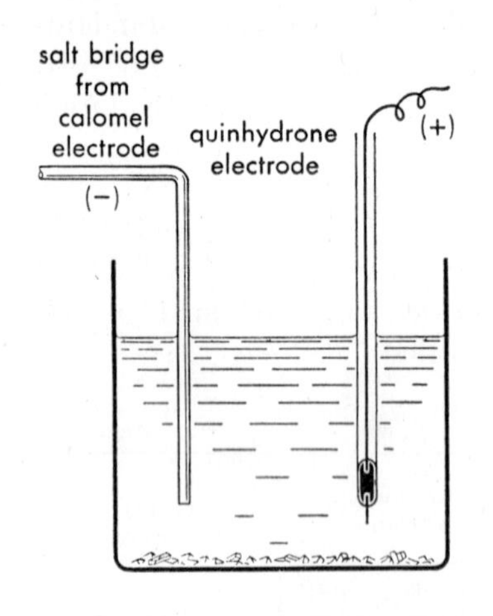

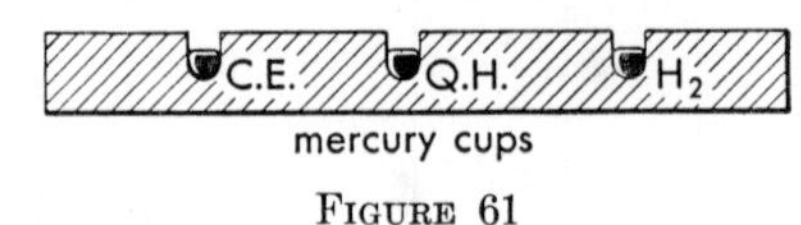

FIGURE 61

The E.M.F. of the sample is obtained with the quinhydrone electrode as follows: About 0.1 g. of solid quinhydrone is added to the solution and stirred for a few minutes, the platinum or gold electrode and salt bridge are placed in the solution and the cell illustrated in Fig. 61 is formed. Note that the calomel electrode is now connected to the negative side of the potentiometer. The use of glass mercury cups will facilitate the interchange of connections.

The potentiometer is adjusted with the standard cell as previously described, and the E.M.F. of the sample is obtained. Approach the setting on the slide-wire from the high and low readings; the average of both is recorded.

Calculations From the measured values of the E.M.F. calculate the *p*H, using equations 231 and 234 for the hydrogen and quinhydrone electrodes respectively. If the measurements have been carefully made, the results should agree with the values given in Table 33.

With the aid of equations 230 and 233, calculate the activity of the hydrogen ion.

Further suggested experiments The *p*H of various weak acids and bases and their salts may be measured. The E.M.F. of cells such as $M \mid M^+ \parallel H_3O^+ \mid H_2$, **Pt** may be measured and either the standard potential of the metal or the activity of hydrogen ion can be found. The effect of neutral salts on the activity of hydrogen ion may be measured, using a hydrogen ion indicator electrode in combination with a calomel reference electrode.

REFERENCES

Auerbach and Smolczyk, *Z. physik, Chem.*, **110,** 65 (1924)
Clark, W. M., *The Determination of Hydrogen Ions*, 3d ed., The Williams and Wilkins Company, Baltimore, **1928**
Hovorka and Dearing, *J. Am. Chem. Soc.*, **56,** 243 (1943)
Michaelis, L., *Hydrogen Ion Concentration*, tr. by W. A. Perizweig, The Williams and Wilkins Company, Baltimore, **1926**

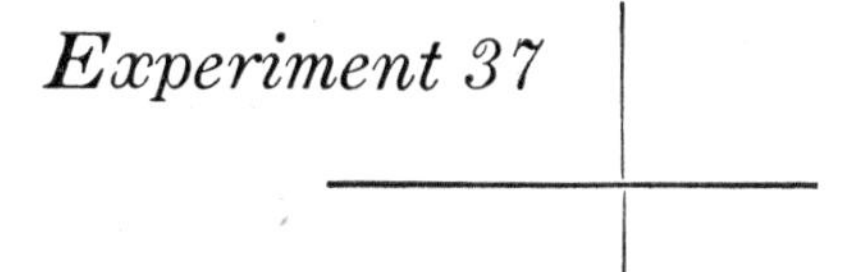

Potentiometric Analysis Applied to Acidimetry and Alkalimetry

In this experiment, the quinhydrone indicator electrode has been selected to follow the change in *p*H during a neutralization reaction. A calomel half cell has been chosen as the reference electrode.

Since neutralization is a reaction involving the appearance or disappearance of hydrogen ions, practically any hydrogen ion indicator can be used to measure the concentration of hydrogen ion during the neutralization process. When a quinhydrone electrode is used, the operation must start with an acid sample in the cell, and this is neutralized by adding base from a buret. The reverse process cannot be employed as quinhydrone undergoes decomposition in alkaline solution.

Apparatus Quinhydrone electrode; calomel electrode; quinhydrone; approximately 0.1 *M* HCl and 0.1 *M* acetic acid; standard 1 *M* or 0.5 *M* NaOH; potentiometer and accessories; 10-ml. micro buret or 50-ml. buret.

In this and other experiments where the absolute potential need not be known, the apparatus and circuit suggested by Hildebrand[1] may be used. (See Fig. 62.) If a *p*H meter with a glass electrode, or other types of commercial titrimeters are available, they may be substituted.

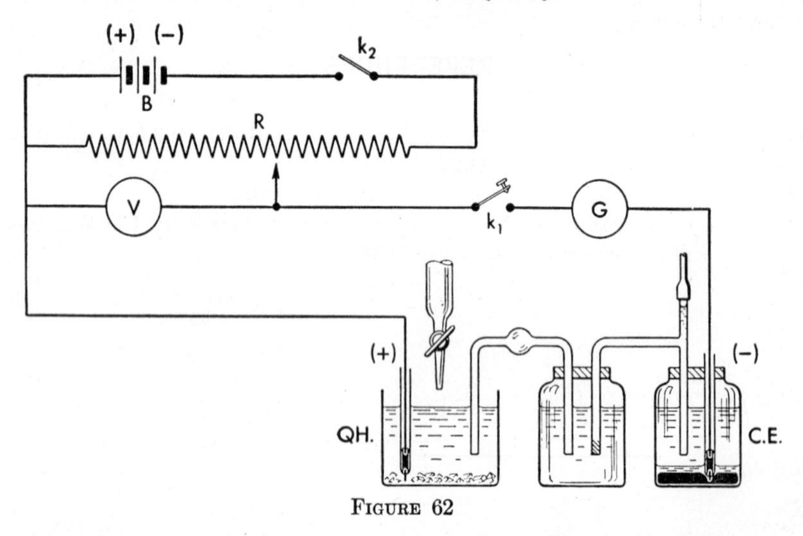

FIGURE 62

The Hildebrand potentiometer consists of a 700-ohm rheostat, a portable galvanometer (0.5 μa. sensitivity), two dry cells, S.P.S.T. switch k_2, tapping key k_1, and a 0–3-volt voltmeter with scale marked in 0.1-volt units. The unknown cell is connected into the circuit as shown, the correct polarity being observed. The resistance R is changed until the galvanometer G does not deflect upon tapping key k_1. The voltmeter reading is recorded and corresponds to the E.M.F. of the cell. The S.P.S.T. switch k_2 is used to take the working cell out of the circuit when not in use.

Procedure Pipet 50 ml. of approximately 0.1 *M* HCl solution into a 150-ml. beaker, add about 0.1 g. of solid quinhydrone and stir for a few minutes. The salt bridge from the calomel half cell and a bright platinum or gold electrode is placed in the beaker. The calomel electrode is connected to the negative lead of the potentiometer.

[1] *J. Am. Chem. Soc.*, **35**, 847 (1913)

If the student potentiometer is used, measure the E.M.F. as described in Expt. 31. A total of 4 ml. of standard 1.0 M NaOH is added in 1-ml. portions from a micro buret; stir for about one-half minute after each addition and obtain the voltage of the cell. The titration is completed with 0.2-ml. portions until 4.96 ml. has been added; finally 0.05-ml. portions are added until the endpoint has been passed by 0.15–0.30 ml.

The above procedure is repeated in detail using an approximately 0.1 M solution of acetic acid.

Determine the concentration of the acids by the usual volumetric procedures employing phenolphthalein as the indicator.

If the procedure is carried out with an ordinary 50-ml. buret, 100-ml. samples of acid are taken. The concentration of base should be approximately 0.5 M and is added in quantities five times as large as those previously given.

TABLE 34

ml. OF BASE	E VOLTS	pH	$a_{H_3O^+}$	$\Delta E/\Delta V$

Calculations Calculate the pH of each solution, using equation 234, page 191.

Calculate the activity of hydrogen ion present at each step in the titration (see eq. 230, p. 190). This is omitted if the Hildebrand method was used.

Prepare a graph employing pH as the ordinate and volume V of base in milliliters as abscissa. A graph using activity of hydrogen ion as ordinate and V in milliliters is also prepared.

The equivalence point is obtained by a graphical procedure. Plot the E.M.F. in volts as ordinate and volume of base added as abscissa. Indicate the equivalence point on the curve by a mark such as |/|. Calculate the molarity of the original acid from this value; compare the result obtained by the volumetric standardization.

A second procedure for determining the equivalence point is as follows: Calculate ΔE by subtracting the voltage of each successive reading from the previous one. Do the same for the volume readings. Obtain the ratio $\Delta E/\Delta V$.

A graph employing $\Delta E/\Delta V$ as ordinate and volume of added base (total) as abscissa is prepared. It is only necessary to employ data in the immediate neighborhood of the equivalence point in order to locate it.

Calculate the molarity of the acids using this procedure. Which of the above procedures should be the more reliable?

The dissociation constant of acetic acid may be obtained from the known value of E for the original solution. Employing the calculated value of the activity of the hydrogen ion in the original solution, assume that the acetate ion has the same activity and that the activity of the undissociated acetic acid is equal to its concentration, and calculate the dissociation constant.

At the midpoint of a titration of a weak acid, the hydrogen ion activity has the same numerical value as the dissociation constant. Obtain K, the dissociation constant, by applying this statement to the results.

REFERENCES

Gabbard, *J. Am. Chem. Soc.*, **69,** 533 (1947)

The salt error of the quinhydrone electrode.

Hildebrand, *ibid.*, **35,** 847 (1913)

Kolthoff, I. M., and Furman, N. H., *Potentiometric Titrations,* 2d ed., John Wiley & Sons, Inc., New York, **1931**

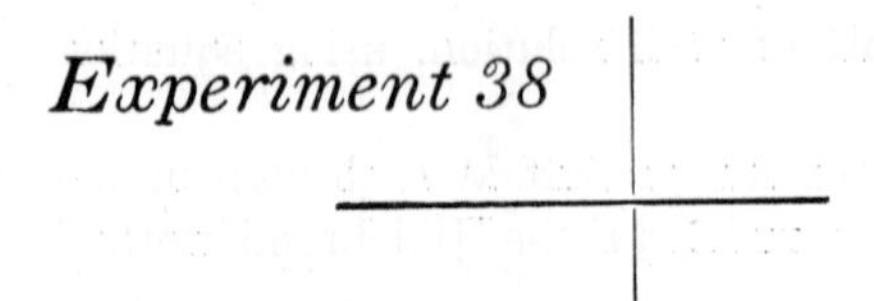

The Determination of Silver by Potentiometric Titration

If a cell such as the following is arranged

$$-\mathrm{Hg} \mid \mathrm{Hg_2Cl_2}, \mathrm{KCl}(1\ N) \mid \mathrm{KNO_3}(1\ N) \mid \mathrm{Ag^+} \mid \mathrm{Ag(s)}+$$

it can be used to determine the endpoint of the reaction

$$\mathrm{Ag^+} + \mathrm{Cl^-} \rightleftharpoons \mathrm{AgCl(s)}.$$

As chloride ion is added to the left side of the cell, the concentration of silver ion decreases since it is removed as an insoluble silver salt. Simultaneously the E.M.F. of the cell will change.

If the salt bridge completely eliminates the junction potential, the E.M.F. of the cell is given by

$$E_{cell} = 0.2805 - E^{\circ}_{Ag} + 0.0591 \log \frac{[Ag]}{[Ag^+]} \quad \text{at } 25°\text{C}. \tag{235}$$

where E° is the standard potential of the silver electrode and is a constant, [Ag] is the activity or concentration of silver metal (a constant), and $[Ag^+]$ is the activity or concentration of silver ion. Grouping the constant terms together

$$E_{cell} = k - 0.0591 \log [Ag^+] \quad \text{at } 25°\text{C}. \tag{236}$$

Thus the concentration of silver ion at any time during the titration depends upon the amount of chloride ion which has been added, and the E.M.F. of the cell varies logarithmically.

In most practical potentiometric titrations, it is only necessary to obtain the relative change of E.M.F. per unit volume of titrating reagent. Thus if $[Ag_1^+]$ and $[Ag_2^+]$ represent two different concentrations of silver ion during the titration and the condition $[Ag_1^+] > [Ag_2^+]$ is assumed

$$\Delta E = E_1 - E_2 = k - 0.0591 \log [Ag_1^+] - k + 0.0591 \log [Ag_2^+]$$
$$\Delta E = 0.0591 \log [Ag_2^+]/[Ag_1^+] \tag{237}$$

That is, the greatest change in potential is to be expected when the change of the concentration ratio is the largest.

The conditions at the equivalence point or endpoint are such that equal amounts of reagent produce the greatest relative change in the concentration of the substance being titrated. One practical method of determining the endpoint consists of adding equal increments of titrating reagent; the endpoint is considered to be the point where the greatest change in the E.M.F. occurs.

A second procedure is, in effect, to construct tangents to the curve of E.M.F. versus milliliters of reagent and obtain the tangent $\Delta E/\Delta V$. The rate of change of the slope of the tangents is greatest at the endpoint.

It is not necessary to use an accurate potentiometer when only changes in E.M.F. are measured and any simplified form, such as the Hildebrand type (see Expt. 37), may be employed.

Apparatus Silver wire; De Khotinsky cement or equivalent; calomel half cell; potentiometer [1] and accessories; 50-ml. buret; an approximately 0.1 *M* silver nitrate solution; a standard solution (approximately 0.1 *M*) of sodium chloride prepared by weighing the requisite amount of dried C.P. salt; motor stirrer (optional).

[1] Any of the commercial titrimeters may be substituted.

A silver wire electrode is made by sealing a piece of wire into 3-mm. glass tubing with cement, connection to the outside circuit being made with an alligator clip. The wire is polished with fine emery paper.

To prepare the salt bridge, dissolve 3 g. of agar in 100 ml. of water by heating on a steam bath until a clear solution is obtained, add 10 g. of potassium nitrate, and stir until the salt is dissolved. The warm gel is poured into inverted **U** tubes and allowed to solidify. The salt bridge may be kept from drying out if placed in a solution of potassium nitrate of similar concentration (10 g. per 100 ml.).

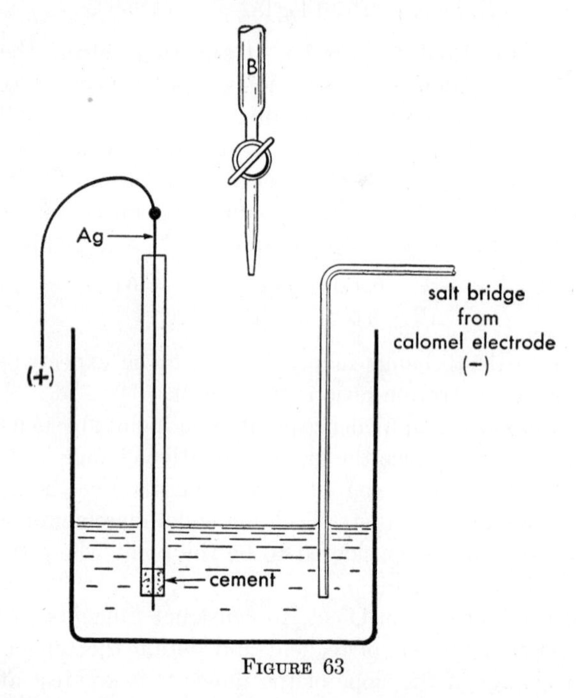

FIGURE 63

Procedure Accurately pipet 25 ml. of the silver nitrate solution into 200 ml. of water in a 400-ml. beaker. Arrange the apparatus as shown in Fig. 63, noting that the calomel half cell is connected to the positive lead of the potentiometer. The silver wire electrode should be completely immersed in the solution. Standardize the working cell of the potentiometer according to directions given in Expt. 31.

Introduce the silver-calomel cell into the circuit by changing the position of the D.P.D.T. switch and measure the E.M.F. Add 4 ml. of the standard sodium chloride solution and stir for about two minutes or until the E.M.F. of the cell is constant. Continue to titrate with 4-ml.

portions until a total of 20 ml. has been reached, stirring vigorously before determining the E.M.F. The reagent is now added in 0.2-ml. quantities until the equivalence point has been passed by at least 0.5 ml.

If a duplicate titration is to be made, clean the silver wire with emery paper to remove the adherent silver chloride, otherwise the electrode may function as a chloride ion indicator electrode. In any case, clean the wire at the end of the experiment.

Calculations Prepare a graph using E.M.F. in volts as ordinate and milliliters of reagent as abscissa. This graph may be constructed as the titration progresses to give an approximate knowledge of the endpoint and aid in regulating the increments of reagent to be added. From an inspection of the graph, indicate the endpoint with a mark |/| across the curve. Calculate the molarity of the silver nitrate.

Prepare a graph using $\Delta E/\Delta V$ as ordinate and volume V of reagent as abscissa (see Expt. 37), using the data only in the immediate neighborhood of the endpoint. Indicate the endpoint from an inspection of the curve and mark it. Calculate the molarity of silver nitrate from these data.

If the silver nitrate has been standardized by an accepted volumetric procedure, compare the results.

Further experimental suggestions The titration may be studied with 0.01 M, 0.001 M, and 0.0001 M silver nitrate solutions in order to determine the effect of concentration on the endpoint. Silver nitrate may also be titrated with OH^-, $CrO_4^{=}$, Br^-, I^- ions and the effect of the ion product on the endpoint may be correlated.

REFERENCE

Kolthoff, I. M., and Furman, N. H., *Potentiometric Titrations*, 2d ed., John Wiley & Sons, Inc., New York, **1931**

Experiment 39

Potentiometric Analysis Applied to Redox Reactions

In the potentiometric titrations described in Expts. 37 and 38, the reactions taking place at the indicator electrode were reversible; *i.e.*, upon opposing the cell voltage with a slightly greater E.M.F., the reverse reaction could be made to take place. In many redox reactions, this is not the case. For example, in the titration of iodine with thiosulfate, one of the reactions is reversible, namely $I_2 \rightleftharpoons 2I^-$, but the change of thiosulfate ion to tetrathionate ion is not; $2S_2O_3^= \longrightarrow S_4O_6^=$. Another example is the titration of oxalate by permanganate; in this case neither reaction is reversible.

Potentiometric methods can be applied to many such irreversible reactions; measurable potentials are obtained with suitable indicator electrodes, and change markedly with concentration so that the endpoint in a titration is obvious. It is necessary, however, to establish empirically whether such a titration is sufficiently accurate to be used for quantitative analysis.

Apparatus Calomel electrode; platinum-point electrode; salt bridge (KCl); potentiometer and accessories; 50-ml. buret; approximately 0.02 *M* $KMnO_4$; pure potassium iodide; potassium ferrocyanide trihydrate; Mohr's salt (ammonium ferrous sulfate hexahydrate). The Hildebrand potentiometer (Expt. 37) may be used in place of the student type.

Procedure The following substances may be titrated with an approximately 0.02 *M* solution of potassium permanganate:

a) Accurately weigh about 0.6600 g. of potassium iodide and dissolve in 100 ml. of an approximately 0.125 *M* sulfuric acid solution.

b) Accurately weigh about 1.6880 g. of potassium ferrocyanide trihydrate and dissolve in 100 ml. of an approximately 0.75 *M* sulfuric acid solution.

c) Accurately weigh about 1.5600 g. of Mohr's salt [$(NH_4)_2Fe(SO_4)_2 \cdot 6H_2O$], and dissolve in 100 ml. of an approximately 0.2 *M* sulfuric acid solution.

The platinum-point electrode and the salt bridge from the calomel half cell are placed in the beaker containing the solution to be analyzed (see Fig. 61, p. 194). The calomel electrode is connected to the positive lead of the potentiometer.

Add 5 ml. of the permanganate solution, stir for one minute or until the measured E.M.F. does not change. Continue to titrate with 5-ml. portions until a total of 35 ml. has been added, whereupon 1-ml. portions are used until a total of 39 ml. has been reached. Finally add the reagent in 0.2-ml. quantities until the endpoint has been passed by about 0.5 ml. The E.M.F. is determined after each addition of reagent.

TABLE 35

ml. of $KMnO_4$	E.M.F.	$\Delta E/\Delta V$

Calculations During the titration construct a graph, using E.M.F. (volts) as ordinate and volume (milliliters) as abscissa. In this way the approach of the equivalence point or endpoint may be approximately foretold and the increments of reagent may be regulated accordingly.

From an inspection of the graph, indicate the endpoint by a mark |/| across the curve. Calculate the molarity of the potassium permanganate from this result.

Prepare a graph employing $\Delta E/\Delta V$ as ordinate and total volume (V) as the abscissa from the measurements in the immediate neighborhood of the endpoint (see Expt. 37). Obtain the endpoint from this curve and calculate the molarity of the potassium permanganate.

If the potassium permanganate is standardized by the usual volumetric method, the result may be compared with that of the potentiometric method.

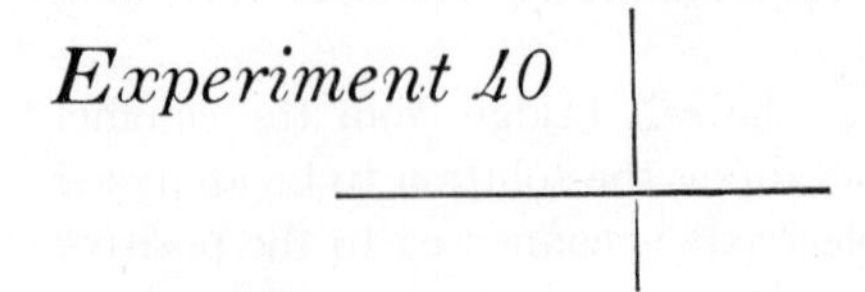

Experiment 40

The Preparation and Purification of Colloids

The size of colloidal particles is intermediate between those of molecules and of macro particles. The following scheme illustrates this:

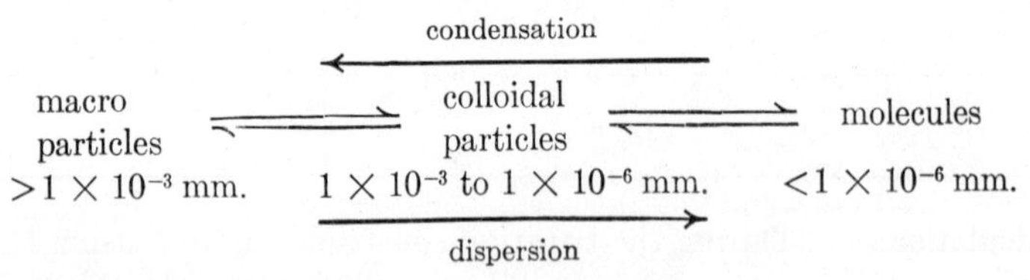

It is evident that colloid particles could be prepared by either dispersing large particles into smaller ones of colloidal size, or by grouping together many molecules to form particles of larger size. The former process is called dispersion or peptization, while the latter is called condensation. Examples of these methods are illustrated in the following experiments.

Colloidal hydrous ferric oxide by condensation Place 300 ml. of distilled water in a beaker and heat to boiling. Remove the burner, quickly add 3 ml. of a concentrated solution of $FeCl_3$, and rapidly mix the solution. Note that the color of the solution is much deeper than if the $FeCl_3$ had been diluted with an equal volume of cold water. Examine with a Tyndall light source and observe the Tyndall cone. Retain the sol for further use.

Colloidal arsenious sulfide by condensation Transfer one gram of As_2O_3 (weighed on a platform balance) slowly and with vigorous stirring to 100 ml. of hot distilled water. Observe that As_2O_3 is not easily wetted by water. Filter when cool. Saturate 200 ml. of water with hydrogen sulfide gas (HOOD) and mix with the As_2O_3 (H_3AsO_3) solution in a flask. Pass hydrogen sulfide gas into the mixture three to five minutes more. An intensely colored yellow sol results. Stopper the flask and retain for further use. Examine the sol with a Tyndall beam.

Colloidal hydrous ferric oxide by dispersion (peptization) Add 3 *M* NH_4OH solution to 100 ml. of an approximately 0.1 *M* solution of $FeCl_3$ until precipitation is complete. Wash the hydrous ferric oxide precipitate with water by decantation several times. Pour off as much water as possible from the last washing or filter; transfer some of the precipitate to a test tube. Add a few milliliters of concentrated $FeCl_3$ solution and warm until the precipitate disappears. Pour when cool into 100 ml. of cold water. Examine the sol with a Tyndall beam.

Colloidal cadmium sulfide by dispersion (peptization) Add 3 *M* NH_4OH solution to 100 ml. of an approximately 0.1 *M* solution of $CdCl_2$ contained in a 500-ml. Erlenmeyer flask until the precipitate which first forms dissolves. Saturate the solution with H_2S (HOOD) until precipitation is complete. Wash the precipitate by decantation several times with distilled water. After the last washing, suspend the precipitate in 300 ml. of H_2O and saturate with H_2S until the CdS is completely peptized. Boil off the excess H_2S and stopper. Examine the sol with a Tyndall beam. Keep the sol for several weeks and observe if flocculation takes place in this time.

The purification of colloids Since excess electrolyte produces coagulation of sols, it is advantageous to remove most of the ions. This may be done by the use of dialyzing membranes which are permeable to both solvent and ionic solutes but impermeable to colloidal particles. Various types of membranes may be used, such as parchment paper, collodion, and cellophane. Since dialysis is a process involving diffusion, it will take place more rapidly at higher temperatures.

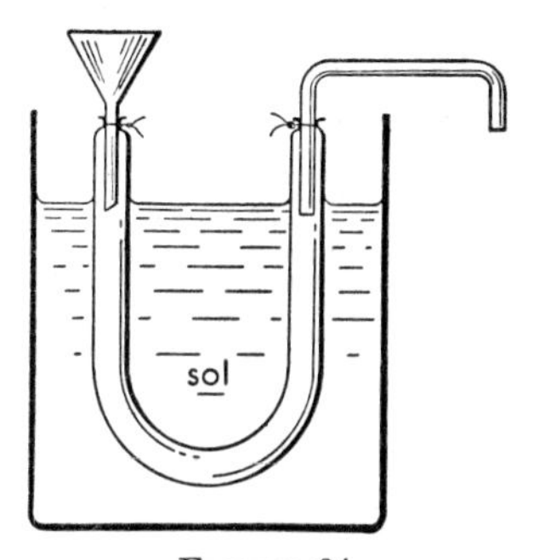

FIGURE 64

Tie one end of cellophane tubing membrane around the lower end of a funnel, the other end around a piece of glass tubing, and mount as shown in Fig. 64, with the aid of clamps. Pour warm distilled water in through the funnel to fill the membrane completely. Place the colloidal suspension in the beaker and heat to 70–90°, and every 5–15 min. pour a fresh portion of warm distilled water through the funnel. The process may be made continuous, if desired, by placing a container of water some distance above the funnel and arranging a controlled flow siphon to feed into the funnel. Dialysis should be allowed to proceed several hours or even days when a sol of high purity is desired.

The hydrous ferric oxide and the arsenious sulfide sols are dialyzed.

Test the first portion of distilled water from the dialyzing membrane with a solution of KCNS to show that ferric ion is passing through the membrane from the hydrous ferric oxide sol. The water from the arsenious sulfide sol may likewise be tested with a solution of lead acetate to show the presence of sulfide ion. Osmosis of water through the semipermeable membrane into the solution takes place, but may not be noticed, as evaporation from the hot solution may obscure this effect.

REFERENCES

Hauser, E. A., and Lynn, J. E., *Experiments in Colloid Chemistry,* McGraw-Hill Book Company, Inc., New York, **1940**

Johnson and La Mer, *J. Am. Chem. Soc.*, **69,** 1184 (1947)
Particle size of sulfur sols and the Tyndall effect.

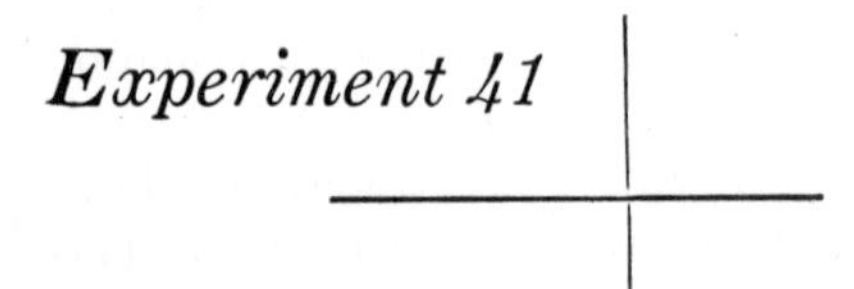

The Properties of Colloids

Most aqueous inorganic (hydrophobic) colloids are stabilized by adsorbed ions, which confer negative or positive charges to the individual particles. All the particles of a given sol have charges of the same sign, and the forces of repulsion prevent them from colliding and coagulating in spite of their Brownian motion. The addition of salts, especially ones having multivalent ions of opposite charge, leads to instability, eventually resulting in flocculation of the sol. Similarly, mixing two sols whose particles have charges of opposite sign leads to coagulation.

a) Place 10 ml. of dialyzed colloidal ferric oxide in each of three test tubes. Determine the amounts of 5 N NaCl and of 0.1 N Na_2SO_4 that will cause flocculation. Reserve the third test tube for comparison. Use a buret to deliver the NaCl solution and a graduated 1-ml. pipet for the Na_2SO_4, and shake after each addition. What is the ratio of the amounts required to cause flocculation on the basis of 0.1 N solutions?

b) Repeat the above experiment with dialyzed colloidal arsenious sulfide with the following salts: 5 N NaCl, 0.1 N $BaCl_2$, and 0.01 N

$AlCl_3$. What is the ratio of the amounts required to cause flocculation on the basis of 0.01 *N* solutions?

c) Place 10 ml. of colloidal arsenious sulfide sol in each of several test tubes. To the first tube, add 1 ml. of the iron oxide sol, to the second add 0.1 ml., to the third add 2 ml., and observe if flocculation takes place. Try varying the proportions if the above ratios are not effective, as flocculation depends upon the purity and concentration of the sols. After the proportion has been found approximately, try to establish the limits more closely. A buret will be suitable for measuring the amount of sol. It will be observed that smaller concentrations will cause flocculation when the sols are allowed to stand. Evidently a time factor should be included when estimating the amount required to cause flocculation.

The experiment may be performed with sols that have not been dialyzed. The results are not so satisfactory as mutual coagulation may not occur due to the various ions remaining from the initial reactants.

d) Certain hydrophylic colloids when present in a suspension of a hydrophobic sol may stabilize it against flocculation by electrolytes. When this action takes place, the hydrophylic colloid is said to be a protective colloid. This may be illustrated by adding about 1 g. of gum arabic to 10 ml. of water and warming until it "dissolves" (actually it is undergoing peptization by the solvent). Add 1 ml. of this solution to 10 ml. of the arsenious sulfide sol and determine the amount of $AlCl_3$ solution necessary to cause flocculation. Compare with the unprotected sol.

e) The presence and sign of the charge on the colloidal particle may easily be shown by cataphoresis. When a current flows through a solution of an electrolyte, migration of the ions takes place, and likewise charged colloidal particles will migrate to the oppositely charged electrodes. The speed of migration of colloid particles is approximately one-tenth that of ions; the particles are much larger but also have a much greater number of charges per particle. The following experiment will show the direction of migration of the colloid particle.

Fill the side arms *A* and *B* of a cell (Fig. 65) almost up to the cross arms with approximately 1 *N* KCl solution, and put in place the two graphite electrodes. Carefully pour the sol (either As_2S_3 or Fe_2O_3) into the tube *C* or *D* until it flows over the KCl solution. The electrodes are connected to a 110-volt direct current outlet or to a 45-volt *B* battery. The current is allowed to pass through the sol for about thirty minutes. The migration can easily be observed by comparing tubes *C* and *D*. The charge of the colloid can be ascertained if the polarity of the electrodes is known. The polarity may be obtained by touching both electrodes to a moistened strip of starch iodide paper and observing at which electrode iodine is set free.

While the experiment works well with a dialyzed sol, the same procedure may be used with an undialyzed one. However the presence of

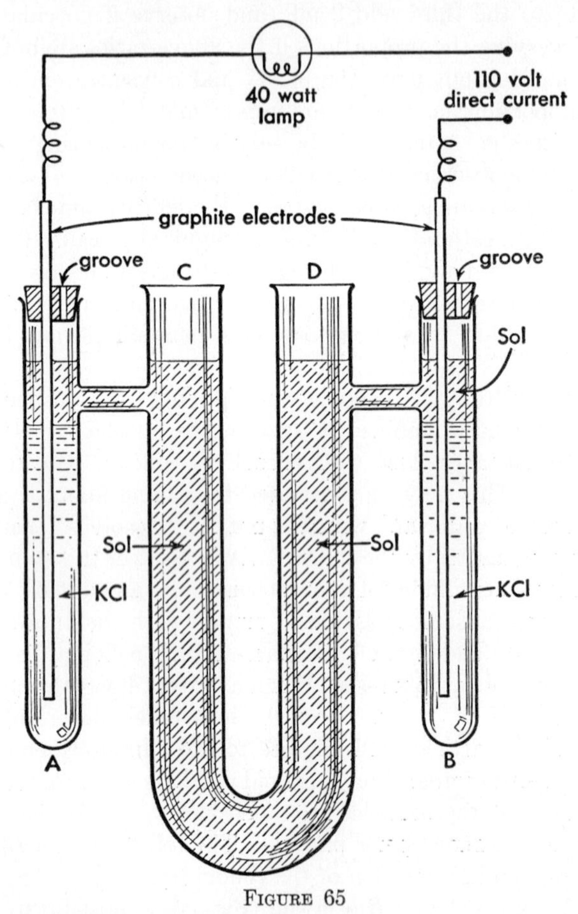

FIGURE 65

many ions allows more gas evolution to take place and this may produce complicating effects. A simple U tube may be employed with less satisfactory results (the KCl solution being omitted).

Experiment 42

Surface Active Substances

When a drop of one liquid is placed upon a second with which it is immiscible, two things may happen. The first liquid may either draw together and form a lenslike drop, or it may spread completely in a thin film over the surface of the second liquid. Substances which behave in the latter manner are known as surface active substances. In the following experiment the thickness of these films and also the area occupied by a single molecule will be measured.

Procedure Clean a long shallow photographic tray (8×40 in.) thoroughly with soap and repeat with a cleansing powder, with the aid of a brush. Do not allow the fingers to come into contact with the inside or edge of the tray. Rinse thoroughly first with tap water and then with distilled water, and finally fill the tray brimful with distilled water. Dust talcum powder over the surface of the water (use a cloth bag and strike it with a pencil). With the aid of a strip of paper equal in length to the width of the tray, push the powder down to one end and remove it with the paper. This process cleans the surface of the water, as the talcum powder tends to adsorb any oily or film-forming substances. Repeat this cleansing procedure once more.

Prepare a solution containing about 0.512 g. of palmitic acid per liter of benzene by accurately weighing the acid. Add 0.25 ml. of the above solution to the water near one end of the tray. The benzene evaporates rapidly and leaves a monomolecular film of palmitic acid on the surface. Dust the film lightly with talcum powder in order to make it visible. Gently blow the film to one end of the tray and mark the position of its limit. Next measure the area occupied by the film.

Calculations In order to calculate the thickness of the film, it is first necessary to calculate the volume of palmitic acid dissolved in the benzene solution placed on the water. Assume the value of 0.857 g./ml. for the density of the solid acid. From the known volume of acid and the measured area, calculate the thickness of the film. The calculation will show its thickness to be about 10^{-7} cm., which is in the range of molecular dimensions, and accordingly the film is said to be monomolecular.

Calculate the number of molecules in the weight of palmitic acid taken, using 6.02×10^{23} for the Avogadro number (the formula of palmitic acid is $C_{15}H_{31}COOH$). From the number of molecules taken and their measured area, calculate the area covered by one molecule on the surface of water. Langmuir found the area to be 21×10^{-16} cm.^{2}

Further experimental suggestions A film balance may be used to obtain the pressure-area relations of these films.

REFERENCES

Blodgett, *J. Am. Chem. Soc.*, **56,** 495 (1934); **57,** 1007 (1935)
Blodgett and Langmuir, *Phys. Rev.*, **51,** 964 (1937)
Harkins, *J. Am. Chem. Soc.*, **39,** 354, 541 (1917)
Holmes, H. N., *Laboratory Manual of Colloid Chemistry*, 3d ed., John Wiley & Sons, Inc., New York, **1934**
Langmuir, *J. Am. Chem. Soc.*, **39,** 1848 (1917)

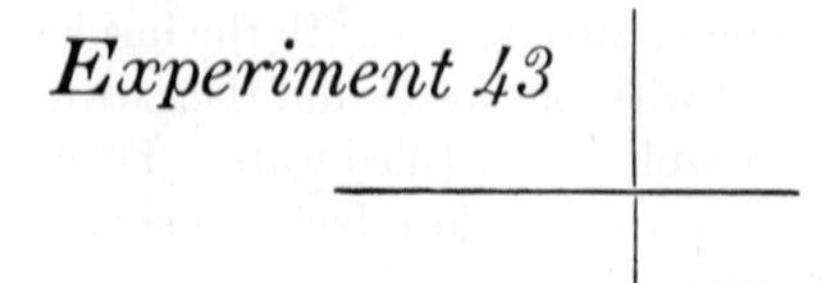

Interfacial Tension

The surface tension of a liquid is determined by the nature of the second phase in contact with it. While the surface tensions of most liquids are slightly different when in contact with air or vapor of the sample, they are considerably different if the second phase is another liquid.

While static methods, such as are used in this experiment, are useful to study interfacial tension, dynamic methods are also employed to obtain fuller information about the nature of the interface. This is necessary, for it has been found that the interfacial tension between certain substances changes with time.

The equation for the interfacial tension of two liquids such as water and benzene, which are present in a capillary tube as shown in Fig. 66, may be derived as follows. At equilibrium, the downward force due to the hydrostatic pressure of the two liquids is $\pi r^2 h_w d_w g$ plus $\pi r^2 h_b d_b g$, where g is the acceleration of gravity (980 cm./sec.^{2}). The corresponding upward force is composed of the surface tension of benzene $2\pi r\gamma_b$ and the interfacial tension $2\pi r\gamma_{1,2}$, both acting over the inner circumference of the capillary; hence

$$\underbrace{2\pi r\gamma_b + 2\pi r\gamma_{1,2}}_{\text{upward force}} = \underbrace{\pi r^2 h_w d_w g + \pi r^2 h_b d_b g}_{\text{downward force}}$$

Canceling and solving, there is obtained:

$$\frac{2\gamma_{1,2}}{r} = (h_w d_w + h_b d_b)g - \frac{2\gamma_b}{r} \tag{238}$$

Apparatus The capillary tube for this experiment is best obtained from a broken thermometer (110° range). With the aid of a sharp file, scratch the lower end of the tubing where the bulb has been joined to the stem. Upon breaking at the mark, a capillary such as shown in Fig. 66 should be obtained. The capillary is mounted in a rubber stopper and is thoroughly cleaned by drawing fresh warm chromate cleaning solution through it. It is advisable to fill the capillary with the chromate mixture some time before it is to be used in order to insure absolute cleanliness.

The interfacial tension of benzene-water or toluene-water is particularly suited for student work.

Procedure It is advantageous if the capillary that was used in Expt. 9 is available, as its effective radius will be known. Otherwise, the height of rise of benzene must be obtained and the effective radius calculated. This may be done

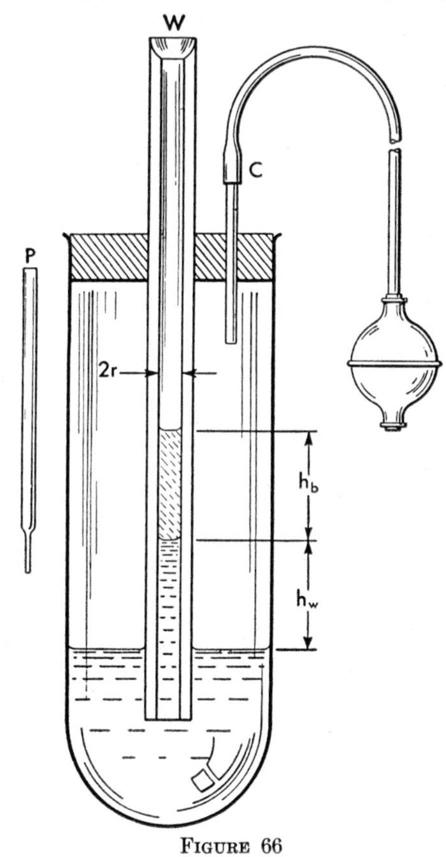

FIGURE 66

after the experiment below is finished; rinse the capillary first with methanol, then with pure benzene, and proceed as in Expt. 9.

Place distilled water in the large test tube and mount the capillary vertically. Connect a hand bellows (atomizer bulb) to the outlet C and force water up the capillary so that it fills the well W. A small quantity of benzene is transferred to the well with the aid of a micro pipet. Upon disconnecting the hand bellows, the liquids will recede in the capillary. The column of benzene should be 2–4 cm. long in order to obtain reasonable accuracy of measurement. Repeat the procedure if insufficient benzene has been taken.

With the aid of a hand lens, determine the degree mark where the capillary enters the water and also the positions of the interface and upper surface of the benzene. To convert degree readings into length (centimeters), place the thermometer stem between two meter sticks. Select two rather widely separated marks along the stem and obtain the corresponding reading in centimeters. Repeat at least three times and obtain the average ($1° = x$ cm.).

Calculations The interfacial tension $\gamma_{1,2}$ may be calculated from equation 238. The quantity $2\gamma_b/r$ may be calculated from the known surface tension of benzene and the effective radius r of the capillary, or from the measured rise of the pure substance ($2\gamma_b/r = hdg$). This quantity must always be measured by the capillary rise method if the surface tension of liquid b when saturated with water is not the same as for the pure substance. In the present experiment, the surface tensions of dry and wet benzene or toluene are very nearly the same, and no large error is made in using the surface tension of the dry liquid.

The accuracy of the experimental results decreases as the interfacial tension decreases: as the quantities $(h_w d_w + h_b d_b)g$ and $2\gamma_b/r$ approach each other, the small errors in determining them are greatly magnified in the final result. In the present experiment, the results obtained should be within ± 3 per cent of the accepted values. Obtain the maximum error of the derived result employing the procedures illustrated in Expt. 9.

Further experimental suggestions The procedure may be modified somewhat by using the apparatus of Expt. 9, so that the pressure necessary to force the interface back to the level of the water in the test tube is measured. The equation for calculating the interfacial tension is then

$$\frac{2\gamma_{1,2}}{r} = h_b d_b g - \frac{2\gamma_b}{r} + P_m \qquad (239)$$

where P_m is the manometric pressure in dynes/cm.^{2}

The interfacial tension of the system aniline-water may be studied; it is somewhat more difficult. The aniline should be redistilled before use and saturated solutions of water in aniline and aniline in water must be prepared by shaking the two liquids together in a separatory funnel (no grease on stopcock) and separating the layers.

The interfacial tension of liquids more dense than water, such as CCl_4, $CHCl_3$, and CS_2, may be measured. The position of water and organic liquid is accordingly reversed in the capillary. The subscripts b and w in equation 238 are interchanged (b represents the organic liquid) in order to calculate the results.

If a Cenco–du Noüy tensiometer is available, the change in the surface tension of a dilute (0.003 N) solution of sodium oleate with time may be measured. Since the instrument is accompanied with complete directions for operation and calibration, the procedure will not be given here.

REFERENCES

Harkins and Jordan, *J. Am. Chem. Soc.*, **52,** 1571 (1930)

Surface tension by the pull on a ring.

Holmes, H. N., *Laboratory Manual of Colloid Chemistry*, 3d ed., John Wiley & Sons, Inc., New York, **1934**

Mack and Bartell, *J. Am. Chem. Soc.*, **54,** 936 (1932)

Measurement of interfacial tension.

Steinbach, *J. Chem. Ed.*, **21,** 582 (1945)

Zuidema and Pilz, *Anal. Chem.*, **20,** 1244 (1948)

Interfacial tension by the ring method.

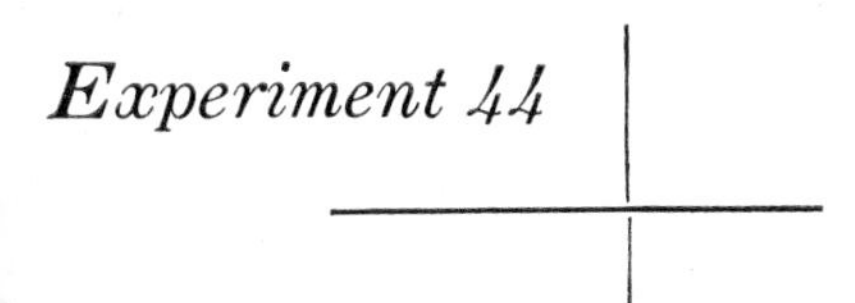

Adsorption of Acetic Acid

Adsorption is specific in nature, as its magnitude depends upon the specific nature of both the adsorbate and the adsorbent. When a porous solid, such as activated carbon, is shaken with a dilute solution of acetic acid, an equilibrium is established between the amount adsorbed and the concentration of acid remaining in the solution, at a given temperature. It is also found that the total amount of material adsorbed varies directly with the mass of activated charcoal used.

The relationship between the amount adsorbed and concentration is not a linear one, and depends upon some function of C raised to a fractional power. The above information may be collected into the following equation (the Freundlich isotherm)

$$\frac{x}{m} = kC^n \tag{240}$$

where x is the amount of material adsorbed by a given mass m of adsorbent, k is a specific constant and is dependent upon the nature of both adsorbate and adsorbent, C is the equilibrium concentration of adsorbate in the solution, and n is a constant, the value of which is specifically related to the adsorbate.

Apparatus Twelve 250-ml. Erlenmeyer flasks; six funnels; filter paper (9 cm.); phenolphthalein indicator; buret (50 ml.); 0.50 M acetic acid; 0.10 M NaOH; 250- and 500-ml. volumetric flasks; 10-, 25-, 50- and 200-ml. pipets; stirring rods; granulated activated charcoal. Preliminary activation of the charcoal by heating in a covered crucible may give a product having greater adsorptive powers.

Procedure Accurately weigh to the nearest milligram about 4 g. of the charcoal into each of six numbered flasks, employing the weighing bottle technique. Prepare acetic acid solutions of 0.50 M, 0.25 M, 0.125 M, 0.0625 M, 0.03125 M, and 0.01562 M by quantitatively diluting 250 ml. of each more concentrated sample to 500 ml. in a volumetric flask. Pipet 200 ml. of each into a flask containing charcoal; stopper and let stand for at least one hour, swirling the contents at frequent intervals. The flasks may be stored in a constant temperature bath if desired, though it is not absolutely necessary if the room temperature is reasonably constant.

In the meantime, an approximately 0.1 M sodium hydroxide solution is standardized, using 0.6–0.8 g. samples of potassium acid phthalate.[1] The 0.5 M acetic acid solution is standardized against 0.1 M NaOH solution by titrating three 10-ml. samples of the acid, using phenolphthalein as the indicator.

In order to determine the equilibrium concentration of acetic acid, decant the solutions from the activated charcoal into clean dry flasks, or filter if necessary. Pipet duplicate 10-ml. samples from each of the two most concentrated solutions and titrate with standard 0.1 M NaOH

[1] Sulfamic acid may also be used for standardization, with methyl red as the indicator.

solution. Remove duplicate 25-ml. portions from the third most concentrated solution, and duplicate 50-ml. portions from each of the last three and titrate as before. The data are entered in Table 36.

TABLE 36

WEIGHT OF ACTIVATED CARBON m	INITIAL C_o OF HAc MOLES/LITER	EQUILIBRIUM C_e OF HAc MOLES/LITER	GRAMS ADSORBED x	$\frac{x}{m}$	$\log \frac{x}{m}$	$\log C_e$

Calculations Calculate the initial concentration (C_o) of acetic acid in moles/liter for each sample. The equilibrium concentration (C_e) of acetic acid in moles/liter is calculated by the relation:

$$\text{ml. of HAc} \times \text{molarity} = \text{ml. of NaOH} \times \text{molarity}$$

The amount of acid adsorbed is $C_o - C_e$, in moles/liter. This may be converted to grams (x) of acid adsorbed by the relation:

$$(C_o - C_e) \times \text{mol. weight of acid} \times V \text{ in liters of sample} = x$$

Calculate the amount of acid adsorbed per gram of adsorbent (x/m).

Plot x/m as ordinate against C_e as abscissa, and use a French curve or spring brass wire to draw the curve.

In order to evaluate the constants k and n in equation 240 it is best to change to the logarithmic form

$$\log \frac{x}{m} = \log k + n \log C_e \tag{241}$$

and plot $\log x/m$ as ordinate against $\log C_e$ as abscissa. Draw the best straight line to represent the points.

The constant n is evaluated by obtaining the slope of the line, using two widely separated points. It will be observed that when $C_e = 1$, $n \log C_e = 0$ and hence

$$\log \frac{x}{m} = \log k \tag{242}$$

The point where $\log C_e$ is equal to zero is found and the antilogarithm of the corresponding value of x/m is equal to k. An alternative, but not very accurate, method of obtaining the value of k is to determine the x/m value when $C_e = 1$ from the plot of x/m and C_e. Since the measurements may not include an equilibrium concentration as great as 1 M, it may be necessary to extrapolate the curves for both above procedures to this concentration. Obtain k by both methods.

Another method of evaluating k is as follows: When x/m is equal to unity, $\log x/m$ is zero, and equation 241 simplifies to

$$n \log C_e = -\log k \tag{243}$$

Evaluate k by this method and compare all values. Why should one of the methods be more satisfactory than the others?

The maximum error of the slope n and the intercept $\log k$ can be obtained from the graph. The deviations Δx and Δy for each observed point from the straight line are obtained. The quantities $\Sigma \Delta x/n$ and $\Sigma \Delta y/n$ (n in this case is equal to the number of points) may be considered as representing the average error of any one of the n observations. The deviations (Δ) are added together irrespective of sign; upon dividing by the number n of observations, the average error is obtained.

Assume that the following data were obtained, the errors being computed as above:

Log C_e	Log x/m
0.500 ± 0.01	0.590 ± 0.01
-1.500 ± 0.01	-0.225 ± 0.01

The maximum error of the slope ($\pm\Delta n$) may be obtained by calculating normal and maximum (or minimum) values, thus

$$\pm\Delta n = \frac{0.600 - (-0.235)}{0.490 - (-1.49)} - \frac{0.590 - (-0.225)}{0.500 - (-1.500)}$$

$$\pm\Delta n = 0.42 - 0.41 = 0.01$$

or

$$n = 0.41 \pm 0.01$$

Calculate the maximum error of the slope n and the intercept k, selecting points from the graph, and obtain their average error.

Further experimental suggestions Benzoic acid or any of the various substituted benzoic acids may be employed. Activated alumina may be used as adsorbent. A chromatographic column may be set up as described by Nestler and Cassidy.

REFERENCES

Alexander, J., *Colloid Chemistry, Theoretical and Applied*, vols. i and ii, Chemical Catalog Company, New York, **1926** and **1928**

Freundlich, H., *Colloid and Capillary Chemistry*, tr. by H. S. Hatfield, E. P. Dutton & Co., New York, **1926**

Harkins and Gans, *J. Am. Chem. Soc.*, **53,** 2804 (1931)

An adsorption method for determining the surface area of a powder

Nestler and Cassidy, *ibid.*, **72,** 680 (1950)

Use of chromatography to obtain adsorption isotherms

Experiment 45

The Rate of Inversion of Sucrose

Chemical reactions are classified as unimolecular if only one molecule is involved, bimolecular if two molecules are involved in the chemical change, etc. In a pseudo-unimolecular reaction, one of the reactants is present in either a large excess or a constant amount; even though the reaction may be kinetically bimolecular or trimolecular, the other reactant (not present in excess) disappears from the reaction mixture as in a unimolecular process. A better method of classification is to state the order of the reaction, which is the sum of the exponents of the concentrations in the differential kinetic equation.

The reaction of sucrose with water in the presence of hydrogen ions (which act catalytically) to form an equimolar mixture of glucose and fructose may be represented as

$$\underset{\text{sucrose}}{C_{12}H_{22}O_{11}} + H_2O \xrightarrow{H_3O^+} \underset{\text{glucose}}{C_6H_{12}O_6} + \underset{\text{fructose}}{C_6H_{12}O_6}$$

The rate is given by the following equation:

$$-\frac{dC}{dt} = k'C_{\text{sucrose}} \times C_{H_2O} \times C_{H_3O^+} \tag{244}$$

When the experimental conditions are such that the concentrations of water and hydrogen ions are essentially constant during the reaction, the differential equation for the observed rate of disappearance of sucrose may be written as

$$-\frac{dC}{dt} = kC_{\text{sucrose}} \tag{245}$$

This reaction may be classified as pseudo-unimolecular or first order while kinetically it is either trimolecular or stepwise.

The concentration of sucrose may be readily measured by the polarimetric method. Since sucrose is dextrorotatory and an equimolecular mixture of glucose and fructose is slightly levorotatory, the amount of sucrose present at any given time may be determined by measuring the angle of rotation.

Apparatus Polarimeter; light source (sodium vapor lamp is preferable but 100-watt lamp will serve); water-jacketed polarimeter tubes; pure cane sugar; 100-ml. pipet; approximately 2 *M* HCl; 100-ml. volumetric flask; 500-ml. glass-stoppered bottle.

Procedure A solution of pure cane sugar is prepared by dissolving approximately 20 g. in distilled water and diluting to 100 ml. in a volumetric flask. Place the flask in a thermostat maintained at 25 ± 0.05°C. Pipet exactly 100 ml. of approximately 2 *M* HCl into a glass-stoppered bottle and place in the thermostat.

While waiting for the solutions to come to temperature, locate the zero setting of the polarimeter with distilled water in one of the tubes. Obtain and record at least four readings of the zero point, approaching it from opposite sides each time. Review Expt. 11 for more complete details.

When ready pour the sugar solution into the acid and mix rapidly and thoroughly. Rinse the polarimeter tube twice with small portions of the reaction mixture and then fill it completely, being careful not to trap air bubbles. Place the tube in the polarimeter and obtain the angle of rotation; record the time when the reading is taken. This will be used as the initial point in calculating the rate.

TABLE 37

Time (min.)	α	$\alpha - \alpha_\infty$	$\log(\alpha - \alpha_\infty)$	k Calc. Eq. 248

Av. k

If the polarimeter tube is not provided with a constant temperature jacket, the room temperature should be constant to ±1°C.; or fresh portions may be taken each time from a sample bottle which is kept in the thermostat. If the latter procedure is followed, it will be necessary to make up a much larger volume of solution than that specified above. Obtain the angle of rotation every ten minutes during the first hour and every twenty to thirty minutes for the next two to three hours. At the end of this time, empty the polarimeter tube and rinse with distilled water.

The sample which has been left in the thermostat may be removed, if necessary. It should be allowed to stand at least two days before determining the final angle of rotation α_∞ of completely inverted sucrose. Be sure to rinse the polarimeter tube with the sample before obtaining the angle of rotation and obtain four readings, the final temperature being the same as the initial ($\pm 0.5°$ or better).

The tube is rinsed thoroughly and filled with distilled water and the zero point of the polarimeter is determined once again. While the actual setting of the zero point does not enter into the calculations, the reading is obtained in order to determine if any change has occurred.

Calculations Prepare a plot of time in minutes (abscissa) and the angle of rotation (α) as ordinate, using $t = 0$ at the time of the first reading.

Prepare a plot of log ($\alpha - \alpha_\infty$) as ordinate and t (min.) as abscissa and draw the best straight line through the points. Employing two widely separated points on the graph, determine the slope of the curve. The velocity constant k is obtained by multiplying the slope by 2.303.

Calculate the half-life period from the equation

$$t_{\frac{1}{2}} = 0.693/k \tag{246}$$

Referring to the plot of log ($\alpha - \alpha_\infty$) and t, obtain the value of α from the calculated value of $t_{\frac{1}{2}}$. What is its relation to ($\alpha_o - \alpha_\infty$)?

The integration of equation 245 gives

$$k = \frac{2.303}{t - t_o} \log \frac{C_o}{C} \tag{247}$$

The initial concentration C_o of the sucrose may be expressed in terms of the difference between the initial and final readings of the polarimeter, namely α_o and α_∞. The concentration of sucrose C at the time t is proportional to the difference between the angle of rotation α at the time t and α_∞ at the time $t = \infty$. Equation 247 may then be written as

$$k = \frac{2.303}{t - t_o} \log \frac{(\alpha_o - \alpha_\infty)}{(\alpha - \alpha_\infty)} \tag{248}$$

Substitute at least five different experimental values in this equation and calculate the values of the velocity constant and their average. The value of α_o may be taken as the original polarimeter reading ($t = 0$) or the value of log ($\alpha_o - \alpha_\infty$), obtained from the logarithmic plot, may be used in the computation of k. Compare the result obtained with this equation and that of the graphical method.

Further experimental suggestions Other concentrations of HCl may be employed and the values of k obtained should be approximately proportional to C_{HCl}.

Other strong acids as H_2SO_4 and CCl_3COOH may be used as catalysts.

If readings are taken at suitable time intervals, k may be evaluated by the Guggenheim method.[1] In this case it is unnecessary to obtain α_∞.

[1] Guggenheim, *Phil. Mag.* [7], **2**, 538 (1926)

REFERENCES

Guggenheim, *Phil. Mag.*, [7] **2,** 538 (1926)
Pennycuick, *J. Am. Chem. Soc.*, **48,** 6 (1926)
Roseveare, *ibid.*, **53,** 1651 (1931)

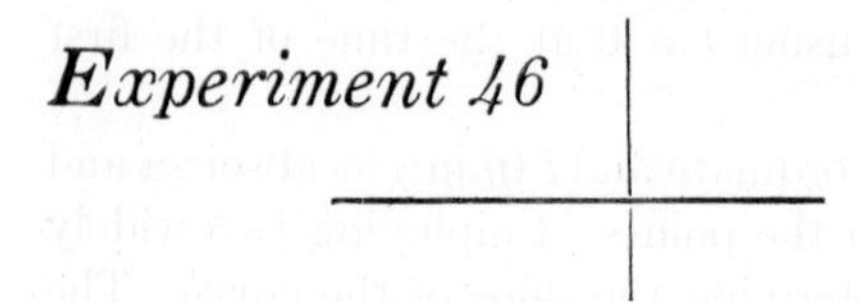

Experiment 46

The Velocity of an Ionic Reaction

In this experiment the velocity of oxidation of iodide by persulfate ion is to be studied. The ionic equation for the reaction is

$$S_2O_8^{=} + 2I^- \longrightarrow I_2 + 2SO_4^{=} \tag{249}$$

The rate equation has been found to be of the second order, indicating that the reaction takes place in consecutive steps. The velocity is proportional to the first power of the persulfate and iodide ion concentrations respectively, and the rate equation may be written as

$$-\frac{d[S_2O_8^{=}]}{dt} = k[S_2O_8^{=}][I^-] \tag{250}$$

Classical theory neglects any variation of the rate "constant" k with change in the solvent, in the concentration of the reactants, or addition of inert salts to change the total ion concentration. It is well known that such variations do exist and result in increased or decreased rates as the ionic strength of the solution is increased; in some cases the variation is large, in others, small. The effect is large and positive in the persulfate-iodide reaction.

The Brönsted-Bjerrum theory explains these salt effects quantitatively for dilute solutions. It is assumed that the ions A and B react rapidly to reach equilibrium with an intermediate critical complex (AB). The concentration of the critical complex is small as it may decompose reversibly into the initial reactants, or slowly and irreversibly into the products, or it may slowly react with another ion or molecule to form the final products:

$$A + B \rightleftharpoons (AB) \longrightarrow \text{products}$$

The valence, or electric charge, of (AB) is assumed to equal the sum of the charges of A and B:

$$Z_{(AB)} = Z_A + Z_B$$

The observed rate is assumed to be proportional to the concentration [AB]:

$$-\frac{d[A]}{dt} = k'[AB] \qquad (251)$$

If (AB) is in equilibrium with A and B

$$K_{eq.} = \frac{[AB]}{[A][B]} \cdot \frac{f_{AB}}{f_A f_B} \qquad (252)$$

where the f's are the activity coefficients whose change with ionic strength gives rise to the salt effect.

If equation 252 is solved for [AB] and this is substituted in equation 251, setting $k'K_{eq.} = k_a$, there is obtained

$$-\frac{d[A]}{dt} = k_a[A][B]\frac{f_A f_B}{f_{AB}} \qquad (253)$$

The quantity $f_A f_B/f_{AB}$ is called the kinetic activity factor F. Comparing equations 250 and 253, it is seen that

$$k = k_a\frac{f_A f_B}{f_{AB}}, \qquad (254)$$

where k is the observed rate constant for any experiment at a given ionic strength, while k_a is a true constant for various experiments at different ionic strengths, and equal to k only if the factor $F = 1$. This would be true at infinite dilution and the value of k_a can sometimes be determined by extrapolating a plot of k or log k to zero ionic strength.

For dilute solutions the theoretical value of F can be obtained from the simplified Debye-Hückel equation:

$$\log f = -0.51Z^2\sqrt{\mu} \qquad \text{for water solution, 25°C.} \qquad (255)$$

Combining with equation 254, the following may be obtained:

$$\log k = \log k_a + 1.02Z_A Z_B\sqrt{\mu} \qquad (256)$$

In the persulfate-iodide reaction, $Z_A Z_B = (-2) \cdot (-1) = 2$. The rate constant k should increase with ionic strength since k_a remains constant.

The persulfate-iodide reaction has often been studied by determining the amount of iodine formed from time to time after mixing the original solutions. However, since some of the iodine combines with remaining iodide ion to form tri-iodide ion, viz., $I_2 + I^- \rightleftharpoons I_3^-$, the rate "constant" k changes with time and a correction must be made. In this experiment, small known amounts of sodium thiosulfate are added to the initial solutions; as iodine is formed (eq. 249) it reacts very rapidly:

$$I_2 + 2S_2O_3^{=} \longrightarrow 2I^- + S_4O_6^{=} \tag{257}$$

No iodine is visible in the solution until all thiosulfate has been oxidized, and during this time the iodide concentration does not change since it is being regenerated. The reaction is of the type known as a clock reaction, since with starch present, the sudden appearance of a blue color can be timed quite precisely. In more concentrated solutions there is direct oxidation of thiosulfate by persulfate

$$2S_2O_3^{=} + S_2O_8^{=} \longrightarrow S_4O_6^{=} + 2SO_4^{=} \tag{258}$$

but this reaction is almost inappreciable with the concentrations used here.

Apparatus One 100-ml. buret; pipets; volumetric flasks; 150- or 250-ml. beakers; potassium persulfate; sodium thiosulfate; potassium nitrate; 0.2 per cent starch solution; watch with second hand.

To obtain results comparable with those in the literature, water which has been redistilled from alkaline permanganate should be used, all salts recrystallized, standard solutions made very carefully, and all experiments performed at constant temperature. However, results which are consistent among themselves may be obtained with ordinary chemicals and distilled water and with the experiments carried out at room temperature provided the latter is reasonably constant.

It is advisable to recrystallize the potassium persulfate if a test shows that it contains much sulfate. Prepare a saturated solution at 50–55°C., filter, and cool to about 5°C. in an ice bath. Filter with suction and dry by sucking air through the moist crystals. Store in a desiccator until completely dry.

The potassium iodide crystals should have no brown color. The sodium thiosulfate crystals should be of the clear pentahydrate. This salt effloresces and it is best to take crystals from a freshly opened bottle.

Procedure Prepare the following solutions by accurately weighing the salts and making up in volumetric flasks:

$K_2S_2O_8$	0.01 *M*	250 ml.	KI	0.10 *M*	250 ml.
$Na_2S_2O_3$	0.001 *M*	1000 ml.	KNO_3	0.4 *M*	250 ml.

A 0.2 per cent starch solution is made in the usual manner and need not be exact.

The reaction mixtures indicated in Table 38 are prepared by pipetting the potassium iodide, potassium nitrate, starch, and sodium thiosulfate solutions into one clean dry beaker and the potassium persulfate solution into another. The water may be added to either, from a pipet or a 100-ml. buret. It is convenient to prepare the first four or six solutions, then mix at one-minute intervals.

At definite recorded times mix the pairs of solutions by pouring one into the other and then back and forth a few times. The beaker should be placed on a clear white background with good illumination. At 25° the blue color due to iodine will appear in approximately five minutes in the most rapid cases, and the time can be ascertained within five seconds or less. The time of appearance of iodine is recorded in each case.

TABLE 38

Expt.	ml. 0.1 *M* KI	ml. 0.001 *M* $Na_2S_2O_3$	ml. 0.4 *M* KNO_3	ml. 0.2 % Starch	ml. 0.01 *M* $K_2S_2O_8$	ml. H_2O	Time	
							Start	End
1	10	10	25	5	10	40		
2	10	10	25	5	20	30		
3	10	10	25	5	30	20		
4	10	20	25	5	30	10		
5	10	30	25	5	30	0		
6	20	10	25	5	10	30		
7	30	10	25	5	10	20		
8	10	10	20	5	20	35		
9	10	10	15	5	20	40		
10	10	10	10	5	20	45		
11	10	10	5	5	20	50		
12	10	10	0	5	20	55		

Calculations The rate constant k is calculated in each case using equation 250 in the following form:

$$\frac{\Delta x}{\Delta t} = k[S_2O_8^{=}][I^{-}] \tag{259}$$

In equation 259, Δx indicates moles per liter of $S_2O_8^{=}$ used up at the appearance of iodine, and inspection of equations 249 and 257 shows that this is equal to one-half the moles per liter of thiosulfate present initially. Δt is the elapsed time and may be expressed in minutes. The iodide concentration is constant and the fact that Δx is in no case greater than 5 per cent of $[S_2O_8^{=}]$ permits using the original persulfate concentration in the increment equation 259 with little error. In cases where the persulfate and iodide concentrations vary widely, it is of course necessary to use the integrated form of equation 250 in the calculation of k.

Record the values of Δt, k, and log k in Table 39. Calculate the ionic strength μ of each solution and record the square root in Table 39.

TABLE 39

EXPT.	$[S_2O_8]$	[I]	$[S_2O_3]$	$[KNO_3]$	$\sqrt{\mu}$	Δt	k	$\log k$
1	0.001	0.01	0.0001	0.1				
2	.002	.01	.0001	.1				
3	.003	.01	.0001	.1				
4	.003	.01	.0002	.1				
5	.003	.01	.0003	.1				
6	.001	.02	.0001	.1				
7	.001	.03	.0001	.1				
8	.002	.01	.0001	.08				
9	.002	.01	.0001	.06				
10	.002	.01	.0001	.04				
11	.002	.01	.0001	.02				
12	.002	.01	.0001	.00				

The ionic strength of each mixture is the sum of the values for all positive and negative ions

$$\mu = \Sigma \tfrac{1}{2}(c_+ z_+^2 + c_- z_-^2) \qquad (260)$$

where c_+ and c_- are the molarity of positive and negative ions and the z's are the charges.

Note the comparative constancy of the values of k in expts. 1–7 of Table 39, and if there is a definite trend (as in expts. 3–5) try to explain it. Plot log k (ordinate) against $\sqrt{\mu}$ (abscissa) and draw a smooth curve through the points. The deviation from the straight line of equation 256 indicates that the simplified Debye-Hückel equation for activity coefficients is not accurate at these ionic strengths. Draw a tangent with a slope of $1.02\, Z_A Z_B (=2.04)$ to the curve at the lower ionic strengths. The intercept is the constant k_a.

Further experimental suggestions The concentrations given in Table 38 may be varied if desired. For example in expts. 8–12, 0.001 M persulfate and 0.02 M iodide may be substituted for those given in the table and should give almost the same values of Δt. Temperature coefficients can be measured if suitable temperature control is available. The timing may be done with a photoelectric colorimeter, with or without starch, if a sufficiently sensitive instrument is available.

REFERENCES

King and Jacobs, *J. Am. Chem. Soc.*, **53,** 1704 (1931)
King and Knudsen, *ibid.*, **60,** 687 (1938)
King and Steinbach, *ibid.*, **52,** 4779 (1930)
Price, *Z. physik. Chem.*, **27,** 474 (1898)
Sturtevant, *J. Am. Chem. Soc.*, **59,** 699 (1937)

Experiment 47

Raoult's and Henry's Laws

An ideal solution is defined as one which obeys Raoult's law, *i.e.*, the partial vapor pressure of each component is equal to the vapor pressure of that component in the pure state times its mole fraction in the mixture. This definition assumes that the partial vapor pressure is a correct measure of the "escaping tendency" of a component; if the vapor does not follow the ideal gas law this is not exact. In this case the fugacity of the vapor is used rather than its pressure. The fugacity may be calculated when the pressure, real density, and ideal density are known. In terms of fugacity, Raoult's law is

$$f = f^\circ \cdot x \tag{261}$$

where f refers to the fugacity of a given component in the solution, f° to the fugacity of the pure component, and x is its mole fraction.

Generally the components of a mixture do not follow Raoult's law exactly. Positive and negative deviations from this law were illustrated in Expt. 20. Similar deviations, in terms of fugacity, are shown in Figs. 67 and 68. The fugacity curves (solid lines) approach the straight lines of Raoult's law as x_A and x_B approach unity (pure A or pure B). The per cent deviation is greatest toward the other side of the graph (dilute solutions of A in B or B in A).

For these dilute solutions, Henry's law applies over a limited range of composition, *i.e.*, the vapor pressure is proportional to the mole fraction, but the constant of proportionality is f^*. This is shown by the lines C of Figs. 67 and 68, where

$$f_B = f_B^* x_B \tag{262}$$

Rather than employing pressure or fugacity, which are absolute quantities, it is sometimes advantageous to use the concept of activity, which is a relative quantity. Activity may be defined as the ratio of fugacity in the measured state to that in a chosen standard state. The standard state generally selected for the liquid solvent is the pure component ($x_A = 1$), which leads to the relations:

$$a_A = f_A/f_A^{\circ} \quad \text{or} \quad a_A = p_A/p_A^{\circ} \tag{263}$$

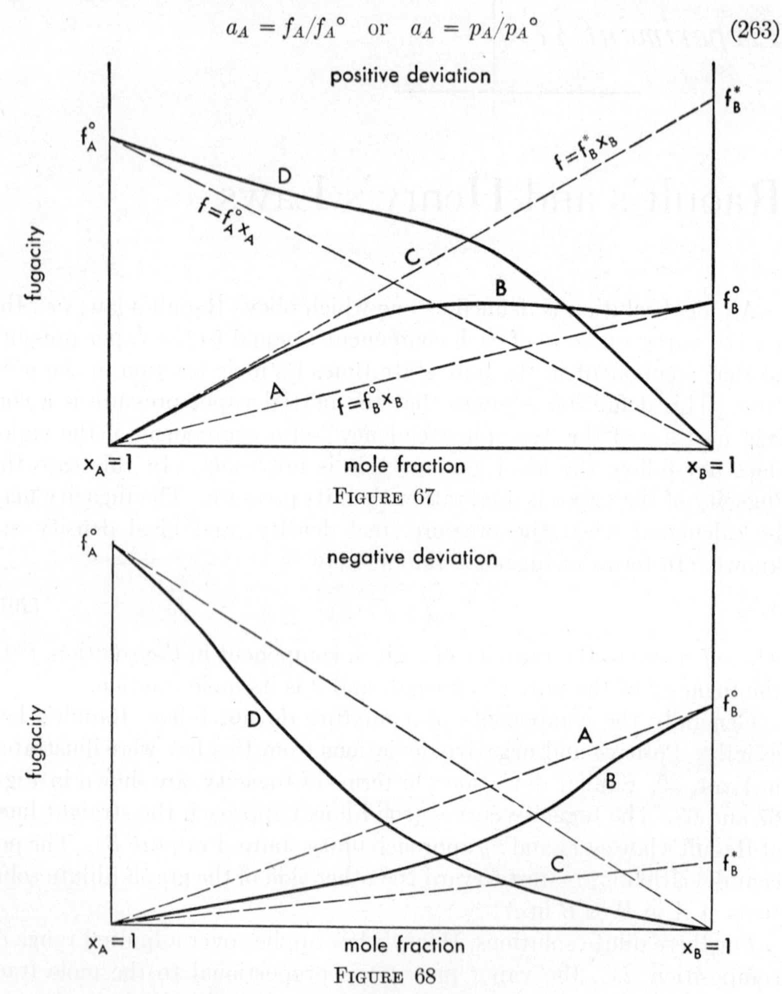

FIGURE 67

FIGURE 68

If Raoult's law is obeyed, the activity equals the mole fraction, or

$$a_A/x_A = 1 \tag{264}$$

Otherwise the ratio in equation 264 may be greater or less than unity, as shown in Figs. 69 and 70.

For two completely miscible liquids, the standard state for the second component B may be similarly chosen as pure $B(x_B = 1)$. However, if only dilute solutions of B in A are considered, the standard state selected is often the infinitely dilute solution of B in A ($x_B \longrightarrow 0$). The activity, a_B, of solute B is then defined as

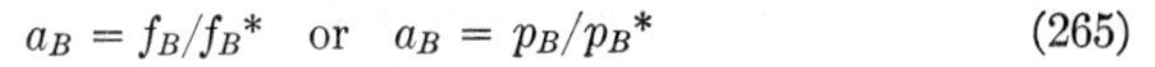

$$a_B = f_B/f_B^* \quad \text{or} \quad a_B = p_B/p_B^* \tag{265}$$

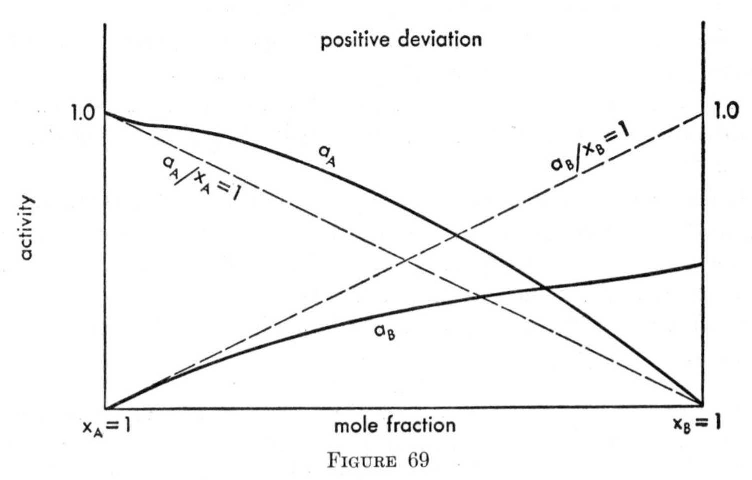

FIGURE 69

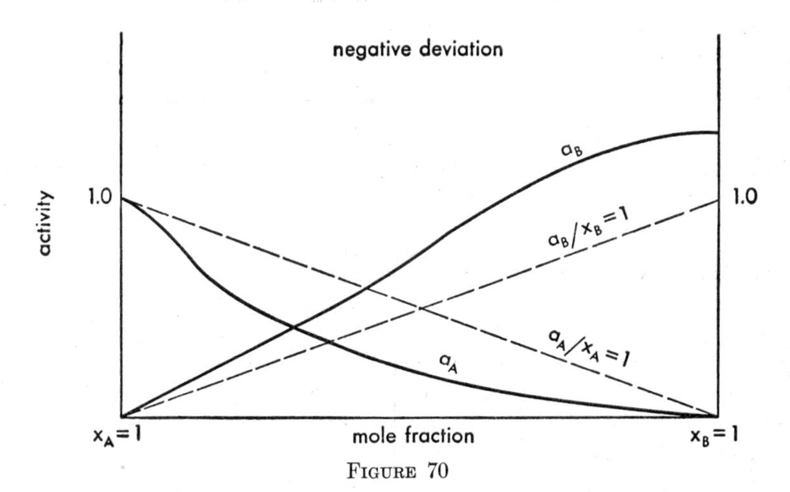

FIGURE 70

where f_B^* and p_B^* are the fugacity and vapor pressure pure B would possess if it had the same properties as in dilute solution.

The standard state selected for the solute B thus differs materially from pure B, and curves a_B and a_A in Figs. 69 and 70 illustrate this distinction. However, in dilute solutions where Henry's law is valid

$$a_B = x_B \quad \text{or} \quad a_B/x_B = 1 \tag{266}$$

When B exhibits positive deviations from Raoult's law in dilute solutions, it shows negative deviations from Henry's law in more concentrated solutions, and vice versa; thus $a_B < x_B$ or $a_B > x_B$. This results simply because of the choice of the standard state for the solute.

Apparatus The pressure measuring apparatus from Expt. 13 is connected to the vapor sampling apparatus of Expt. 20 (with side arm attached to the inner tube) as shown in Fig. 71. A steel needle valve is more convenient than a simple capillary leak. It is attached at the end of the tube near stopcock B.

Refractometer; thermometer T_1 in 0.1 or 0.2 degree; thermometer T_2 in whole degrees; asbestos squares; capillary medicine droppers. The temperature of the refractometer prisms should be controlled and should correspond to the values given in Table 41.

Procedure The binary systems shown in Table 40 will be found suitable for study.

TABLE 40

Component A Component B	Ethanol (Absolute) Benzene	Acetone Benzene	Acetone Chloroform
Recommended temperature for study	60–65°	50–55°	50–55°

The refractive index of these systems is given in Table 41; from these data construct a curve on large graph paper (17 × 22 in.) so that the composition may be ascertained by reference to this curve. Divide the

TABLE 41

Mole Fraction	Ethanol (A) Benzene (B)	Mole Fraction	Acetone (A) Benzene (B)	Mole Fraction	Acetone (A) Chloroform (B)
Benzene (B)	n_D^{18}	Acetone (A)	n_D^{16}	Chloroform (B)	n_D^{25}
1.0000	1.5024	0.0000	1.5036	0.0000	1.35621
0.84147	1.4869	.0700	1.4962	.00864	1.36454
.70230	1.4716	.1275	1.4885	.19356	1.37417
.57918	1.4568	.2516	1.4723	.29150	1.38332
.46945	1.4425	.3668	1.4558	.38525	1.39196
.37100	1.4283	.4521	1.4426	.46925	1.39943
.28217	1.4146	.5697	1.4284	.55912	1.40757
.20176	1.4011	.7531	1.4011	.65892	1.41618
.12844	1.3878	.8815	1.3803	.78771	1.42692
.06152	1.3749	1.0000	1.3609	.88809	1.43487
.00000	1.3622			1.00000	1.44309

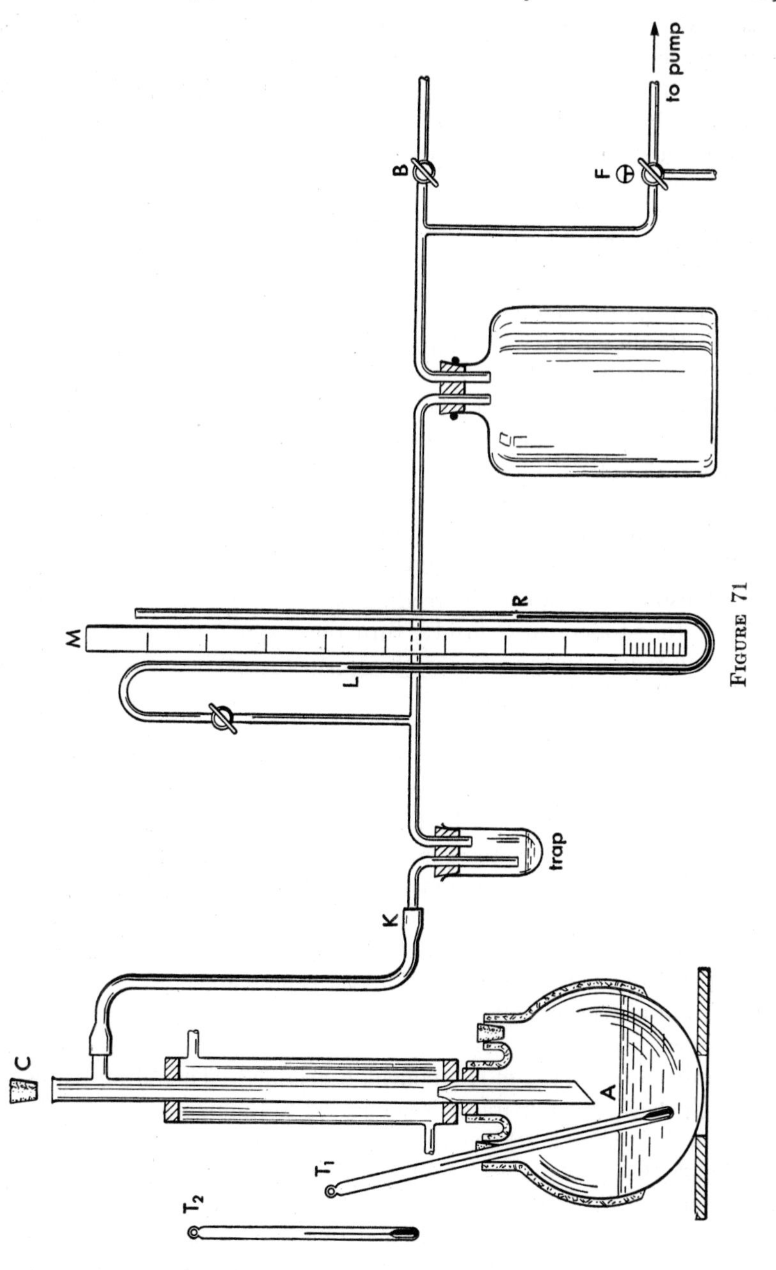

FIGURE 71

refractive index range in two and use the left-hand ordinate to represent the lower half of the range and the right-hand ordinate to represent the upper range. In this way two curves may be drawn and the mole fraction can be estimated to ± 0.001 units. If the points do not fall upon a straight line, a length of No. 18 spring brass wire or a spline is bent to fit the points.

Place 150 ml. of A in the flask and add a few boiling stones to prevent superheating. To minimize fractionation of vapor in the flask a number of asbestos squares are placed under it. This precaution deflects the heat from the Bunsen flame away from the sides of the flask.

Heat the liquid to its boiling point and remove the burner after a small amount of liquid has collected in the throat of the condenser. Remove the condensed liquid with a long capillary dropper and discard. Repeat this several times especially if the samples are cloudy. Finally remove a sample of the condensed vapor and determine its refractive index; record the reading in Table 42. Transfer a sample from the flask to a test tube and, when cool, obtain the refractive index. The two readings should agree to ± 0.00015 units if the sample is pure and should also correspond to the reading in Table 41.

Place the stopper in C firmly, turn the water aspirator or pump on fully, and reduce the pressure in the apparatus. When the temperature of the boiling liquid is approximately 0.2–0.4° below that selected (see Table 40), the three-way stopcock is turned so that the flask is isolated from the pump and the atmosphere; a small ($\frac{1}{2}$ in.) Bunsen flame is placed under the flask. Upon opening and closing the air leak at B so that the pressure increases slightly, the temperature can be adjusted to the selected value. In case the temperature is too high, the pressure is reduced as before. The temperature should be held to ± 0.05°C. Obtain the barometric pressure and the manometer readings. The vapor pressure of pure A is obtained from these data and the result should agree within ± 1 mm. of that recorded in the literature. This furnishes a good test of the apparatus. Atmospheric pressure is restored in the apparatus with the three-way stopcock F.

Approximately 5 ml. of component B is added. The burner is placed under the flask, the apparatus is connected to the pump through F, and the leak B is closed. When the boiling temperature again drops 0.2–0.4° below that selected, isolate the flask from the pump and atmosphere with stopcock F. Open and shut the leak so that the pressure increases in small increments until the desired temperature is obtained. Allow boiling to continue for three to five minutes; then obtain and record the manometer readings. Remove the flame and immediately turn the stopcock F so that the flask communicates with the atmosphere. A sample of the condensed vapor is removed with the medicine dropper and immediately transferred to the refractometer; it is absolutely necessary to use the small side hole provided in the prism box. Obtain the refractive index. A sample of the liquid phase is removed and transferred to a small test tube and tightly stoppered. Obtain the refractive index when cool.

Continue to add B in 5-ml. portions until a total of 25 ml. has been added, each time determining the manometer reading and the refractive index of liquid and condensed vapor phases. Component B is then added in 20-ml. portions until a total of 125 ml. has been added, the same data being collected as above. The student may repeat the procedure at any given concentration in order to check the precision of the apparatus and of operation. It should be possible to check the composition of the vapor to ± 0.0003 units of refractive index.

To investigate the system rich in component B, place 150 ml. of pure B in the flask. Proceed exactly as with component A by first discarding cloudy condensate and then by measuring the refractive index of the liquid and condensed vapor phase. Finally the vapor pressure of B is measured at the selected temperature of operation. Component A is added in 5-ml. portions until a total of 40 ml. has been added, whereupon 15-ml. portions are added until a total of 115 ml. has been reached. The refractive index of the liquid and condensed vapor phase is obtained each time as well as the manometer readings.

TABLE 42

150 ml. A (solvent) B = ____ mm. t = ____ $°C_{corr}$.

ml. of B	n Liquid / $_l x_B$	n Vapor / $_v x_B'$	R mm.	L mm.	P mm.	p_A mm. Solvent	p_B mm. Solute	a_A Solvent	a_B Solute	$\frac{a_A}{x_A}$	$\frac{a_B}{x_B}$

The entire experiment takes approximately eight hours to perform. It may be shortened and only the beginning portion (about eight points) of the curve need be obtained to give sufficient information for the calculation of the activities over a limited range of concentration.

Calculations Obtain the mole fraction of the liquid and condensed vapor phases from the measured refractive index and the composition curve constructed from Table 41. Calculate the partial pressure p_A and p_B of A and B in the vapor phase, respectively, using Dalton's law of partial pressures, namely $p_A = P_v x_{A'}$ and $p_B = P_v x_{B'}$, where P is the total pressure and ${}_v x_{A'}$ and ${}_v x_{B'}$ are the mole fractions of A and B in the condensed vapor. The total pressure P is given by $P = B + R - L$, where B is the barometric pressure and L and R are the left and right readings of the manometer. An alternative method may be used for calculating the partial pressure of the second component, namely, $p_A = P - p_B$.

Plot the total pressure P (ordinate) against the mole fraction (abscissa). Employ graph paper with a 22-in. ordinate and a 17-in. abscissa. On the same paper, plot the partial pressures of A and B against the mole fraction. Use the right ordinate for B and the left ordinate for A.

Calculate the activity a_A of the solvent using equation 263. To obtain the activity a_B of the solute, plot ${}_l x_B/p_B$ (the ratio of the mole fraction of B in the liquid state to the partial vapor pressure of B) as ordinate against ${}_l x_B$ as abscissa. Complete the curve and extrapolate to ${}_l x_B = 0$. The numerical value of ${}_l x_B/p_B$ when ${}_l x_B = 0$ corresponds to $1/p_B{}^*$. The activities may then be calculated with equation 265.

The same calculations can be made by assuming B to be the solvent and A the solute if data for the proper range is available. Plot the activities a_A (left ordinate) and a_B (right ordinate) against mole fraction as in Figs. 69 and 70. Calculate a_A/x_A and a_B/x_B over the range of compositions investigated.

REFERENCES

Carley and Bertelsen, *Ind. Eng. Chem.*, **41,** 2806 (1949)

Gilmont, *Anal. Chem.*, **20,** 474 (1948)

Absolute and differential manometer.

Redlich and Schulz, *J. Am. Chem. Soc.*, **66,** 1007 (1944)

Todd, *Anal. Chem.*, **20,** 148 (1948)

Vacuum pressure regulator.

See Experiment 20 for further references.

Experiment 48

Equilibrium in a Heterogeneous Ionic Reaction

In this experiment the equilibrium reaction between solid lead sulfate, lead iodide, and sulfate and iodide ions in solution will be studied. The equation for the reaction may be written

$$PbI_2(s) + SO_4^{=} \rightleftharpoons PbSO_4(s) + 2I^- \qquad (267)$$

The equilibrium constant in terms of concentrations and activity coefficients is

$$K_a = \frac{[I^-]^2 \cdot f_{I^-}^2}{[SO_4^{=}] \cdot f_{SO_4^{=}}} \qquad (268)$$

This may also be written as

$$K_a = K_c \frac{f_{I^-}^2}{f_{SO_4^{=}}} \qquad (269)$$

where K_c is the concentration ratio as determined by analysis. Since K_a is a true constant it is evident that K_c must vary with changing ionic strength.

For low ionic strengths the activity coefficients are given by the simplified Debye-Hückel equation:

$$\log f = -0.51\, Z^2\sqrt{\mu} \qquad \text{in water, } 25° \qquad (270)$$

Taking logs of equation 269 and substituting from equation 270 for $\log f_{I^-}$ and $\log f_{SO_4^{=}}$, there results

$$\log K_c = \log K_a - 1.02\sqrt{\mu} \qquad (271)$$

According to equation 271, upon plotting $\log K_c$ against $\sqrt{\mu}$ a straight line with a slope of -1.02 should be obtained. The intercept, $\log K_a$, is equal to the value approached by $\log K_c$ as the ionic strength approaches zero. Actually since equation 270 is valid only in dilute solutions the curve obtained in this experiment will approach or follow the theoretical slope only in the more dilute solutions.

It should be noted that K_a is also the ratio of the activity solubility product constants. For the saturated solutions of PbI and $PbSO_4$ the solubility product constants are, respectively

$$K_a' = [Pb^{++}][I^-]^2 f_{Pb^{++}} f_{I^-}{}^2$$

$$K_a'' = [Pb^{++}][SO_4^=] f_{Pb^{++}} f_{SO_4^=} \qquad (272)$$

and their ratio is

$$K_a = \frac{K_a'}{K_a''} = \frac{[I^-]^2 f_{I^-}{}^2}{[SO_4^=] f_{SO_4^=}} \qquad (273)$$

as given previously. Since $f_{I^-}{}^2$ and $f_{SO_4^=}$ do not change to the same extent with ionic strength, the ion concentration products K_c' and K_c'' will not vary to the same extent and their ratio (K_c) is not constant as μ changes.

Apparatus 10-, 20-, 50-ml. pipets; 100-ml. buret; funnels; solid C.P. $PbSO_4$. Standard solutions of 0.02 *M* $AgNO_3$ (1 liter), 0.10 *M* KI (1 liter), and 0.5 *M* KNO_3 (250 ml.) are prepared by carefully weighing the pure solid salts.

Procedure Prepare 100 ml. of each solution listed in Table 43 in the first two columns by diluting standard solutions in 100 ml. volumetric flasks. The KI solutions are measured with pipets, and the KNO_3 solution may be added to the flasks from a buret. Each solution is diluted to the mark with water. Add one gram of solid lead sulfate weighed on a platform balance to each flask, stopper, and shake occasionally over a period of 24 hours or longer. The samples may be kept in a thermostat if desired, but room temperature is satisfactory if the variation is not more than ±1°.

To analyze, filter a portion of each solution into a clean dry flask, using dry filter paper and funnels. Remove a 10-ml. sample with a dry pipet or one that has been rinsed with the solution, and titrate with 0.02 *M* $AgNO_3$ solution. No indicator is necessary; at the endpoint the previously colloidal silver iodide suddenly flocculates. Since quite accurate values must be obtained, the titrations must be done with care; the solution is added from the buret slowly so that drainage is uniform, and the last 0.5–1.0 ml. should be added dropwise with the mixture well shaken or swirled after each drop. Approximate titration values obtained at 25° are given in Table 43 as a guide.

Several 10-ml. portions of the original 0.1 *M* KI solution should be titrated with the 0.02 *M* $AgNO_3$ in the same manner. If the solutions are correctly made and the buret and pipet are accurate this titration will require exactly 50 ml.

TABLE 43

[KI]	[KNO_3]	ml. $AgNO_3$	FINAL [I^-]	FINAL [$SO_4^=$]	μ	$\sqrt{\mu}$	K_c	log K_c
0.10		31.0						
.09		29.0						
.08		27.0						
.07		24.5						
.06		22.0						
.05		19.0						
.04		16.0						
.03		12.5						
.02		8.5						
.05	0.04	18.5						
.05	.08	18.0						
.05	.12	17.5						
.05	.16	17.0						
.05	.20	16.5						

An alternative procedure which is somewhat more accurate is as follows: Prepare the solutions of KI with the aid of a 100-ml. buret; the solution of KNO_3 and the water are delivered from 50-ml. burets. A total of 100 ml. of each solution is made in a 250-ml. Erlenmeyer flask. Remove a 10-ml. portion with a pipet and titrate with silver nitrate to determine the exact initial iodide concentration. The roughly weighed samples of lead sulfate are added to each flask and the above procedure is followed to determine the final equilibrium iodide concentration. This procedure avoids the small but important errors which may arise in the quantitative dilution method.

Calculations The equilibrium iodide concentration is calculated directly from the titration value of the sample. The equilibrium sulfate ion concentration is one-half the difference between the initial and the final iodide concentrations (since one mole of sulfate appears for each two moles of iodide ion which react).

Calculate the ion concentration ratio $K_c = [I^-]^2/[SO_4^=]$ and tabulate values of log K_c. Calculate the ionic strength μ for the solutions at equilibrium with the two solid salts, ignoring the very small concentration of lead ion in the solution. Tabulate values of μ and $\sqrt{\mu}$.

Plot log K_c as ordinate and $\sqrt{\mu}$ as abscissa and draw a smooth curve through the points, extrapolating it to $\sqrt{\mu} = 0$. Obtain the value of K_a from the extrapolation. Draw a straight line tangent to the curve at $\sqrt{\mu} = 0$ or through the points at the lower values of $\sqrt{\mu}$. Compare the slope of the straight line with the theoretical value (eq. 271).

Further experimental suggestions Instead of increasing the ionic strength by adding potassium nitrate, stronger potassium iodide solutions may be used. In this case a more concentrated silver nitrate solution should be prepared for the titrations.

Solid lead iodide may be brought to equilibrium with potassium sulfate solutions, or mixtures of the two solids may be used with both iodide and sulfate present initially in the solutions as done by Findlay.[1]

Other salts may be used for similar equilibrium reactions.

REFERENCES

Acree, *J. Am. Chem. Soc.*, **65,** 1765 (1943)
Numerical values of the constants in the Debye-Hückel equation.
Findlay, *Z. physik. Chem.*, **34,** 409 (1900)
Newton, *J. Am. Chem. Soc.*, **50,** 3258 (1928)

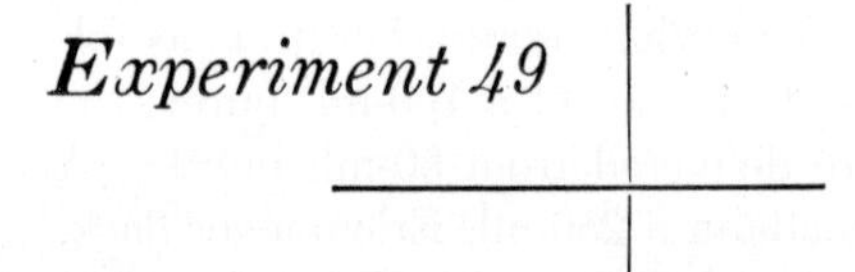

The Activity Coefficient of Silver Acetate

When a slightly soluble salt such as silver acetate is dissolved in water, the equilibrium between the ions and solid salt is given by

$$AgAc(s) \rightleftharpoons Ag^+ + Ac^- \tag{274}$$

The activity solubility product for the above reaction is

$$K_a = a_{Ag^+} \times a_{Ac^-} \tag{275}$$

Since $a_+ = f_+C_+$ and $a_- = f_-C_-$, upon substituting in equation 275 there is obtained

$$K_a = f_+C_{Ag^+} \times f_-C_{Ac^-} \tag{276}$$

or

$$K_a = f^2(C_{Ag^+} \times C_{Ac^-}) \tag{277}$$

where f is defined as the mean activity coefficient; that is

$$f^2 = f_+ \times f_- \tag{278}$$

[1] *Z. physik. Chem.*, **34,** 409 (1900)

It may be noted that $C_{Ag^+} \times C_{Ac^-}$ or K_c was used to define solubility product in the older literature, and it is clear that K_a and K_c become more alike numerically, the closer f approaches unity. For a pure solution of a very slightly soluble salt, K_a and K_c are sensibly the same. If the ionic strength is increased as by adding some other soluble salt, the activity coefficient f decreases in the range of dilute solutions, and K_c must increase in order that K_a remain constant. An increase in the numerical value of K_c corresponds to increased solubility of salt.

If no salt with a common ion is present

$$C_{Ag^+} = C_{Ac^-} = C \tag{279}$$

and C may be used to represent the molar solubility of the salt. In a series of saturated solutions containing another salt to vary the ionic strength

$$K_a = f_o^2 C_o^2 = f_1^2 C_1^2 =, \text{ etc.} \tag{280}$$

In this equation f_o and C_o refer to a solution of zero ionic strength; by convention $f_o = 1$ and C_o can be obtained by extrapolation if necessary.

The Debye-Hückel equation gives the relation between the ionic strength μ, the mean activity coefficient f, the valence Z of the ions, and a constant A related to the ionic diameters:

$$-\log f = \frac{Z_+ Z_- \, 0.51\sqrt{\mu}}{1 + A\sqrt{\mu}} \tag{281}$$

This more accurate form of the Debye-Hückel equation is found to be necessary to represent the data for the solubility of silver acetate and in general for moderately insoluble salts. From the relations expressed in equations 280 and 281, there is obtained

$$\log \frac{C}{C_o} = \frac{0.51\sqrt{\mu}}{1 + A\sqrt{\mu}} \tag{282}$$

since $Z_+ = Z_- = 1$ and $\log f_o = 0$ ($f_o = 1$ when $\mu = 0$).

Apparatus 25-ml. pipet; 100-ml. volumetric flasks; sample withdrawing tubes; ten to twenty 250-ml. Erlenmeyer flasks; 100-ml. buret; 10 glass-stoppered bottles (125 ml.); KNO_3 which has been dried for several hours at 150°; silver acetate; saturated solution (about 40 per cent) of ferric ammonium sulfate; one liter of 0.1 M potassium thiocyanate, prepared by accurately weighing the solid salt.[1]

Procedure Weigh ten 2-g. samples of silver acetate on a platform balance and transfer each to a glass-stoppered bottle. Solutions of KNO_3 corresponding to those of Table 44 are prepared by diluting a standard

[1] Kolthoff and Sandell, *Quantitative Analysis*, p. 544

1 M solution, which has been prepared by weighing the solid salt. A 100-ml. buret may be used to deliver the necessary amount of salt solution into 100-ml. volumetric flasks, which are diluted to the mark. The solutions are then transferred to the sample bottles.

If the sample bottles are to be rotated mechanically in a thermostat, the glass stoppers are wired firmly in place and sealed with a molten mixture of beeswax and rosin. Samples may be withdrawn for analysis any time after two hours. Otherwise, the bottles are stored in a thermostat at 25 ± 0.1°C. and shaken several times over a period of twenty-four hours or longer before removing samples for analysis.

Remove a bottle from the thermostat and dry the outside. A sample withdrawing tube, prepared as in Expt. 14, is connected to a 25-ml. pipet with a small piece of rubber tubing. Withdraw a sample (employ suction and a suction release tube, see Expt. 14) and transfer to a flask. Add 1 ml. of ferric alum indicator solution, 5 ml. of 6 M HNO_3, and 15 ml. of distilled water, and titrate with standard thiocyanate solution; the first indication of the approach to the endpoint is an orange-red color. Continue the titration carefully with vigorous agitation until a brownish tinge appears which is permanent upon shaking. This is the well-known Volhard method [1] for the determination of silver. Repeat with a duplicate sample.

Each solution is analyzed as above, using a dry sample withdrawing tube with a fresh plug of cotton for each sample. All silver acetate and silver thiocyanate residues are placed in bottles provided for that purpose, as the silver may be recovered later.

Calculations The concentration C_1 of silver acetate may be obtained by using the relation $V_1C_1 = V_2C_2$, where V_1 = ml. of AgAc sample, V_2 = ml. of KCNS, C_2 = molarity of KCNS.

The ionic strength of the solution is calculated by

$$\mu = \Sigma CZ^2/2 \tag{283}$$

where C is the molarity and Z is the charge (or valence) for each ion. The total ionic strength is the sum of that for KNO_3 and AgAc. The contribution of the latter salt is relatively large in dilute solutions, but becomes unimportant in the concentrated ones. Also calculate the square root of the ionic strength.

Prepare a graph, plotting log solubility of AgAc (ordinate) against the square root of the ionic strength (abscissa). Extrapolate the curve to zero ionic strength and obtain the value of the ideal solubility C_o. Since the line has a distinct curvature even at low ionic strength, it is difficult

[1] Kolthoff and Sandell, *loc. cit.*

to obtain an accurate value for $\log C_o$ and hence C_o. The difficulty arises from the relatively large solubility of silver acetate.

For this reason it is advantageous to employ equation 282. Plot $\log C$ as ordinate against the quantity $0.51\sqrt{\mu}/(1 + 1.480\sqrt{\mu})$ as abscissa. Extrapolate to zero ionic strength to obtain $\log C_o$ and C_o.

The mean activity coefficient f of silver acetate in each salt solution is calculated, using the relation $f = C_o/C$, which can be obtained from equation 280, since $f_o = 1$.

The constant A, if desired, may be evaluated from the data or the curve, by substituting in the following:

$$\log \frac{C_2}{C_1} = \frac{0.51\sqrt{\mu_2}}{1 + A\sqrt{\mu_2}} - \frac{0.51\sqrt{\mu_1}}{1 + A\sqrt{\mu_1}} \qquad (284)$$

The average value of A is obtained from several trials.

The constant A is related to the average diameter d of silver and acetate ions by the equation

$$A/(0.3283 \times 10^8) = d \qquad (285)$$

Calculate the average diameter d of the ions.

The activity solubility product constant K_a of silver acetate in each of the salt solutions is calculated using equation 280.

If a series of K_c values (concentration solubility product) are calculated from the equation $K_c = C^2$, the necessity of employing K_a for moderately insoluble salts will become evident.

The value of $\log C_o$ may also be calculated from several individual data by substituting C in equation 282 with $A = 1.480$. Several such calculations should be made, and the average value of C_o can be compared with the graphical extrapolation.

TABLE 44

CONCN. KNO_3 MOLAR	ml. 0.1 M KCNS	CONCN. AgAc MOLAR	$\log C$	f	K_a	K_c	A
0.00							
.05							
.10							
.20							
.30							
.40							
.50							
.60							
.70							
.80							
1.00							

REFERENCES

Jones and Hickman, *J. Am. Chem. Soc.*, **69**, 536 (1947)
Kolthoff, I. M., and Sandell, E. B., *Textbook of Quantitative Inorganic Analysis*, The Macmillan Company, New York, **1936**
MacDougall, F. M., *Physical Chemistry*, The Macmillan Company, New York, **1936**
——, *J. Am. Chem. Soc.*, **52**, 1390 (1930)
Randall and Vietti, *ibid.*, **50**, 1526 (1928)

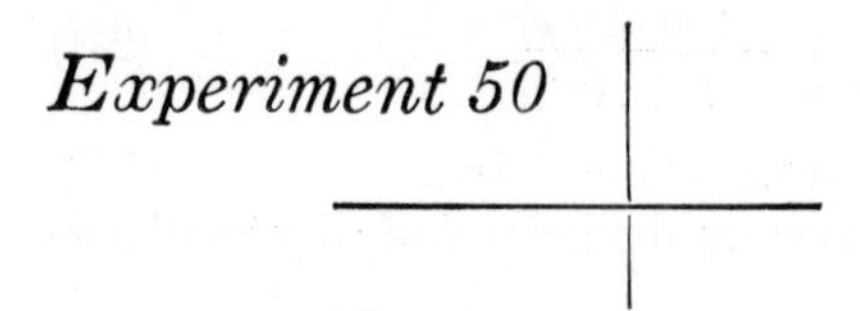

Experiment 50

The Activity Coefficient of a Weak Electrolyte

Part A: Solubility Measurements

The activity coefficient of a weak electrolyte or nonelectrolyte in aqueous solutions of various ionic strengths may be determined from solubility measurements. If the solid solute is in contact with a series of aqueous solutions containing various concentrations of an inert salt such as KCl the activity of the solid and dissolved solute in the different solutions must be equal, and

$$a_s = {}_0a_w = {}_1a_w = {}_2a_w = \cdots \tag{286}$$

Experimentally it is found that the addition of a neutral salt to a saturated aqueous solution of a weak electrolyte may increase (salt in) or decrease (salt out) its solubility. Since the activity of the solute can not change, the activity coefficient f_w in the following relation must vary with the concentration C:

$$a_s = {}_0C_w \times {}_0f_w = {}_1C_w \times {}_1f_w = {}_2C_w \times {}_2f_w = \cdots \tag{287}$$

Since the concentration of solute can be determined experimentally, the activity coefficients can be obtained if any one of them is known or can be assumed. The activity is defined numerically by being set equal to unity, or equal to concentration, in a selected standard state. In the present case we are interested in the change in activity coefficient with ionic strength, and it is customary to set activity equal to the concentration ($_0C_w$) in a hypothetical solution of zero ionic strength. The coefficient $_0f_w$ is then equal to unity in the same solution. While a solution of a weak electrolyte always contains some ions, it will be possible to obtain $_0C_w$ by extrapolation, and thus calculate $(f_w)_{1,2,3}$ (eq. 287). Equation 287 may be arranged in a form that is more readily employed for the purpose of calculation; upon taking logarithms and noting that $\log {}_0f_w = 0$, then

$$\log (f_w)_{1,2,3} \cdots = \log {}_0C_w - (\log C_w)_{1,2,3} \cdots \tag{288}$$

The change in solubility of a weak electrolyte or a nonelectrolyte, and likewise its activity coefficient in inert salt solutions, cannot be predicted from the Debye equation. The solubility effects are specific, as they depend upon the particular nature of the solvent salt (neutral salt). However, for a given solvent salt the following equation has been found to apply over a wide range of concentrations

$$\log [{}_0C_w/(C_w)_{1,2,3}] = [\log f_w]_{1,2,3} = kX \tag{289}$$

where X is the concentration of neutral salt and k is the salting out constant. Equation 289 applies only to those cases where the addition of solvent salt decreases the solubility.

If the weak electrolyte is an acid, such as benzoic acid, dissociation in the aqueous phase reduces the amount of molecular acid present. The concentration of the undissociated part can be calculated if the dissociation constant[1] of the acid is known in the various salt solutions. In the present experiment, this correction will be neglected since it is small (about 1 per cent).

Part B: Distribution Measurements

The activity of a weak electrolyte may also be obtained by measuring its distribution between salt solutions and a solvent immiscible with water. For example, if solid benzoic acid (HB) is in contact with pure water (w) and benzene (b), the following equilibrium exists:

$$\begin{array}{c} n\,(\mathrm{HB})_s \rightleftharpoons n_w(\mathrm{HB}) \rightleftharpoons n_b(\mathrm{HB}) \rightleftharpoons {}_b(\mathrm{HB})_n \\ \quad\quad\quad\quad \Updownarrow \quad\quad\quad\quad\quad\quad\quad\quad \\ \quad\quad\quad\quad H^+ + B^- \quad\quad\quad\quad\quad\quad \end{array} \tag{290}$$

The equilibrium is complicated by the partial dissociation of the acid in the aqueous phase into hydrogen (H_3O^+) and benzoate (B^-) ions. In

[1] Chase and Kilpatrick, *J. Am. Chem. Soc.*, **53**, 2598 (1931)

the benzene phase, dissociation of dimeric acid[1] into monomer will be negligible if the solution is more than half saturated; *i.e.*, $n = 2$ in equation 290.

The dimeric benzoic acid behaves nearly ideally in benzene solution and its activity may be set proportional to its (dimeric) concentration, $a_{b_2} = C_{b_2} \cdot f_{b_2}$, where the activity coefficient f_{b_2} is a constant whose numerical value depends on the standard state chosen for reference. It does not vary with the concentration of the acid or of KCl in an aqueous phase in contact with the benzene, since the salt is insoluble in benzene.

If we were concerned with benzene solutions only, we should set $f_{b_2} = 1$. However, in order to make use of the data from distribution experiments, the standard state chosen in Part A may be retained, namely an aqueous solution of zero ionic strength where ${}_of_w = 1$. The essential equilibrium of equation 290 is

$$2_w(\mathrm{HB}) \rightleftharpoons {}_b(\mathrm{HB})_2 \tag{291}$$

and consequently

$$K_a = a_{b_2}/a_w^2 = 1 \tag{292}$$

where a_{b_2} and a_w are the activities of dimer in the benzene phase and monomer in the water phase respectively. K_a is equal to unity since the activity of any component is taken to be the same in all phases in equilibrium with each other.[2] Then

$$\frac{C_{b_2} f_{b_2}}{C_w^2 f_w^2} = 1 \tag{293}$$

and

$$f_{b_2} = \frac{C_w^2 f_w^2}{C_{b_2}} \tag{294}$$

or for the special case of zero ionic strength (${}_0f_w = 1$)

$$f_{b_2} = \frac{{}_0C_w^2}{C_{b_2}} \tag{295}$$

The Nernst distribution constant ${}_dK_c$ is generally defined as

$${}_dK_c = C_b/C_w^2 \tag{296}$$

where C_b and C_w are the concentrations as determined by analysis and expressed in terms of monomer in both phases. Thus

$$f_{b_2} = \frac{{}_0C_w^2}{\frac{1}{2}C_b} = \frac{2}{{}_dK_c} \tag{297}$$

[1] Wall, *J. Am. Chem. Soc.*, **64**, 472 (1942)

[2] Strictly the full equilibrium should be considered $2_w(\mathrm{HB}) \underset{}{\overset{K_a'}{\rightleftharpoons}} 2_b(\mathrm{HB}) \overset{K_a''}{\rightleftharpoons} {}_b(\mathrm{HB})_2$ where K_a' and K_a'' are the respective equilibrium constants. It is found that $K_a' \cdot K_a'' = K_a$ as given in equation 292.

Having calculated f_{b_2} from values of ${}_aK_c$ (aqueous solutions of zero ionic strength or where f_w is known) it can be employed to determine f_w in other aqueous solutions.

Apparatus 5-ml. and 50-ml. pipets; 50-ml. buret; 25-ml. and 200-ml. graduated cylinders; rubber-stoppered bottles (250 ml.); Erlenmeyer flasks; separatory funnels (250 ml.); benzoic acid; benzene; phenolphthalein indicator; C.P. KCl or NaCl; standard 0.05 M NaOH; standard 0.1 or 0.2 M NaOH.

Procedure Accurately weigh sufficient KCl or NaCl to prepare 250 ml. of the solutions given in Table 45.

It is assumed that in both parts of this experiment the temperature is the same. If the room temperature is reasonably constant (±1°), a thermostat will not be necessary.

TABLE 45

M of Neutral Salt	Part A: ml. NaOH	Part A: Moles/Liter	Part B: ml. NaOH Aqueous Phase	Part B: Moles/Liter	Part B: ml. NaOH Benzene Phase	Part B: Moles/Liter
0.00						
0.50						
1.00						
1.50						
2.00						
2.50						
3.00						

Part A. Transfer approximately 125 ml. of water or salt solution to clean dry bottles (or flasks). Approximately 1-g. samples of benzoic acid are weighed (platform balance) and transferred to each of the solutions, which are then shaken vigorously at ten-minute intervals over the period of one hour or longer. The solutions are filtered into dry flasks, using dry filter paper and funnels.

Duplicate 50-ml. samples are withdrawn from each flask and titrated with 0.05 M NaOH using phenolphthalein indicator.

Part B. Transfer approximately 125 ml. of water or salt solution (Table 45) to clean dry separatory funnels. Add 25 ml. of benzene to each, and add also approximately 1.5 g. of solid benzoic acid (weighed on a platform balance). Shake at ten-minute intervals for one hour or more.[1]

[1] If a thermostat is employed, a rubber policeman should be placed over the tip of the separatory funnel.

Withdraw most of the aqueous phase from each sample into a dry flask and titrate duplicate 50-ml. samples with 0.05 M NaOH. Separate and discard the remainder of the water layer; withdraw duplicate 5-ml. portions of the benzene layer, run into flasks containing 50 ml. of pure water, and titrate with 0.1 or 0.2 M NaOH. Install a safety trap between the mouth and pipet when withdrawing benzene solutions. Rinse the pipet with each new solution, or rinse with benzene and dry.

Calculations *Part A.* Calculate the concentration of benzoic acid in moles/liter for each solution.

Prepare a graph employing log concentration of benzoic acid (ordinate) and concentration of neutral salt (abscissa). Extrapolate the curve to the ordinate to obtain log ${}_0C_w$ and ${}_0C_w$ (the concentration of solute in a solution of zero ionic strength). This value should correspond very closely to the concentration of the acid in pure water solution.

The activity coefficient is calculated by using either equation 287 or 288. Use of the latter may save some computations.

Plot log $(f_w)_{1,2,3}\cdots$ (ordinate) against the concentration of neutral salt (abscissa) and obtain the salting out constant.

Part B. The results of the distribution experiments may be employed in several different ways to gain information about the system.

Calculate the "concentration distribution constant," ${}_dK_c$, employing equation 296. Obviously ${}_dK_c$ should not be a constant if $(f_w)_{1,2,3}\cdots$ is different in each salt solution.

If Part A has been performed, f_{b2} may be calculated employing equation 294 with the values of $(f_w)_{1,2,3}\cdots$ for each salt solution. Observe whether f_{b_2} shows any trend with salt concentration and if not, calculate the $A.M.$ and its probable error.

Calculate f_{b_2} from the experiment with water only, using equation 295. If the experiment was carried out near 25°C., look up the solubility of benzoic acid in water and in benzene at this temperature and calculate f_{b_2} from these values. Equation 295 should be valid for saturated solutions, and f_{b_2} should not change much with temperature over a few degrees. What is the percentage difference in these two values?

Using f_{b_2} as obtained above, calculate $(f_w)_{1,2,3}\cdots$, where the subscripts refer to each of the salt solutions; solve equation 294 for f_w for this calculation. If Part A was performed, compare the activity coefficients obtained for each salt solution. Plot log f_w against the concentration of neutral salt and obtain the salting out constant (eq. 289).

Further suggested experiments The assumption that n (eq. 290) is constant and equal to 2 may be tested by measuring the distribution ratio with several concentrations of benzoic acid in pure water and benzene. If f_w and f_b are both constant

$$\frac{1}{n}\frac{C_b}{C_w{}^n} = {}_dK_c \qquad (298)$$

where $\frac{1}{n} C_b = C_{bn}$. Then

$$\log C_b = \log (n_dK_c) + n \log C_w \qquad (299)$$

and a plot of $\log C_b$ against $\log C_w$ should have the slope of n if the latter is constant.

The solubility of the nitro benzoic acids [1] or chloro and hydroxy benzoic acids [2] may be studied.

REFERENCES

Chase and Kilpatrick, *J. Am. Chem. Soc.*, **53**, 2589 (1931)
Kolthoff, *ibid.*, **57**, 973 (1935)
LaMer and Greenspan, *ibid.*, **57**, 969 (1935)
Osol and Kilpatrick, *ibid.*, **55**, 4430 (1933); **57**, 1053 (1935)
Randall and Failey, *ibid.*, **49**, 2678 (1927)
Smith and White, *J. Phys. Chem.*, **33**, 1953 (1929)
Sykes and Robertson, *J. Am. Chem. Soc.*, **55**, 2621 (1933)
Wall, *ibid.*, **64**, 472 (1942)

[1] Sykes and Robertson, *J. Am. Chem. Soc.*, **55**, 2621 (1933)

[2] See articles by Osol and Kilpatrick, LaMer and Greenspan, and Kolthoff in the references.

LOGARITHMS

N	0	1	2	3	4	5	6	7	8	9	Proportional Parts								
											1	2	3	4	5	6	7	8	9
10	0000	0043	0086	0128	0170	0212	0253	0294	0334	0374	4	8	12	17	21	25	29	33	37
11	0414	0453	0492	0531	0569	0607	0645	0682	0719	0755	4	8	11	15	19	23	26	30	34
12	0792	0828	0864	0899	0934	0969	1004	1038	1072	1106	3	7	10	14	17	21	24	28	31
13	1139	1173	1206	1239	1271	1303	1335	1367	1399	1430	3	6	10	13	16	19	23	26	29
14	1461	1492	1523	1553	1584	1614	1644	1673	1703	1732	3	6	9	12	15	18	21	24	27
15	1761	1790	1818	1847	1875	1903	1931	1959	1987	2014	3	6	8	11	14	17	20	22	25
16	2041	2068	2095	2122	2148	2175	2201	2227	2253	2279	3	5	8	11	13	16	18	21	24
17	2304	2330	2355	2380	2405	2430	2455	2480	2504	2529	2	5	7	10	12	15	17	20	22
18	2553	2577	2601	2625	2648	2672	2695	2718	2742	2765	2	5	7	9	12	14	16	19	21
19	2788	2810	2833	2856	2878	2900	2923	2945	2967	2989	2	4	7	9	11	13	16	18	20
20	3010	3032	3054	3075	3096	3118	3139	3160	3181	3201	2	4	6	8	11	13	15	17	19
21	3222	3243	3263	3284	3304	3324	3345	3365	3385	3404	2	4	6	8	10	12	14	16	18
22	3424	3444	3464	3483	3502	3522	3541	3560	3579	3598	2	4	6	8	10	12	14	15	17
23	3617	3636	3655	3674	3692	3711	3729	3747	3766	3784	2	4	6	7	9	11	13	15	17
24	3802	3820	3838	3856	3874	3892	3909	3927	3945	3962	2	4	5	7	9	11	12	14	16
25	3979	3997	4014	4031	4048	4065	4082	4099	4116	4133	2	3	5	7	9	10	12	14	15
26	4150	4166	4183	4200	4216	4232	4249	4265	4281	4298	2	3	5	7	8	10	11	13	15
27	4314	4330	4346	4362	4378	4393	4409	4425	4440	4456	2	3	5	6	8	9	11	13	14
28	4472	4487	4502	4518	4533	4548	4564	4579	4594	4609	2	3	5	6	8	9	11	12	14
29	4624	4639	4654	4669	4683	4698	4713	4728	4742	4757	1	3	4	6	7	9	10	12	13
30	4771	4786	4800	4814	4829	4843	4857	4871	4886	4900	1	3	4	6	7	9	10	11	13
31	4914	4928	4942	4955	4969	4983	4997	5011	5024	5038	1	3	4	6	7	8	10	11	12
32	5051	5065	5079	5092	5105	5119	5132	5145	5159	5172	1	3	4	5	7	8	9	11	12
33	5185	5198	5211	5224	5237	5250	5263	5276	5289	5302	1	3	4	5	6	8	9	10	12
34	5315	5328	5340	5353	5366	5378	5391	5403	5416	5428	1	3	4	5	6	8	9	10	11
35	5441	5453	5465	5478	5490	5502	5514	5527	5539	5551	1	2	4	5	6	7	9	10	11
36	5563	5575	5587	5599	5611	5623	5635	5647	5658	5670	1	2	4	5	6	7	8	10	11
37	5682	5694	5705	5717	5729	5740	5752	5763	5775	5786	1	2	3	5	6	7	8	9	10
38	5798	5809	5821	5832	5843	5855	5866	5877	5888	5899	1	2	3	5	6	7	8	9	10
39	5911	5922	5933	5944	5955	5966	5977	5988	5999	6010	1	2	3	4	5	7	8	9	10
40	6021	6031	6042	6053	6064	6075	6085	6096	6107	6117	1	2	3	4	5	6	8	9	10
41	6128	6138	6149	6160	6170	6180	6191	6201	6212	6222	1	2	3	4	5	6	7	8	9
42	6232	6243	6253	6263	6274	6284	6294	6304	6314	6325	1	2	3	4	5	6	7	8	9
43	6335	6345	6355	6365	6375	6385	6395	6405	6415	6425	1	2	3	4	5	6	7	8	9
44	6435	6444	6454	6464	6474	6484	6493	6503	6513	6522	1	2	3	4	5	6	7	8	9
45	6532	6542	6551	6561	6571	6580	6590	6599	6609	6618	1	2	3	4	5	6	7	8	9
46	6628	6637	6646	6656	6665	6675	6684	6693	6702	6712	1	2	3	4	5	6	7	7	8
47	6721	6730	6739	6749	6758	6767	6776	6785	6794	6803	1	2	3	4	5	5	6	7	8
48	6812	6821	6830	6839	6848	6857	6866	6875	6884	6893	1	2	3	4	4	5	6	7	8
49	6902	6911	6920	6928	6937	6946	6955	6964	6972	6981	1	2	3	4	4	5	6	7	8
50	6990	6998	7007	7016	7024	7033	7042	7050	7059	7067	1	2	3	3	4	5	6	7	8
51	7076	7084	7093	7101	7110	7118	7126	7135	7143	7152	1	2	3	3	4	5	6	7	8
52	7160	7168	7177	7185	7193	7202	7210	7218	7226	7235	1	2	2	3	4	5	6	7	7
53	7243	7251	7259	7267	7275	7284	7292	7300	7308	7316	1	2	2	3	4	5	6	6	7
54	7324	7332	7340	7348	7356	7364	7372	7380	7388	7396	1	2	2	3	4	5	6	6	7

LOGARITHMS

N	0	1	2	3	4	5	6	7	8	9	Proportional Parts								
											1	**2**	**3**	**4**	**5**	**6**	**7**	**8**	**9**
55	7404	7412	7419	7427	7435	7443	7451	7459	7466	7474	1	2	2	3	4	5	5	6	7
56	7482	7490	7497	7505	7513	7520	7528	7536	7543	7551	1	2	2	3	4	5	5	6	7
57	7559	7566	7574	7582	7589	7597	7604	7612	7619	7627	1	2	2	3	4	5	5	6	7
58	7634	7642	7649	7657	7664	7672	7679	7686	7694	7701	1	1	2	3	4	4	5	6	7
59	7709	7716	7723	7731	7738	7745	7752	7760	7767	7774	1	1	2	3	4	4	5	6	7
60	7782	7789	7796	7803	7810	7818	7825	7832	7839	7846	1	1	2	3	4	4	5	6	6
61	7853	7860	7868	7875	7882	7889	7896	7903	7910	7917	1	1	2	3	4	4	5	6	6
62	7924	7931	7938	7945	7952	7959	7966	7973	7980	7987	1	1	2	3	3	4	5	6	6
63	7993	8000	8007	8014	8021	8028	8035	8041	8048	8055	1	1	2	3	3	4	5	5	6
64	8062	8069	8075	8082	8089	8096	8102	8109	8116	8122	1	1	2	3	3	4	5	5	6
65	8129	8136	8142	8149	8156	8162	8169	8176	8182	8189	1	1	2	3	3	4	5	5	6
66	8195	8202	8209	8215	8222	8228	8235	8241	8248	8254	1	1	2	3	3	4	5	5	6
67	8261	8267	8274	8280	8287	8293	8299	8306	8312	8319	1	1	2	3	3	4	5	5	6
68	8325	8331	8338	8344	8351	8357	8363	8370	8376	8382	1	1	2	3	3	4	4	5	6
69	8388	8395	8401	8407	8414	8420	8426	8432	8439	8445	1	1	2	2	3	4	4	5	6
70	8451	8457	8463	8470	8476	8482	8488	8494	8500	8506	1	1	2	2	3	4	4	5	6
71	8513	8519	8525	8531	8537	8543	8549	8555	8561	8567	1	1	2	2	3	4	4	5	5
72	8573	8579	8585	8591	8597	8603	8609	8615	8621	8627	1	1	2	2	3	4	4	5	5
73	8633	8639	8645	8651	8657	8663	8669	8675	8681	8686	1	1	2	2	3	4	4	5	5
74	8692	8698	8704	8710	8716	8722	8727	8733	8739	8745	1	1	2	2	3	4	4	5	5
75	8751	8756	8762	8768	8774	8779	8785	8791	8797	8802	1	1	2	2	3	3	4	5	5
76	8808	8814	8820	8825	8831	8837	8842	8848	8854	8859	1	1	2	2	3	3	4	5	5
77	8865	8871	8876	8882	8887	8893	8899	8904	8910	8915	1	1	2	2	3	3	4	4	5
78	8921	8927	8932	8938	8943	8949	8954	8960	8965	8971	1	1	2	2	3	3	4	4	5
79	8976	8982	8987	8993	8998	9004	9009	9015	9020	9025	1	1	2	2	3	3	4	4	5
80	9031	9036	9042	9047	9053	9058	9063	9069	9074	9079	1	1	2	2	3	3	4	4	5
81	9085	9090	9096	9101	9106	9112	9117	9122	9128	9133	1	1	2	2	3	3	4	4	5
82	9138	9143	9149	9154	9159	9165	9170	9175	9180	9186	1	1	2	2	3	3	4	4	5
83	9191	9196	9201	9206	9212	9217	9222	9227	9232	9238	1	1	2	2	3	3	4	4	5
84	9243	9248	9253	9258	9263	9269	9274	9279	9284	9289	1	1	2	2	3	3	4	4	5
85	9294	9299	9304	9309	9315	9320	9325	9330	9335	9340	1	1	2	2	3	3	4	4	5
86	9345	9350	9355	9360	9365	9370	9375	9380	9385	9390	1	1	2	2	3	3	4	4	5
87	9395	9400	9405	9410	9415	9420	9425	9430	9435	9440	0	1	1	2	2	3	3	4	4
88	9445	9450	9455	9460	9465	9469	9474	9479	9484	9489	0	1	1	2	2	3	3	4	4
89	9494	9499	9504	9509	9513	9518	9523	9528	9533	9538	0	1	1	2	2	3	3	4	4
90	9542	9547	9552	9557	9562	9566	9571	9576	9581	9586	0	1	1	2	2	3	3	4	4
91	9590	9595	9600	9605	9609	9614	9619	9624	9628	9633	0	1	1	2	2	3	3	4	4
92	9638	9643	9647	9652	9657	9661	9666	9671	9675	9680	0	1	1	2	2	3	3	4	4
93	9685	9689	9694	9699	9703	9708	9713	9717	9722	9727	0	1	1	2	2	3	3	4	4
94	9731	9736	9741	9745	9750	9754	9759	9763	9768	9773	0	1	1	2	2	3	3	4	4
95	9777	9782	9786	9791	9795	9800	9805	9809	9814	9818	0	1	1	2	2	3	3	4	4
96	9823	9827	9832	9836	9841	9845	9850	9854	9859	9863	0	1	1	2	2	3	3	4	4
97	9868	9872	9877	9881	9886	9890	9894	9899	9903	9908	0	1	1	2	2	3	3	4	4
98	9912	9917	9921	9926	9930	9934	9939	9943	9948	9952	0	1	1	2	2	3	3	4	4
99	9956	9961	9965	9969	9974	9978	9983	9987	9991	9996	0	1	1	2	2	3	3	3	4

Index

100
75
25

65.3
58
7.3

$\frac{7.3}{65.3}$

.112
65.3) 7.300
653
770
653
1170
1306